PONDWE_
OF
GREAT BRITAIN
AND IRELAND

B.S.B.I. HANDBOOK No. 8

C. D. PRESTON
Institute of Terrestrial Ecology

ILLUSTRATED BY
L. T. ELLIS

WITH ADDITIONAL DRAWINGS BY
MEGAN DOWLEN, KARIN DRACOULIS, G. LYALL
& MARGARET TEBBS

BOTANICAL SOCIETY OF THE BRITISH ISLES
London
1995

ISBN 0-901158-24-0

Published by the Botanical Society of the British Isles
c/o Natural History Museum
Cromwell Road, London SW7 5BD
Typeset by the Botanical Information Company Ltd
Printed by Jaggerprint Victoria, Kingston-upon-Thames

CONTENTS

PREFACE

The first B.S.B.I. Handbook, *British Sedges*, was published in 1968. In 1970, F. H. Perring persuaded J. E. Dandy to agree to write an illustrated booklet on the genus *Potamogeton* which would be issued in the Handbook series but would not be a formal descriptive handbook like its predecessor. There were, however, many other calls on Dandy's time and in 1972 the B.S.B.I. Publications Committee were disappointed to learn that he regarded the book as "very much a project for the future". Matters had progressed no further by the time that Dandy died in 1976.

It must have been clear to the Publications Committee that there was no chance of replacing Dandy with anyone of comparable expertise. Nevertheless, the Committee still wanted to publish a Pondweeds Handbook and by 1983 three authors had been recruited to write one. I was asked to prepare distribution maps for inclusion in it. I had no knowledge of *Potamogeton*, but this did not matter as Dandy had left details of the many thousands of specimens he had determined in a card index. By the time that the draft distribution maps were ready there had been no progress with the text. By then I had become interested in the genus, and to encourage the others I began to draft accounts of one or two of the more distinctive species. Fools rush in where angels fear to tread!

I am grateful to the late Sir George Taylor for his encouragement at the start of the project and for the loan of his copy of the manuscript monograph which he had written with J. E. Dandy. I also thank N. T. H. Holmes, who prepared initial drafts of several of the species accounts and who would have been an author of the book had he not been overwhelmed by other commitments. My greatest debt is, however, to N. F. Stewart, who taught me how to identify pondweeds when I first became involved with the genus and who has subsequently helped in innumerable other ways. It is unlikely that this Handbook would have been written had he not offered such generous encouragement and assistance.

Many botanists have joined me for fieldwork, or have collected living material or sent dried specimens at my request. For such assistance I thank Mrs P. P. Abbott, B. A. Adams, Dr J. R. Akeroyd, S. Beesley, Mrs S. L. Bell, R. P. Bowman, A. Branson, J. H. Bratton, Mrs M. Briggs, Miss E. Buckle, I. Butterfield, Dr C. J. Cadbury, A. O. Chater, Mrs P. Copson, Mrs J. M. Croft, Mrs G. Crompton, Dr Q. C. B. Cronk, C. Doarks, D. Doogue, R. G. Ellis, I. M. & Mrs P. A. Evans, Dr J. S. Faulkner, Lady R. FitzGerald, R. S. Forbes,

S. Foster, Dr L. Friday, Dr C. E. Gibson, Dr R. Goodwillie, P. Hackney, Dr G. Halliday, P. Harmes, Mrs S. C. Holland, P. M. Hollingsworth, Dr M. G. B. Hughes, Dr G. Hutchinson, Mrs C. & M. A. R. Kitchen, Miss V. Morgan, D. Morgana, Mrs C. W. Murray, Dr A. E. Newton, H. J. Noltie, R. Northridge, Mrs M. Norton, P. H. Oswald, Mrs A. and D. A. Pearman, Dr T. C. G. Rich, Miss M. J. P. Scannell, P. D. Sell, Mrs J. E. Smith, Dr S. J. Smith, Miss H. E. Stace, C. R. Stevenson, N. F. Stewart, Mrs O. M. Stewart, D. Synnott, B. H. Thompson, Dr A. Walker, R. M. Walls, A. C. Waterman, K. J. Watson, Dr S. D. Webster, Mrs I. Weston, R. S. Weyl, Mrs H. & J. Williamson, S. Wolfe-Murphy and Miss S. E. Yates. The heart-warming friendship and hospitality that I have received during my travels has made the fieldwork particularly enjoyable. In addition to the botanists listed above, I should also like to thank the spouses who tolerated with such good grace the invasion of their homes by an aquatic botanist with all his smelly and dripping collections. A contribution towards fieldwork expenses was made by the B.S.B.I. from the Welch bequest.

I have made full use of the herbarium and library of the Department of Plant Sciences, University of Cambridge (**CGE**), and am most grateful for access to these rich collections. Similarly, I must thank the Natural History Museum (**BM**) for access to specimens and books and for the extended loan of J. E. Dandy's card index. I have also visited, or borrowed material from, the herbaria at Aberdeen (**ABD**), Belfast (**BEL**), Cardiff (**NMW**), Copenhagen (**C**), Dorchester (**DOR**), Dublin (**DBN, TCD**), Edinburgh (**E**), Exeter (**RAMM**), Glasgow (**GL**), Kew (**K**), Lancaster (**LANC**), Leicester (**LSR, LTR**), Liverpool (**LIV**), London (**SLBI**), Loughborough (**UTLH**), Manchester (**MANCH**), Munich (**M**), Newcastle upon Tyne (**HAMU**), Norwich (**NWH**), Oxford (**OXF**), Reading (**RNG**), Stirling (**STI**), Uppsala (**UPS**), Warwick (**WARMS**) and Zürich (**Z, ZT**).

During the later stages of the preparation of the Handbook, P. M. Hollingsworth has been studying the population biology of British *Potamogeton* species as a research student jointly supervised by Dr R. J. Gornall of Leicester University and myself. I am grateful to both these colleagues for much helpful discussion and to Peter Hollingsworth for contributing the chapter on chromosome numbers. I have included only a few brief references to this unpublished work; the detailed results will be published elsewhere.

I am grateful to P. T. Harding, head of the Biological Records Centre (B.R.C.) at Monks Wood, for his support over the period in which the book has been written. The distribution maps were prepared by B.R.C. and much of the work has fallen to the database managers Mrs D. M. Greene, H. R. Arnold and J. C. M. Dring, to the data inputters Mrs L. Ling and Mrs W. Forrest, and in particular to my fellow botanist at B.R.C., Mrs J. M. Croft. Details of the sources of records are given later but I am particularly grateful to the B.S.B.I. vice-county recorders for their contribution and to the Scottish Loch Survey and the Northern Ireland Lake Survey teams for access to the large numbers of voucher specimens they collected. Financial support for this aspect of the work was provided by the Nature Conservancy Council, Joint Nature Conservation Committee and Natural Environment Research Council, and some records were added during a project jointly financed by the National Rivers Authority.

Most of the drawings were made (usually from fresh material) by L. T. Ellis, who has devoted many hours of meticulous attention to the task. Margaret Tebbs drew the figures which illustrate the introductory chapters, and Megan Dowlen not only prepared some plates herself but also recruited Karin Dracoulis and Graeme Lyell to complete the remaining drawings. Clive Jermy designed the cover. I am grateful to all the artists for their major contribution to this book.

I thank Mrs J. Gaunt, Mrs L. Guerin and Mrs J. Rushton for typing the species accounts and Mrs Gaunt for also scanning the illustrations into the computer so that they could be sent to the printer on disk.

It has been a pleasure to work with A. O. Chater, appointed by the Publications Committee to oversee the production of the Handbook. His encouragement and sagacious counsel, and his detailed comments on the manuscript, have been invaluable. P. D. Sell has given me much useful advice during the preparation of the species accounts. R. M. Burton, Mrs G. Crompton, T. ap Rees and J. Vögel drew my attention to books and papers which I might otherwise have missed. H. J. Noltie valiantly read the entire manuscript, and Mrs J. M. Croft, P. T. Harding, M. O. Hill, N. T. H. Holmes, J. O. Mountford and Dr S. J. Smith commented on parts of the text. Finally, I am grateful to P. H. Oswald for planning the layout of the book and to both him and H. Synge for their work in seeing it through the press.

November, 1994   C. D. Preston

This is the last of seven handbooks to be edited for the B.S.B.I. by A. O. Chater, who retired as editor following his retirement from the Natural History Museum. We could not have hoped to find a better editor for our handbooks, and the enormous amount of work that Arthur has devoted to the task has been a major factor in the success of the series. We thank him warmly for his invaluable contribution.

D. A. Pearman   M. Walpole
President, B.S.B.I.   *Chairman, B.S.B.I. Publications Committee*

INTRODUCTION

This book is an illustrated guide to the British and Irish representatives of two plant families, the Potamogetonaceae (which contains the large genus *Potamogeton* and the monotypic *Groenlandia*) and the closely related Ruppiaceae (which comprises a single genus, *Ruppia*). The species and hybrids of *Potamogeton* are traditionally regarded by British botanists as difficult to identify. It is certainly true that even some botanists who can reliably identify all but the most critical of terrestrial plants can make elementary errors in tackling pondweeds. There are a number of reasons inherent in the nature of the plants which contribute to this. There are often considerable differences between the first leaves produced by a species in spring and the later foliage, and mature plants of some taxa can also vary greatly according to habitat conditions. The numerous hybrids also complicate identification. However, I believe that in most cases the mistakes that arise in identifying pondweeds are not caused by any difficulty of the material but by a number of other reasons, most of which can be overcome by anyone who wishes to tackle the group. Most botanists only attempt to identify those specimens which they chance to come across, rather than deliberately trying to see a range of material both in the field and in the herbarium. When identifying plants, they struggle to interpret structures with a hand-lens rather than examining them under a binocular microscope. If the pondweeds are tackled systematically, the British and Irish plants should not provide insuperable problems to anyone who has an eye for plants and who is prepared to devote two or three seasons to their study. It should, of course, be possible to master the more restricted range of species present in a smaller area more rapidly.

The scope of this work has been determined by the fact that it is intended as an identification guide rather than a taxonomic monograph. The user I have had in mind when writing the book is a botanist who is reasonably familiar with the commoner British or Irish plants and with the use of standard floras, such as Clapham, Tutin and Warburg's (1981) *Excursion Flora of the British Isles* or Stace's (1991) *New Flora of the British Isles*, but does not necessarily have any previous experience of aquatic plants. I have based the descriptions on morphological characters which can be seen with the unaided eye, the hand lens or the binocular microscope. It is certainly possible to identify almost all well-collected specimens by these characters alone. I have neither investigated nor described microscopic features such as stem anatomy. References to the key literature dealing with stem anatomy, pollen morphology, fruit structure and the identification of subfossil fruits are provided for those who want to follow up these more specialised fields.

This book covers Britain and Ireland, and the descriptions of species and hybrids are (unless stated) based solely on material from our area. However, the pondweed flora of the British Isles is particularly rich, and the Handbook may therefore be useful in identifying plants found elsewhere in Europe. The only taxa recorded in Europe but not in the British Isles are *P. vaginatus*, a northern species known from Norway, Sweden and Finland, and several rare hybrids. I expect that most problems in using the book in mainland Europe will be caused by the greater variability there of species such as *Potamogeton nodosus*, *P. pectinatus* and *Ruppia maritima*, rather than by the presence of additional taxa.

The current taxonomy and nomenclature of the British and Irish *Potamogeton* species was worked out over many years by J. E. Dandy, who collaborated with G. Taylor during the first and most productive period of his studies of the genus. Dandy and Taylor themselves built on the earlier work of British botanists such as A. Fryer, European students such as J. O. Hagström and American specialists such as M. L. Fernald. Dandy's final views on the European species are summarised in *Flora europaea* (Dandy 1980) and his treatment of the British and Irish hybrids in Stace's *Hybridization* (Dandy 1975). The many thousands of specimens in numerous herbaria determined by Dandy and Taylor have been of immense value in the preparation of this work.

As the book is an identification guide, the species accounts concentrate on morphological descriptions. However, I have tried to include enough autecological information in the introductory chapters and in the species accounts to help the reader to understand the taxa as living, growing and reproducing organisms. I hope that this will not only lead to more accurate identifications, but also make the study of the group a much more stimulating experience.

HISTORY OF PONDWEED STUDIES IN BRITAIN AND IRELAND

This chapter outlines the taxonomic history of the Potamogetonaceae and the Ruppiaceae in the British Isles. This history begins with the first published reference to *Potamogeton* in the 16th century, and the present chapter takes the story up to the death of J. E. Dandy in 1976. A detailed treatment of the taxonomic history of the plants in our area would require a comparison of developments here with those taking place simultaneously in mainland Europe. I have not been able to undertake a detailed study of the European literature in writing this account, but the major continental studies which have influenced the treatment of the British and Irish taxa are outlined. Unless stated, species and hybrids are referred to by their current names: these may not be the names which appear in the works cited.

The prehistory of pondweeds

Pondweeds are neither useful nor decorative, and it is doubtful whether they attracted much notice before the advent of botanical science. Laird (1986) describes a late 15th-century carved misericord in St George's Chapel, Windsor, as a "loop of opposite-leaved pondweed surrounding yellow water-lily leaves", commenting that it shows "what was probably a sample (freshly collected from the nearest stream) of the abundant opposite-leaved pondweed, *Groenlandia densa*". I have not seen the misericord, but I would not have identified the plant portrayed in the photograph as *G. densa*, and I doubt whether it represents any aquatic plant.

The recognition of the genus *Potamogeton*, 1548–1696

William Turner included "*Potamogeton*" in his book *The Names of Herbes*, first published in 1548, saying that "it maye be named in englishe Pondplantayne, or swymmynge plantayne, because it swymmeth aboue pondes and standyng waters". Stearn (in Turner 1965) equates Turner's *Potamogeton* with *P. natans*, but he admits that the identifications of the species in *The Names of Herbes* "are necessarily based on scanty evidence and hence must be regarded as tentative".

John Gerarde (1597) included two species in Chapter 283 of his *Herball*, "Of Pondweede, or water Spike". His *Potamogeiton latifolium* is our *Potamogeton natans* and his *Potamogeiton angustifolium* is *Persicaria amphibia*. Broad-leaved Pondweed survives in books as the English name for *P. natans*; it arose because the leaves were broad in relation to those of *Persicaria amphibia*.

The modern concept of the genus *Potamogeton* developed during the 17th century. In the 1633 edition of Gerarde, "Very much Enlarged and Amended by Thomas Johnson", five species which would now be included in the Potamogetonaceae are added, but they are split between three different chapters. To Gerarde's *P. angustifolium* and *P. latifolium* Johnson added plants which can be recognised as our *P. lucens* and *P. perfoliatus*. In a chapter which deals with a very heterogeneous assemblage of aquatic plants with divided leaves (including *Hottonia, Ranunculus* and *Utricularia*) he reproduced an instantly recognisable picture of *Potamogeton pectinatus* under the name *Millefolium tenuifolium*, but his description applies to a completely different plant, apparently a Batrachian *Ranunculus*. The two most interesting additions to the revised *Herball* are *Potamogeton crispus* and *Groenlandia densa*, which were added to the chapter which describes *Trapa natans* (as *Tribulus aquaticus*). The descriptions of these species had been drawn up from living material by Johnson's friend John Goodyer of Hampshire, described by Johnson as "the only assistant I had in this worke". Both Goodyer's descriptions are remarkable for their originality and accuracy, and they mark the start of the critical study of pondweeds in our islands. He described *P. crispus* under the phrase name *Tribulus aquaticus minor quercus floribus*, noting its "flat, knottie stalks [stems] ... bearing but one leafe at every joint ... so wrinckled and crompled by the sides that it seemeth to be torne, of a reddish greene colour: the foot-stalkes [peduncles] are something [corrected to "somewhat" in the 1636 reprint] long and thicke, and rise up from amongst those leaves, which alwaies grow two one opposite against another, in a contrarie manner to those that grow below ... neare the top of which foot-stalke groweth small grape-like huskes, out of which spring very small reddish floures like those of the Oke ... the lower part of the stalke hath at every joint small white threddie roots, somewhat long, wherby it taketh hold in the mudde ...." The description of *Tribulus aquaticus minor, muscatellae floribus* (*Groenlandia densa*) notes most of the significant differences between this species and *P. crispus*. "This hath not flat stalkes like the other but round, kneed, and alwaies bearing two leaves at every joint, one opposite against another, greener, shorter and lesser than the other, sharpe pointed, not much wrinckled or crumpled by the edges ... the floures grow on short small foot-stalks, of a whitish green colour like those of *Muscatella Cordi* [*Adoxa moschatellina*] ...

two floures at the top of every foot-stalke, one opposite against another ... the roots are like the former ... this groweth abundantly in the river by Droxford in Hampshire ... greene, both winter & Sommer." These descriptions were illustrated by plates taken from other works: that of *P. crispus* is excellent, but unfortunately the illustration of *Groenlandia densa* is simply a rather cruder picture of *P. crispus*, and despite Goodyer's text these two species continued to be confused by some authors for another century.

The next significant contribution was made by John Ray, who taught himself botany in Cambridge at a time when numerous aquatic plants could be found within the town and in the nearby fenland. Ray's first botanical publication, *Catalogus Plantarum circa Cantabrigiam nascentium* (1660), included all the species in Gerarde (1633), listed under the three 'genera' *Millefolium*, *Potamogeiton* and *Tribulus*. Ray noted that his *Millefolium aquaticum* was the plant illustrated in Gerarde (1633), not that described. Ray had also begun to suspect that the inclusion of *Persicaria amphibia* in *Potamogeiton* was unjustified, and he noted that "when out of water it somewhat resembles a Persicaria in appearance" (Raven 1942). In addition to the species in Gerarde, Ray also described under *Potamogeiton* three species which were new to science: *Potamogeton compressus*, *P. pusillus* (*sensu lato*) and the "water-grass with small crooked cods", *Zannichellia palustris*, applying long pre-Linnaean phrase-names to each.

In his later publications Ray refined the taxonomic treatment of these plants. In 1670 he moved *P. pectinatus* from *Millefolium* to *Potamogeiton* and also added *Ruppia maritima*, which he had discovered in Essex, to the genus (Ray 1670). He still retained *Potamogeiton angustifolium* in the pondweeds, although he commented that it belonged to *Persicaria*. In *Historia Plantarum* and his pioneer British flora *Synopsis methodica Stirpium britannicarum*, Ray (1686, 1690) transferred the two *Tribulus* species (*P. crispus* and *Groenlandia densa*) to the pondweeds and excluded the *Persicaria*. This brought all the Potamogetonaceae, Ruppiaceae and Zannichelliaceae known to him into a single genus. In the second edition of the *Synopsis* (Ray 1696), he excluded *Zannichellia*, placing it in a group headed "herbae anomalae & incertae sedis, & primo Aquaticae". Thus for the first time in a British flora all the species in the Potamogetonaceae *sensu lato* were brought together in a group from which other taxa were excluded. In Ray's later accounts the variable *P. pectinatus* is described as two distinct species.

Ray's descriptions of the habitats of the pondweeds suggest that he knew the plants well in the field. In *Historia Plantarum* (1686) he wrote of *P. natans*: "In aquis stagnantibus frequentissimum habetur." [It is found very frequently in stagnant waters.]; of *P. crispus*: "In rivulis, praesertim tardiùs fluentibus, frequentissimum est hoc genus." [This kind is very frequent in small streams, especially slower-flowing ones.]; of *P. lucens*: "In fluviis majoribus & leniter fluentibus frequens nascitur." [It frequently grows in larger, slow-flowing rivers.]; and of *Groenlandia densa*: "In rivulis, aquae praesertim purae & limpidae non infrequens Aquis innatat, ..." [In small streams, especially of pure and clear water, it not infrequently floats in the waters, ...].

A long period of little progress, 1696–1827

In contrast to the gradual increase in knowledge in the 17th century, there was remarkably little progress in the next hundred years. This can be illustrated by a comparison of the floras of Ray (1696) and Smith (1800). Ray (1696) recognised ten species of *Potamogeiton*, which correspond to nine currently accepted in the Potamogetonaceae and Ruppiaceae. In the *Flora britannica* Smith (1800) distinguished *Potamogeton* and *Ruppia*, but included only a single additional species, *P. obtusifolius*. The similarity between these two floras does not mean that the taxonomic treatments were static during the century: some taxa were described and later reduced to synonymy, others became confused and (in some cases) were subsequently sorted out as the century progressed, and in one or two cases species reported in regional floras were not taken up nationally. Nevertheless, it is clear that little lasting progress in the study of these plants in Britain and Ireland was made in the period between 1696 and 1800.

One reason for the lack of progress in the first half of the 18th century is almost certainly the malaise which afflicted most branches of natural history in Britain. "In these middle years of the eighteenth century ... British natural history experienced one of its thankfully rare breakdowns in elementary manpower. The intake of recruits proved quite insufficient to keep up the tradition" (Allen 1976). There was a revival of interest in botany in the second half of the century, greatly stimulated by the publications of Linnaeus. This did not result in any increase in the knowledge of pondweeds, perhaps because Linnaeus' account of *Potamogeton* in *Species Plantarum* (1753) shows little advance on the treatment of Ray (1696). British botanists were particularly influenced by the views of Linnaeus after his herbarium was purchased by J. E. Smith, who then used his considerable influence to promote Linnaean taxonomy. Had Linnaeus described or distinguished some of the northern pondweeds, such as *P. alpinus*, *P. filiformis* or *P. praelongus*, it seems likely that his followers in Britain would have detected these plants before the end of the century.

Three new *Potamogeton* taxa were recognised in Britain in the first decade of the 19th century. *P. gramineus* and *P. alpinus* were illustrated by James Sowerby in J. E. Smith's *English Botany* (1804) as *P. heterophyllum* and

P. fluitans respectively. *P. gramineus* had been reported from Scotland by J. Lightfoot (1777) and described as if new to science under the name *P. palustre* by R. Teesdale (1800), but it was only on receipt of a "collection of fine specimens, in various states, sent from Shropshire by the Rev. Mr. [Edward] Williams" that Smith was prepared to admit it to the British flora. In a later volume of *English Botany* Smith (1809) described *P. lanceolatus*; this was the first hybrid to be distinguished in Britain, although its hybrid nature was not recognised for a further 85 years.

Despite these additions to the British list, the last two decades of the 18th century and the first 30 years of the 19th represent one of the few periods when the study of pondweeds in Britain lagged behind that in mainland Europe. Several of the species which Linnaeus had overlooked were described during this period by continental botanists, but these discoveries made little impact in the British Isles.

The discovery of many new taxa, 1827–1880

The considerable progress which had been made in the study of the genus *Potamogeton* in continental Europe was summarised in a monograph of the genus published in the Berlin journal *Linnaea* by Chamisso & Schlechtendal (1827). This provided detailed descriptions of all the species then known. A particular merit of their review was the treatment of the linear-leaved species: *P. acutifolius* and *P. compressus* were recognised as distinct but allied species, as were *P. filiformis* and *P. pectinatus*, and *P. trichoides* was described for the first time. As a direct result of this publication, Hooker (1830, 1831) was able to confirm the presence of both *P. acutifolius* and *P. compressus* in Britain, the former on the basis of collections made by W. Borrer in Sussex.

The publication of Chamisso & Schlechtendal's monograph coincided with the rise of a new generation of British botanists who were keenly aware of the continental literature. C. C. Babington, in particular, considered that the botanists of J. E. Smith's day had been too insular in their approach and had lost touch with taxonomic developments on the continent. He deliberately set out to assess the identity of the British and Irish plants by comparing them with descriptions in the continental literature. An early result of this reassessment was the recognition of *P. coloratus* and *P. polygonifolius*. British botanists had hitherto included these species in a broadly defined *P. natans*: Withering (1787), for example, recognised "floating" and "boggy" varieties of this species. The first published record of *P. polygonifolius* in the British Isles was actually published by Chamisso & Schlechtendal (1827). During his fieldwork in the

Channel Islands, Babington found *P. coloratus*, *P. natans sensu stricto* and *P. polygonifolius*. He outlined the differences in his *Primitiae Florae sarnicae* (1839) and contributed accounts of the two new species to the supplement to *English Botany* (Hooker 1843). Babington also wrote the account of *P. praelongus* for the same volume of the supplement. This distinctive broad-leaved species had been discovered in Scotland in 1832 (Hooker 1835, Brichan 1842) and was soon recognised in several scattered localities.

In 1843 Babington summarised his taxonomic approach in his *Manual of British Botany*. In this flora, he broke away from the highly artificial Linnaean system of plant classification which had survived in Britain until the 1830s. In this system, *Potamogeton* and *Ruppia* had been grouped in the Tetrandria–Tetragynia with quite dissimilar genera (*Ilex*, *Moenchia*, *Sagina*, *Radiola* and *Tillaea*) simply because they possessed four anthers and four carpels in each flower. Babington's *Manual* placed *Potamogeton* and *Ruppia* in the order Potameae, together with *Zannichellia* and *Zostera*. The treatment of the species was notable because *Potamogeton filiformis* was distinguished from *P. pectinatus* and *Ruppia cirrhosa* from *R. maritima* for the first time in a British flora. Babington later added *P. trichoides* to the British list, recognising it amongst material sent to him by K. Trimmer in 1849 (Babington 1850).

As botanists defined the broad-leaved species more precisely than in the past, the commoner hybrids began to be recognised. Babington (1856) was able to add *P.* × *sparganiifolius* from Maam, Co. Galway, to the fourth edition of his *Manual of British Botany*, and Moore (1864) found *P.* × *nitens* in Co. Kerry. These were the first of several interesting hybrids to be discovered in Ireland. Baker & Trimen (1867) reported *P.* × *salicifolius* from Bath, and *P.* × *zizii* was discovered in Cauldshiels Loch (Baker 1879). All these hybrids, like Smith's *P.* × *lanceolatus*, were initially treated as species. Moore (1864) noted that the inflorescences of *P.* × *nitens* fell off before the fruits were mature; Baker & Trimen (1867) reported that none of the British or European material of *P.* × *salicifolius* they had examined was fruiting; more than one botanist searched in vain for fruits on *P.* × *lanceolatus* (Syme 1869, Preston 1989a). However, the significance of these observations was not yet apparent.

The taxonomic treatment of *Potamogeton* and *Ruppia* which developed during the 19th century and was summarised in successive editions of Babington's *Manual* did not achieve universal acceptance. George Bentham (1858) made a determined attempt to persuade British botanists to revert to a broader species concept. Bentham was one of the most able and productive taxonomists, author of works such as *Flora Australiensis* and (with J. D. Hooker) *Genera Plantarum*. In introducing his *Handbook of the British Flora* he said that he had "long been persuaded that the views originally entertained by Linnaeus of what

16

really constitutes a species, were far more correct than the more limited sense to which many modern botanists seem inclined to restrict the term", and consequently the species in his *Handbook* are "limited according to what are conceived to have been the original principles of Linnaeus". In *Potamogeton* Bentham recognised nine species, some of which were very broadly defined. He included *P. coloratus* and *P. polygonifolius* in *P. natans*, attributing the variation in this species to the different environments in which it grew. He also included *P. alpinus* and *P.* × *lanceolatus* in *P. lucens*, both *P. acutifolius* and *P. compressus* in *P. pusillus*, and *P. filiformis* in *P. pectinatus*. Bentham's *Handbook* was written "for the use of beginners and amateurs", and he hoped "to enable persons having no previous knowledge of Botany to name the wild flowers they might gather in their country rambles ... by such characters as may be readily perceived by the unlearned eye". However, it is clear from his introductory remarks that he was convinced of the merits of the broad species concept he adopted and was not just attempting to simplify the subject for his readers.

There was still no consensus about the specific limits in *Potamogeton* and *Ruppia* by 1880. Babington (1874) and J. D. Hooker (1878) recognised virtually the same taxa, but Babington treated them as species whereas Hooker accepted a smaller number of species, many of them divided into subspecies. Syme's (1869) account in the third edition of *English Botany* was similar to Babington's, but he subdivided some of the more variable species into varieties. Bentham's (1878) species concept was even broader than Hooker's, and he did not deal with any infraspecific taxa.

Fryer's studies of the broad-leaved pondweeds, 1880–1912

Alfred Fryer was a native of the Cambridgeshire Fenlands. He was an educated man, who struggled to earn a living from market gardening after the money he had expected to inherit from a rich aunt failed to materialise. Although he was interested in natural history from his schooldays, it was not until 1876 (when he was 50 years old) that he began to record plants systematically. He was encouraged by Babington, who was not only an authority on *Potamogeton* but also the author of the *Flora of Cambridgeshire*. In 1880 Fryer collected his first *Potamogeton*, and he soon began an intensive study of the broad-leaved species. Much of his time was spent examining the pondweeds in the ditches, drains and rivers of his home area, and he supplemented this knowledge by growing plants in a pond and in tanks in his garden. He did little fieldwork outside the Fens and none at all outside East Anglia. However, he received specimens and living plants from other botanists.

Fryer's observations on pondweeds in the wild and in cultivation gave him an accurate appreciation of the variation shown by the Fenland species. He became very familiar with their seasonal variation and their reaction to fluctuations in water level. He therefore refused to give taxonomic recognition to many of the varieties accepted by other authors. He recognised, for example, that *P. natans* var. *linearis* Syme was simply the early growth form of the species which later developed into the typical plant. Once he established that a plant maintained its characters in cultivation, Fryer preferred to describe it as a species. This very narrow species concept has not been maintained by later students, and several of the taxa he recognised are now reduced to synonymy.

The possibility of hybridisation in *Potamogeton* was just beginning to be recognised when Fryer began his studies. There were only three entries under *Potamogeton* in Focke's (1881) compilation of all known plant hybrids, and two of these were probably variants of *P. × salicifolius*. At first Fryer assumed that all the plants which he found in Fenland were species, but after several years he came to the conclusion that some of them must be sterile hybrids. This was a conclusion which Babington, now old and highly conservative, found difficult to accept. However, Fryer was persuaded by the morphology of the hybrids, their sterility and the detailed distribution of the hybrids and their putative parents in the Fenland area which he knew so well. Amongst the first plants which he recognised as hybrids were *P. × fluitans* (Fryer 1890b), *P. × nitens* (Fryer 1889c) and *P. × salicifolius* (Fryer 1890a). He later realised that *P. × zizii* was an apparently fertile hybrid (Fryer 1892b), and he discovered a single colony of *P. × billupsii* (Fryer 1893). He named the latter after his nephew, who assisted him in his botanical work. In his capacity as a national expert in the genus, Fryer received difficult material from other botanists, and he thus came to describe some hybrids new to science, including *P. × bennettii* from Grangemouth (Fryer 1895), *P. × cooperi* from Loughborough and the River Dee near Chester (Fryer 1891) and *P. × lintonii* from Derbyshire (Fryer 1900). He also realised that *P. × lanceolatus*, the plant which had puzzled botanists since it was first described by Smith, was a hybrid between a broad-leaved and a narrow-leaved species (Fryer 1894b). This possibility had been suggested by Professor Buchenau of Berlin in 1882 (Bennett 1882), but had not been taken up by English botanists. Fryer thought that the broad-leaved parent was *P. gramineus*, whereas the current view is that it is *P. coloratus*. Another plant which Fryer described was *P. drucei* (Preston 1988b). He could not decide whether this was a species or a hybrid, and it was to puzzle botanists for nearly 40 years.

From 1886 onwards Fryer published accounts of the pondweeds he had studied for *The Journal of Botany*. These careful and accurate papers contain numerous original observations and are still worth reading. In 1898 he began a monograph *The Potamogetons (Pond Weeds) of the British Isles*, which was illustrated by superb plates drawn by R. Morgan. The monograph was published in parts, three of which were issued by the end of 1900. Publication then stopped, partly because Fryer found that his work as a market gardener was increasingly exhausting as he aged and partly because he had quarrelled with the publisher. He eventually resumed work on the book in 1911, but he died before any more parts could be completed. The monograph was completed by A. H. Evans, who added rather brief and uninformative accounts of the remaining broad-leaved species, and by A. Bennett, who tackled the linear-leaved taxa, and was published in 1915 (Fryer & Bennett 1915).

Affectionate obituaries of Fryer were written by Druce (1913) and by Evans & Britten (1912). For a detailed assessment of his work on *Potamogeton*, including a bibliography of his publications, see Preston (1988a); the taxa he described new to science are discussed by Preston (1988b).

Fryer's contemporaries and successors, 1880–1936

When Fryer died in 1912, the major responsibility for completing his monograph was shouldered by Arthur Bennett. Bennett was a builder and house decorator who devoted "the hours he snatched from his business" to his botanical studies (Druce 1930). His interest in *Potamogeton* was stimulated by his discovery in 1880 of *Potamogeton* × *lanceolatus* in Cambridgeshire, the first and only record from eastern England. He was also interested in other aquatics (for example, he added *Najas marina* to the British flora in 1883), and he made a particular study of *Carex*.

Bennett was a prolific author who contributed 243 notes, papers and reviews to *The Journal of Botany* between 1878 and his death in 1929 (Druce 1929a). Over 50 of these dealt with *Potamogeton*, and in them Bennett described new species and varieties from all five continents. His British and Irish papers included the description of new species, varieties and hybrids, nomenclatural notes, summaries of vice-county distribution, numerous new county records, and snippets from letters sent to him by botanists in Europe and North America. Despite pressing business and domestic preoccupations, including periods of financial hardship, he would always find time to give a name to any difficult or critical material that was sent to him. As a result of his correspondence he was able to describe *P.* × *griffithii*, naming it after J. E. Griffith, who had discovered it in North Wales (Bennett 1883). He also recognised *P. epihydrus* when plants were sent to him from Halifax, adding this to the British flora as a naturalised alien (Bennett 1908a, b, c).

Bennett's work has been criticised by British and American authors. His papers are difficult to read; even his friend Druce (1930) commented that "he had a confused style, and too often overloaded the point with irrelevancies". His identifications were unreliable, and in major matters he was wrong more often than he was right. He reported *P. rutilus* new to Britain on the basis of herbarium specimens from Sussex, Staffordshire and Anglesey (Bennett 1900), all of which proved to be *P. pusillus*. "The Anglesey locality, Llyn Coron, came to be regarded by British botanists as the *locus classicus* for *P. rutilus* in this country, and they visited the lake year after year in search of a species which apparently was never there" (Dandy & Taylor 1938c). Bennett (1907c) claimed to have been particularly cautious before identifying *P. × undulatus* as a British plant, as he was aware of an earlier, erroneous record. Nevertheless, the plant he confidently reported as this hybrid was actually *P. praelongus*. Other species and hybrids which he erroneously claimed as new to Britain were *P. foliosus*, *P. × sudermanicus* and *P. vaginatus* (Bennett 1907a, 1922, 1924). These were actually *P. obtusifolius*, *P. pusillus* and *P. pectinatus* respectively. Although Bennett often wrote of *P. × griffithii* (which he regarded as a species rather than a hybrid), he described the same plant as *P. macvicarii* when it was subsequently collected in Scotland (Dandy & Taylor 1939e). His habit of 'matching' plants by comparing them with herbarium specimens rather than analysing their characters critically almost certainly contributed to the many mistakes he made, especially when identifying the linear-leaved species. Fernald (1932) considered that he "was often more impressed with intangible and undefinable habital characters than with fundamental differences" and therefore relied on a "psychological rather than morphological separation of plants". It is difficult to disagree with Dandy & Taylor's (1938a) conclusion that "any elucidation of taxonomy for which Bennett was responsible was more than offset by the confusion which he left for future workers to resolve". In fairness to Bennett, it should be noted that in a review of the taxonomy of *Potamogeton* on a world scale Wiegleb (1988b) suggested that his publications are a useful source of information for modern students and pointed out that Bennett described more of the currently accepted species than anyone else. Most of the valid species described by Bennett are found in Asia, South America or Australia; they include the eastern Asian *P. fryeri*, which he named after his friend and colleague Alfred Fryer.

Some major European publications appeared during the period when Bennett was the British authority. The importance of the vegetative propagation of *Potamogeton*, rather than reproduction by seed, was highlighted by the biological studies of C. Sauvageau (1893–94) and C. Raunkiaer. Raunkiaer's (1895–99) account of the Danish monocotyledons contains detailed descriptions of the vegetative propagules of many pondweeds, and his illustrations of these features are still the best available. Ascherson & Graebner (1907) produced a world monograph of the Potamogetonaceae for Engler's monumental *Das Pflanzenreich*. Their work was one of synthesis and is still a useful compilation. However, their taxonomic treatment was far too elaborate, and in many species and hybrids they recognised numerous varieties, subvarieties and forms. This approach was not unusual at the time, but it fails to show the understanding of the living plants that is so evident in Fryer's or Raunkiaer's work or to benefit from their published observations. A more significant contribution was J. O. Hagström's *Critical researches on the Potamogetons* (1916), which contained a wealth of original morphological and anatomical observations on both species and hybrids. Hagström contributed greatly to the understanding of the taxa he knew well. He was the first person to appreciate the crucial importance of stipule morphology in the identification of the linear-leaved species, and in particular for distinguishing *P. berchtoldii* from *P. pusillus*. He was, however, prone to misidentify specimens from areas where he had no first hand knowledge of the group. His *P.* × *anglicus* from Surrey was merely *P. polygonifolius*, not the hybrid *P. coloratus* × *polygonifolius*, and in identifying American specimens he "proposed preposterous hybrids (of hypothetical parents thousands of miles apart)" (Fernald 1932). Hagström, like Ascherson & Graebner, recognised numerous infraspecific taxa based on trivial differences or environmental modifications.

After Bennett's death in 1929, the schoolmaster W. H. Pearsall became the British authority on the pondweeds. He lived for many years at Dalton-in-Furness, and most weekends and all family holidays were spent in the Lake District. He was interested in most of the difficult aquatic plant genera, including *Callitriche*, *Potamogeton* and *Ranunculus*. Pearsall surveyed the vegetation of the lakes from a boat with his son, another W.H. Pearsall and apparently the fourteenth member of the family to bear that name (Clapham 1971). This fieldwork led to a joint account of the pondweeds of the Lake District (Pearsall & Pearsall 1921, 1923). The elder Pearsall later provided a detailed account of the taxonomy of the British and Irish pondweeds (Pearsall 1930, 1931). His treatment of the broad-leaved species and hybrids was heavily influenced by Hagström's work, and he therefore divided the more variable species into varieties. He does not explain his concept of the variety. He certainly knew from his own fieldwork, and from the experimental work on *P. perfoliatus* which his son had carried out (Pearsall & Hanby 1925), that some of them represented young growth forms and others were environmental modifications of the mature plant. His failure to reform the taxonomic framework in the light of this knowledge is an unsatisfactory feature of his work. His papers were also marred by his failure to correct some of the misidentifications which had been perpetrated by Bennett.

The modern taxonomic treatment is developed, 1936–1976

One of the young botanists who had submitted specimens of *Potamogeton* to W. H. Pearsall was George Taylor. Taylor had "paddled in water" for as long as he could remember; he collected his first pondweeds in 1926 and refound *P.* × *macvicarii* in Scotland in 1932. After he joined the staff of the British Museum (Natural History) he took part in an expedition to East Africa (1934–35) and made a particular point of collecting aquatics. On his return the *Potamogeton* specimens were worked up by J. E. Dandy. Dandy and Taylor thus joined forces and determined to prepare a monograph of the British species. This project was tackled systematically and thoroughly. Specimens of *Potamogeton* were borrowed from most of the major national herbaria and redetermined, and the details recorded by Dandy in a card index which at the time of his death contained over 20,000 records. Taylor continued his British fieldwork, visiting sites which were known to be rich and areas where the pondweeds had received little attention. His superb specimens were added to the British Museum collection, which already contained those collected by Fryer and Bennett.

In a series of papers published in *The Journal of Botany* between 1938 and 1942 under the general title 'Studies of British Pondweeds', Dandy and Taylor elucidated the taxonomy and distribution of many of the more critical British and Irish species and hybrids. They established the correct names for *P. berchtoldii* and *P. pusillus* and later provided details of all the British specimens they had examined. Similar accounts were provided for two other linear-leaved species which had often been misidentified in Britain, *P. rutilus* and *P. trichoides*, and for the hybrids *P.* × *bennettii*, *P.* × *lintonii* and *P.* × *suecicus*. The identity of a number of hitherto mysterious taxa was cleared up: the British *P. drucei* was shown to be identical to the widespread continental species *P. nodosus*, *P. griffithii* and *P. macvicarii* were shown to be the same hybrid (*P. alpinus* × *praelongus*), and *P. babingtonii* and *P. salignus* were reduced to synonyms of *P.* × *zizii* and *P.* × *salicifolius* respectively. These papers are notable for the clarity with which Dandy and Taylor described and then solved the problems before them, the remorseless way in which they exposed the errors of previous workers, and above all for the evident authority with which they wrote.

Dandy and Taylor did not accept any of the subspecies and varieties which had been set out in Pearsall's account, considering "all the supposed varieties and forms in this country to be developmental states or phases, unworthy of taxonomic recognition" (Taylor 1949). They considered that much of the difficulty which botanists had experienced in identifying pondweeds arose from this multiplicity of names. Once the taxonomy was simplified, Taylor (1949) considered that "any intelligent person who can interpret structure and is capable of making observations resulting from simple dissection should usually have little difficulty in naming specimens".

During their revision of the British and Irish pondweeds Dandy and Taylor became embroiled in a bitter row with J. W. Heslop Harrison of King's College, Newcastle upon Tyne (Dandy & Taylor 1942a, 1944a, Heslop Harrison 1944, Heslop Harrison & Clark 1941b, 1942a). Heslop Harrison and his colleagues were preparing a flora of the Outer Hebrides, and it was as a result of their fieldwork that the rich *Potamogeton* flora of the archipelago was revealed. They made the first record of *P. epihydrus* as a native of Europe and the first correct records of *P. × prussicus* and *P. × suecicus* in Britain. Heslop Harrison was also interested in the ecology of the Hebridean species and hybrids; his ecological observations are summarised in a paper (Heslop Harrison 1949) which provides a striking contrast to the taxonomic work of Dandy and Taylor. Heslop Harrison lent his pondweed specimens to Dandy and Taylor for their monographic work, but he became infuriated when they published their determinations of his plants in a paper which specifically dealt with the pondweeds of the Outer Hebrides (Dandy & Taylor 1940c). There seems to have been some justice to his complaint (which was never directly addressed by Dandy and Taylor in the ensuing controversy), but Heslop Harrison's extreme reaction seems to have been disproportionate to the original offence. It is clear that he found Dandy and Taylor's authoritative style, and their understandable refusal to accept records that they had not themselves confirmed, intensely irritating. He may also have been influenced by the fact that the London pair were colleagues of A. J. Wilmott, the leader of a rival attempt to write a Hebridean flora. Heslop Harrison unwisely chose to challenge Dandy and Taylor's nomenclatural work, coining the name *P. millardii* for the species known to Dandy and Taylor as *P. berchtoldii* (Heslop Harrison *et al.* 1942). Dandy was an expert on nomenclatural matters and demolished Heslop Harrison's arguments with withering sarcasm (Dandy & Taylor 1944a). An unfortunate result of the controversy was that Heslop Harrison refused to allow the junior members of his team to send any material to Dandy and Taylor (with whom they had managed to retain good relations). As a result, a number of their reported discoveries never received expert verification (Preston 1991), and some of the relevant specimens cannot now be traced.

The Journal of Botany ceased publication in 1942, and Dandy and Taylor were temporarily deprived of a convenient outlet for their work. They continued their joint studies of the genus, most notably in a detailed account of the hybrid *P.* × *suecicus* in northern England (1946), in very brief descriptions of *P.* × *cadburyae* and *P.* × *pseudofriesii*, two hybrids new to science (1957), and in the addition of the hybrids *P.* × *grovesii* (also new to science), *P.* × *nerviger* and *P.* × *variifolius* to our flora (Sell 1967). The monograph they planned was drafted in the 1940s and still exists in typescript; it was never submitted for publication. It contains a key to the species and a detailed synonymy and list of specimens (but no description) of each taxon.

Taylor's active participation in the partnership had ceased in 1956, when he left the British Museum for Kew. Dandy's interest in the genus continued even after his retirement in 1966. He was fortunately able to complete accounts of the European species (Dandy 1980) and of the British and Irish hybrids (Dandy 1975) before his death in 1976. In these two publications he summarised the results of 40 years' work on the genus. It is difficult to conceive of a better succinct account of the species than his contribution to *Flora europaea*: the format of the book demanded brevity and every word carries weight. The account of the hybrids is also invaluable, especially when considered in conjunction with the records in his card index. In these two accounts, as in the earlier work he published with Taylor, Dandy set a standard to which later students can aspire but which they can scarcely hope to surpass.

NOMENCLATURE

Scientific names

The scientific names adopted in this book are based on those used by Dandy (1980) for genera, subgenera, sections and species and Dandy (1975) for hybrids. When Dandy prepared his accounts, the hybrid between *Potamogeton gramineus* and *P. polygonifolius* lacked a binomial, but the name *P.* × *lanceolatifolius* is now available for it (Preston 1987). Since Dandy's death Haynes (1986) has lectotypified the species of *Potamogeton* described by Linnaeus, but in most cases he selected lectotypes which also had been chosen (but not published) by Dandy, and even when he departed from Dandy's choice his typification does not lead to any change in the established nomenclature. The names used here do not differ from those used by Stace (1991) and Kent (1992), although the hybrid *P.* × *schreberi* has been discovered in the British Isles since the publication of these works (Preston 1995a). The abbreviations of the authors of scientific names follow Brummitt & Powell (1992).

Synonyms are not cited in the species accounts but are included in the index.

Notes on some potentially misleading names

The application of a number of names in current use has changed over the years. Readers will need to be aware of these changes if they are attempting to interpret literature records correctly. The correct name for one or two taxa is still disputed, and in these cases current authors use different names for the same plant. Notes on the more confusing names are given below.

Potamogeton compressus

The name *Potamogeton compressus* L. was widely used for *P. friesii* in the late 18th and for much of the 19th centuries. Authors who did this would often refer to the true *P. compressus* as *P. zosterifolius*.

Potamogeton fluitans

Several authors have written at some length about the correct application of the name *Potamogeton fluitans* Roth. It seems that Roth's description was based on the sterile hybrid *P. lucens* × *P. natans*, but he included in his account of its distribution a locality for the fertile species *P. nodosus* (Dandy & Taylor 1939a). Some authors have used the name *P. fluitans* for the fertile species and others have applied it to the sterile hybrid; a third school rejects it completely. I follow Dandy in calling the hybrid *P.* × *fluitans* and the species *P. nodosus*. Those who call the species *P. fluitans*, or reject this name completely, usually call the hybrid *P.* × *sterilis*, although *P.* × *crassifolius* is actually an older name for the hybrid (Preston 1988b). This confusion is not likely to concern anyone consulting the British literature, as in our area the species is a rare plant with a well documented history and distribution. It was initially known as *P. drucei*, then *P. nodosus* (Dandy & Taylor 1939a, Preston 1988b). However, there is still no consensus in the wider literature about the correct application of the name *P. fluitans*.

Potamogeton gramineus

The name *Potamogeton gramineus* L. was used for *P. obtusifolius* by many authors from the mid 18th to the mid 19th century. These authors would usually use the name *P. heterophyllus* for the true *P. gramineus*.

Potamogeton pusillus

The name *Potamogeton pusillus* L. was used for many years to cover both of the small 'pusilloid' pondweeds now known as *P. berchtoldii* and *P. pusillus*. The distinction between *P. berchtoldii* and *P. pusillus* was not clarified until 1916, when Hagström demonstrated that one species has open and the other closed stipules. Unfortunately he misapplied the name *P. pusillus* to the species with open stipules, calling the plant with closed stipules *P. panormitanus*. These names were then applied to British material, although British authors often failed to identify the species correctly. In 1938 Dandy & Taylor (1938a) showed that the correct name for the plant with closed stipules was *P. pusillus* and that the species with open stipules should be called *P. berchtoldii*. They followed this paper with a detailed account of the British distribution of the two species (Dandy & Taylor 1940a, b). These names have been accepted by subsequent British and Irish authors, with the notable exception of Heslop Harrison (Harrison *et al.*, 1942). Some American authors, including Haynes (1974), regard the two taxa as varieties of the same species, in which case the name *P. pusillus* covers them both. *P. pusillus* var. *pusillus* is, of course, applied to *P. pusillus sensu stricto* and *P. pusillus* var. *tenuissimus* is the name given to *P. berchtoldii* when it is regarded as a variety. A proposal to reject the name *P. pusillus* because of its confusing history has been rejected, at least for the moment (Brummitt 1986).

Two other narrow-leaved species have often been confused with *P. pusillus* and *P. berchtoldii*. *P. trichoides* was first discovered in Britain in 1848, but the plant was often misidentified and Dandy & Taylor (1938b) had to revise the distribution of the species in our area. Similarly, many early records of *P. rutilus* are erroneous. For further details and a thorough revision of all the early records of this species, see Dandy & Taylor (1938c).

Because the British and Irish species with narrow, linear leaves have been so confused, records which predate Dandy & Taylor's revisions should be accepted only if supported by an expertly determined herbarium specimen. Many modern botanists continue to confuse *P. berchtoldii*, *P. pusillus* and *P. trichoides*, so it is also advisable to exercise a degree of caution even over modern records.

Ruppia maritima

Early authors recognised only one species of *Ruppia*, which they called *R. maritima* L. When two species were distinguished in the 19th century, the name *R. maritima* was applied to the plant with long, coiled peduncles and the name *R. rostellata* to the plant with shorter peduncles. The formal publication of the fact that *R. maritima* was the correct name for the short-peduncled plant did not take place until 1946 (Setchell 1946). However, the fact that *R. maritima* had been misapplied was already known to Dandy (1937a), and the name was correctly used for the short-peduncled plant in the *Check list of British vascular plants* (British Ecological Society 1946). When the name *R. maritima* was adopted for the short-peduncled plant, the appropriate name of *R. spiralis* was taken up for the other species. Gamerro (1968) found an earlier name for *Ruppia spiralis* in *R. cirrhosa*, and this was brought to the attention of British and Irish botanists by Dandy (1969). As the name *R. maritima* has been used in three different senses, historical records should be treated with caution. The meaning a particular author attaches to the name has to be worked out from the date of publication of his work and internal evidence in the work itself.

English names

I have followed the other B.S.B.I. Handbooks which deal with flowering plants in giving English names for species but not hybrids. These names are taken from Stace (1991). If different names are widely used in the American literature, I have added these after Stace's names. The reader would be well advised to ignore the English names. In recent years I have spoken (almost obsessively, I fear) to many people about pondweeds, and I have led field meetings where those present have ranged from beginners to experts. I can remember only one occasion when a pondweed has been referred to by its English name. The conventional wisdom is that "the provision of English names is important in increasing the numbers of people with an interest in and a knowledge of wild plants" (Stace 1991). While this may be true for the more showy groups, I cannot believe anyone prepared to devote time and effort to learning the pondweeds would be deterred if the species with the most flattened stems had to be referred to as "*Potamogeton compressus*" rather than "Grass-wrack Pondweed". In order to understand this arcane English name one has to know that *P. compressus* was formerly known as *P. zosterifolius*, that *zosterifolius* means *Zostera*-leaved and that grass-wrack is an obselete English name for *Zostera*.

SYNOPSIS OF CLASSIFICATION AND ARRANGEMENT OF TAXA

The synopsis below sets out the classification adopted in this book. This classification is discussed in the following chapter. The descriptions of the families, genera, subgenera and sections cover only the British and Irish representatives. The species belonging to each of the higher taxa are listed, with the numbers they have been given in this book. *Potamogeton* hybrids are listed together after the species.

In general I have listed the *Potamogeton* species in the order in which they appear in Stace (1991) and Kent (1992), which in turn follows Clapham, Tutin & Warburg (1952) and Dandy (1958, 1980). The only departure from this order has been to move *P. polygonifolius* and *P. coloratus* from their traditional position after *P. natans* to a position immediately before *P. alpinus*. *P. polygonifolius* and *P. coloratus* were originally confused by British botanists with *P. natans* and later regarded as varieties of that species. However, they lack the phyllodes of *P. natans* and are almost certainly more closely related to *P. alpinus*. Fryer pointed out that the similarity of *P. natans* to *P. polygonifolius* is superficial (Fryer & Bennett 1915), and the relationship of the latter to *P. alpinus* has been recognised by Wiegleb (1988b), who places *P. alpinus*, *P. coloratus* and *P. polygonifolius* in the informal '*P. polygonifolius* group' of species.

Potamogetonaceae

Glabrous perennials of aquatic or (rarely) subterrestrial habitats. Rhizome present or absent; if present, usually well differentiated from the stem, sympodial. Stems terete to flattened, with or without nodal glands. Leaves alternate or opposite; submerged leaves usually present, *either* (a) reduced to phyllodes, *or* (b) arising directly from the nodes, sessile or petiolate, usually with an adaxial stipule, the lamina linear to broadly ovate, linear in cross-section with a conspicuous midrib and 1–12 parallel lateral veins on each side, the midrib not bordered by air channels, the margin entire or denticulate, *or* (c) with a sheathing base and a free lamina, with a ligule at the junction of the sheath and the lamina, the lamina linear to filiform, circular, semicircular, elliptical or caniculate in cross-section with an inconspicuous midrib and 1–2 lateral veins on each side, the midrib bordered by air channels, the margin entire. Floating leaves present or absent; if present, petiolate. Inflorescences with 2 opposite flowers or more than 2 flowers in a dense or interrupted spike; peduncles rigid or flexuous. Flowers hypogynous, with 4 tepals, 4 virtually sessile anthers alternating with the carpels, and (1–)4(–7) carpels, the carpels each with a single ovary, the carpel stalk not elongating after fertilisation. Pollen grains spherical. Fruits indehiscent, without raised tubercles on the surface.

Potamogeton L.

Rhizome, if present, well differentiated from the stem. Leaves (except for those subtending an inflorescence) alternate, submerged or floating, *either* (a) arising directly from the nodes, sessile or petiolate, with stipules present on all leaves, although sometimes fugacious, *or* (b) with a sheathing base and a free lamina, with a ligule at the junction of the sheath and the lamina. Inflorescences with at least three flowers in a spike. Fruits with a stony endocarp. Cotyledon curved in the seed.

Subgenus *Potamogeton*

Rhizome present or absent. Stems terete to flattened, with or without nodal glands. Submerged leaves *either* (a) reduced to phyllodes, *or* (b) arising directly from the nodes, sessile or petiolate, the lamina linear to broadly ovate, linear in cross-section with a conspicuous midrib and 1–12 lateral veins on each side, the midrib not bordered by air channels, the margin entire or denticulate. Floating leaves present or absent. Peduncles rigid.

Section *Potamogeton*

Rhizome present. Stems terete, without longitudinal grooves; nodal glands absent. Submerged leaves reduced to phyllodes or linear-elliptical to broadly ovate, sessile or petiolate, the margins entire or denticulate. Floating leaves present or absent. Stipules rounded to acute at the apex. Plants not producing turions. Beak less than half as long as the rest of the fruit.

1.   P. natans L.
2.   P. nodosus Poir.
3.   P. lucens L.
4.   P. gramineus L.
5.   P. polygonifolius Pourr.

6. P. coloratus Hornem.
7. P. alpinus Balb.
8. P. praelongus Wulfen
9. P. perfoliatus L.

Section *Graminifolii* Fr.

Rhizome usually absent, rarely present (*P. epihydrus*). Stems terete to flattened, without longitudinal grooves; nodal glands sometimes present. Floating leaves absent or rarely present (*P. epihydrus*). Stipules rounded to obtuse at the apex, rarely truncate or emarginate (*P. epihydrus*). Plants often producing turions. Beak less than half as long as the rest of the fruit.

10. P. epihydrus Raf.
11. P. friesii Rupr.
12. P. rutilus Wolfg.
13. P. pusillus L.
14. P. obtusifolius Mert. & W. D. J. Koch
15. P. berchtoldii Fieber
16. P. trichoides Cham. & Schltdl.
17. P. compressus L.
18. P. acutifolius Link

Section *Batrachoseris* Irmisch

Rhizome present. Stems compressed, with a shallow groove running down one or both of the broader sides; nodal glands absent. Submerged leaves linear-oblong to oblong, sessile, the margins serrate especially towards the leaf apex. Floating leaves absent. Stipules truncate or emarginate at the apex. Plants often producing turions. Beak at least half as long as the rest of the fruit.

19. P. crispus L.

Subgenus *Coleogeton* Rchb.

Rhizome present. Stems terete, without nodal glands. Submerged leaves with a sheathing base and a free lamina, with a ligule at the junction of the sheath and the lamina, the lamina linear to filiform, circular, semicircular, elliptical or canaliculate in cross-section with an inconspicuous midrib and 1–2 lateral veins on each side, the midrib bordered by air channels, the margin entire. Floating leaves absent. Peduncles flexuous.

20. P. filiformis Pers.
21. P. pectinatus L.

Potamogeton hybrids

The hybrids are arranged so that plants of similar morphology are grouped together. The hybrids between species in Subgenus *Potamogeton* (22–46) are followed by the one hybrid between the species in Subgenus *Coleogeton* (47). Within Subgenus *Potamogeton*, the first group of hybrids (22–32) can have both floating and submerged leaves. The hybrids in this group with both parents in Section *Potamogeton* (22–30) precede those between a parent in this section and one in Section *Graminifolii* (31–32). All the remaining hybrids have submerged but not floating leaves, with the possible exception of 39, *P.* × *olivaceus*. These include hybrids with both parents in Section *Potamogeton* (33–37), the hybrids of *P. crispus* (Section *Batrachoseris*) with members of Section *Potamogeton* (38–41) and Section *Graminifolii* (42, 43), and those hybrids with both parents in Section *Graminifolii* (44–46).

22. P. × schreberi G. Fisch. (P. natans × nodosus)
23. P. × fluitans Roth (P. lucens × natans)
24. P. × sparganiifolius Laest. ex Fr. (P. natans × gramineus)
25. P. × gessnacensis G. Fisch. (P. natans × polygonifolius)
26. P. × zizii W. D. J. Koch ex Roth (P. gramineus × lucens)
27. P. × lanceolatifolius (Tiselius) C. D. Preston (P. gramineus × polygonifolius)
28. P. × billupsii Fryer (P. coloratus × gramineus)
29. P. × nericius Hagstr. (P. alpinus × gramineus)
30. P. × nitens Weber (P. gramineus × perfoliatus)
31. P. × variifolius Thore (P. berchtoldii × natans)
32. P. × lanceolatus Sm. (P. berchtoldii × coloratus)
33. P. × nerviger Wolfg. (P. alpinus × lucens)
34. P. × salicifolius Wolfg. (P. lucens × perfoliatus)
35. P. × griffithii A. Benn. (P. alpinus × praelongus)
36. P. × prussicus Hagstr. (P. alpinus × perfoliatus)
37. P. × cognatus Asch. & Graebn. (P. perfoliatus × praelongus)
38. P. × cadburyae Dandy & G. Taylor (P. crispus × lucens)
39. P. × olivaceus Baagöe ex G. Fisch. (P. alpinus × crispus)

40. P. × undulatus Wolfg. (P. crispus × praelongus)
41. P. × cooperi Fryer (P. crispus × perfoliatus)
42. P. × lintonii Fryer (P. crispus × friesii)
43. P. × bennettii Fryer (P. crispus × trichoides)
44. P. × grovesii Dandy & G. Taylor (P. pusillus × trichoides)
45. P. × pseudofriesii Dandy & G. Taylor (P. acutifolius × friesii)
46. P. × sudermanicus Hagstr. (P. acutifolius × berchtoldii)
47. P. × suecicus K. Richt. (P. filiformis × pectinatus)

Groenlandia J. Gay

Rhizome present, poorly differentiated from the stem. Leaves opposite, submerged, arising directly from the nodes, sessile, with stipules present only on the leaves which subtend branches or peduncles. Inflorescences with 2 opposite flowers. Fruits without a stony endocarp. Cotyledon spirally coiled in the seed.

48. G. densa (L.) Fourr.

Ruppiaceae

Glabrous perennials of aquatic, brackish habitats. Rhizome present, poorly differentiated from the stem, monopodial. Stems terete, without nodal glands. Leaves (except for those which subtend an inflorescence) alternate, submerged, with a sheathing base and a free lamina, without a ligule at the junction of the sheath and the lamina, the lamina linear to filiform, elliptical in cross-section with an inconspicuous midrib bordered by air channels, lateral veins absent, the margin denticulate at the apex. Floating leaves absent. Inflorescences with 2 flowers *c.* 1.5 mm apart; peduncles flexuous. Flowers hypogynous, without tepals, with 2 virtually sessile anthers and 2–8 carpels, the carpels with a single ovary, the carpel stalk elongating after fertilisation. Pollen grains V-shaped. Fruits indehiscent, with raised tubercles on the surface.

Ruppia L.

The only genus.

49. R. maritima L.
50. R. cirrhosa (Petagna) Grande

CLASSIFICATION AND EVOLUTION

The families

The two families treated in this Handbook, the Potamogetonaceae and the Ruppiaceae, are grouped by Cronquist (1981) in the order Najadales. The other families in this order which are found in the British Isles are the Aponogetonaceae (with the introduced genus *Aponogeton*), Scheuchzeriaceae (*Scheuchzeria*), Juncaginaceae (*Triglochin*), Najadaceae (*Najas*), Zannichelliaceae (*Zannichellia*) and Zosteraceae (*Zostera*). The order also includes the seagrasses in the families Posidoniaceae and Cymodoceaceae, which are found in warmer seas than ours. Two closely related orders, the Alismatales (Alismataceae, Limnocharitaceae and Butomaceae) and Hydrocharitales (Hydrocharitaceae), are classified by Cronquist with the Najadales in the subclass Alismatidae. The Alismatidae is one of the subclasses in the class Liliopsida, commonly known as the monocotyledons.

The families included by Cronquist in the Alismatidae have been consistently grouped together by systematists over the years. This traditional view has recently received support from an analysis of chloroplast DNA, which suggested that the Alismataceae and the Potamogetonaceae were more closely related to each other than to any of the other monocot families tested (Chase *et al.* 1993). Tomlinson (1982) argues that the families of the Alismatidae are members of a natural assemblage, which presumably possess a common ancestor, but that they have undergone adaptive radiation to a remarkable degree. This has led to enormous variation within the group, not least in floral characters.

The two families Potamogetonaceae and Ruppiaceae are closely related. I have treated them as distinct, following Stace (1991) and Kent (1992), who in turn follow Cronquist (1981). However, many recent authors (e.g. Tomlinson 1982, Jacobs & Brock 1982, Dahlgren, Clifford & Yeo 1985, Cook 1990) have treated the Ruppiaceae as a subfamily of the Potamogetonaceae. *Ruppia* resembles *Potamogeton* Subgenus *Coleogeton* in its vegetative structure: these taxa share leaves which have a sheathing base and a linear lamina. However, the rhizomes of *Ruppia* are more poorly differentiated, the leaves lack a ligule at the junction of the sheath and the lamina and the leaf apex is minutely toothed. There are more fundamental differences between the floral morphology of the two families. The flowers of *Ruppia* lack tepals and possess two rather than four stamens, and the carpels have a stalk which usually elongates after fertilisation.

More details of all the families in the Alismatidae can be found in Heywood (1978), Cronquist (1981), Dahlgren, Clifford & Yeo (1985) and Cook (1990).

The genera

All but one of the species in the Potamogetonaceae are included in the genus *Potamogeton*. This is one of the most important of aquatic vascular plant genera, and it is present in all major areas of the world except for the cold deserts of the Arctic and Antarctic and hot deserts elsewhere. Wiegleb (1988b) estimates that there are some 80–90 species, although it is impossible to give a precise total in the absence of a recent world monograph.

One species in the Potamogetonaceae was also included by older authors in *Potamogeton*, as *P. densus*, but is now regarded as sufficiently distinct to be placed in the separate genus *Groenlandia*. The differences which have traditionally been used to delimit *Groenlandia* from *Potamogeton* include the opposite leaves, inflorescences with two flowers, fruits which lack a stony endocarp, and seeds which contain a spirally coiled rather than a curved cotyledon. Recent research on the taxonomic significance of pollen morphology has supported the separation of *Groenlandia* as a distinct genus (Sorsa 1988). Some authors (e.g. Tomlinson 1982, Dahlgren, Clifford & Yeo 1985) claim that *Groenlandia* is an annual and that this is an additional distinction from the species of *Potamogeton*. However, the British populations of *Groenlandia* with which I am familiar overwinter as vegetative shoots and are clearly perennial. My observations correspond exactly to Goodyer's description of the winter-green habit of *Groenlandia* (Gerarde 1633) and to Fryer's description of the life history of the plant (Fryer & Bennett 1915). Furthermore, many linear-leaved species of *Potamogeton* behave as annuals. The genus *Groenlandia* has a more restricted distribution than that of *Potamogeton*, being confined to Europe, S.W. Asia and N. Africa.

The family Ruppiaceae contains a single genus, *Ruppia*; the characters of the genus are therefore those of the family. The genus is found in brackish waters in all temperate, subtropical or tropical parts of the world. It is only rarely found in freshwater habitats.

The species of *Ruppia* are closely related and few in number, and there is nothing to be gained by attempting to subdivide the genus. However, the species of *Potamogeton* are not only numerous but diverse and they can usefully be subdivided. They fall naturally into two subgenera.

The subgenera of *Potamogeton*

The major subdivision of the genus *Potamogeton* is that between Subgenus *Potamogeton* and Subgenus *Coleogeton*. In the British Isles the only members of Subgenus *Coleogeton* are *P. filiformis* and *P. pectinatus*; the European *P. vaginatus* also falls into this group. The two subgenera are easily distinguished in the field and (with a little practice) in the herbarium, even if only vegetative material is available. It is well worth mastering the distinctions between them, as there is then no possibility of confusing unusual variants of the protean *P. pectinatus* (Subgenus *Coleogeton*) with linear-leaved species of Subgenus *Potamogeton*.

The main vegetative difference between the subgenera is that the leaves of species in Subgenus *Potamogeton* arise directly from the stem, with a stipule arising on the upper side of the node and lying between the stem and the leaf. In Subgenus *Coleogeton* there is a sheath which enfolds the stem above the node, and the free leaf lamina arises at the apex of this sheath. A small translucent ligule is present at the junction of the sheath and the lamina. The arrangement of sheath, ligule and lamina parallels that found in the grasses. Leaves with sheathing bases are also found in other aquatic monocots such as *Eleogiton*, *Juncus* and *Ruppia*. For this reason, the members of Subgenus *Coleogeton* are more likely to be confused with plants in other genera than they are with species in Subgenus *Potamogeton*. The leaf of Subgenus *Coleogeton* is a cylinder which in section is circular, semicircular, elliptical or canaliculate and has in the centre an inconspicuous midrib surrounded on each side by one or more air channels. By contrast, the leaf of Subgenus *Potamogeton* has a conspicuous central midrib which in section projects above and below the surface of the otherwise flat lamina.

There are fundamental differences between the subgenera in the reproductive organs. The flowers of Subgenus *Coleogeton* are borne on a very slender and flexuous peduncle, normally flesh pink in colour, and they usually float on the surface of the water. The pollen is released on the surface of the water and pollination takes place at or below the water surface. The peduncles of Subgenus *Potamogeton* range in width from very slender to very robust and in colour from virtually colourless to green. However, all have some rigidity and at anthesis usually hold the inflorescence above the water level, and the flowers can therefore be wind-pollinated.

The species of Subgenus *Coleogeton* are rhizomatous, whereas those in Subgenus *Potamogeton* have a range of growth form. The rhizomes of *Coleogeton* have characteristic ovoid tubers which act as a means of perennation and vegetative spread.

The major division between the pollen types found in the genus *Potamogeton* is that between the pollen of the two subgenera (Sorsa 1988). The chromosome numbers of the subgenera also differ: whereas the British members of Subgenus *Coleogeton* have 2n=78, those in Subgenus *Potamogeton* have 2n=26, 28 or 52. If only the European species of *Potamogeton* were considered there would be a strong argument for considering the two subgenera as distinct genera. However, *P. robbinsii* of North America and *P. serrulatus* of East Asia are said by Hagström (1916) to be significant connecting links between the two groups. However, Les & Sheridan (1990a) performed a cladistic analysis on morphological data derived from Hagström (1916) and suggested that the results did not support Hagström's contention that these two species were connecting links between the two subgenera. A re-evaluation of the position of *P. robbinsii* and *P. serrulatus* would be worthwhile.

Hagström (1916) subdivided the relatively small Subgenus *Coleogeton* into sections on the basis of the structure of their stipular sheaths. He included *P. filiformis* in Section *Connati* and *P. pectinatus* in Section *Convoluti*. However, there is little point in adopting these sections in an identification guide to the British and Irish species. By contrast, the species of Subgenus *Potamogeton* are morphologically diverse and can usefully be subdivided into three sections.

The sections of *Potamogeton* Subgenus *Potamogeton*

Three sections of *Potamogeton* Subgenus *Potamogeton* can be recognised in the British Isles. Two of these sections are themselves divided into subsections by Hagström and many later authors, but these rather fine divisions are not necessary for our purposes. At the world scale the subsections are usually regarded as being the fundamental units in the genus, and there is currently much discussion in the literature about the validity of Hagström's treatment. The description of the sections below refers solely to the British and Irish representatives.

Section *Potamogeton* consists of rhizomatous plants with terete stems. Almost all species have broad submerged leaves (although these are absent in *P. natans*). In addition, many species also have coriaceous floating leaves. Vegetative perennation is usually by elongated buds on the rhizomes; occasionally similar buds are found on short shoots in the lower leaf axils. None of the species produce turions.

The British and Irish members of Section *Graminifolii* are not rhizomatous. The stems are often but by no means always compressed, and several species have well-developed nodal glands. The species have narrow, linear submerged leaves and lack floating leaves. They regularly produce turions. There is one exception to these generalisations, *P. epihydrus*. This is a rhizomatous plant with compressed lower stems, linear submerged leaves and broad floating leaves. It lacks specialised turions. In terms of the European species it is clearly anomalous, but some other North American species combine linear submerged leaves and broad floating leaves. It is interesting to note that this combination of characters has been achieved in Europe by hybrids between Section *Potamogeton* and Section *Graminifolii*.

Potamogeton crispus is sufficiently distinct to be placed in its own section, Section *Batrachoseris*. This is characterised by compressed stems with a groove running down the broader sides, markedly serrate leaves, and fruits with a beak which is at least half as long as the rest of the fruit. Many accounts (e.g. Fryer & Bennett 1915, Clapham, Tutin & Warburg 1952, Stace 1991) claim that the beak is approximately equal in length to the rest of the fruit, but this is an exaggeration. *P. crispus* regularly produces turions of a distinctive form.

The species

The species of *Potamogeton* Section *Potamogeton* are in general well defined 'Linnaean species' which differ in many characters. There are, for example, significant differences between the species in this section not only in morphology but also in life history. The two most closely related species in the section are *P. coloratus* and *P. polygonifolius*, which are usually separable in a vegetative state but sometimes can be identified only if mature fruits are present.

In Section *Graminifolii P. epihydrus* is a distinct plant. However, the differences between the remaining linear-leaved species tend to be much less marked than those between the broad-leaved species, perhaps in part because the plants have a simpler morphology and thus present fewer characters to the taxonomist. There are a number of pairs of similar species such as *P. acutifolius* and *P. compressus*, *P. berchtoldii* and *P. obtusifolius*, and *P. pusillus* and *P. friesii*. Crucial characters separating the species of Section *Graminifolii* include the width and venation of the leaves, the width of the midrib, the morphology of the stipules and the turions, and the number of carpels in the flower. Careful examination is required to establish some of these characters and thus identify the species.

The similarity of two slender-leaved species of Section *Graminifolii*, *P. berchtoldii* and *P. pusillus*, has led Haynes (1974) to treat *P. berchtoldii* as a variety, var. *tenuissimus* Mert. & Koch, of *P. pusillus*. His decision was made because he was unwilling to define the taxa as species on the basis of stipule morphology, and he found that other characters correlated imperfectly with this character. I have preferred to treat these two taxa as species differing in the morphology of the stipules and the shape of the turions, although I recognise that this taxonomy relies on a single character of the stipules to a much greater extent than would be desirable in an ideal world. However, I do not think that *P. berchtoldii* and *P. pusillus* are more closely related to each other than they are to other members of the genus. Vegetative material of *P. berchtoldii* and *P. obtusifolius* can be difficult to distinguish, as the vegetative distinctions between these two taxa are purely quantitative. Similarly, *P. pusillus* can approach *P. friesii* in key vegetative characters such as the venation of the leaves and the presence of two green ribs along the stipules. I prefer to recognise all these taxa as species, acknowledging that they are rather closely allied.

The two species in Subgenus *Coleogeton* differ in habit, sheath morphology and fruit shape.

Definition of species in the genus *Ruppia* is hampered by the fact that the plants possess few taxonomic characters, and the available characters exhibit considerable phenotypic variation. Some authorities recognise only a single, variable species in the genus. However, it does seem possible to distinguish two species, *R. cirrhosa* and *R. maritima*, in the British Isles, and these species are also recognised by other recent authors in western Europe (e.g. Reese 1963, Verhoeven 1979). The vegetative distinctions between these two species are, however, much less clear than is sometimes suggested, and they cannot be relied on for identification.

Evolution of the Potamogetonaceae and Ruppiaceae

The simple vegetative and reproductive structures of the Potamogetonaceae and Ruppiaceae are believed to be the result of reduction from more complex ancestors. "It is a well-known fact – indeed almost a truism – that structural reduction is one of the most marked characteristics of water plants" (Arber 1920). Vegetative material of *Ruppia* and some linear-leaved *Potamogeton* species can easily be confused with some unrelated genera such as *Eleogiton* (Cyperaceae) and *Juncus* (Juncaceae). This similarity is the result of convergent evolution.

The ancestors of the Potamogetonaceae and Ruppiaceae have not been identified. Many authors have regarded the families of the Alismatidae as primitive monocotyledons and have drawn attention to apparent similarities between the Alismatales and aquatic dicotyledons in the Nymphaeales (e.g. *Nymphaea*, *Nuphar*). Cronquist (1981) suggests that the primitive dicots which gave rise to the monocots were probably "something like the modern Nymphaeales" and that the Alismatidae are an ancient group of monocots which diverged from the rest at an early stage. He does not regard the Alismatidae as being directly ancestral to the other monocots. This view has recently received some support from molecular studies which have revealed a link between the monocots and a group of 'paleoherbs' including the Nymphaeaceae (Chase *et al.* 1993). An advantage of the hypothesis that the monocots arose from aquatic dicots is that it provides an evolutionary bottleneck which could explain the absence of secondary thickening in the monocots. However, Dahlgren, Clifford & Yeo (1985) think that the hypothesis that the route of monocot evolution was from proto-Nymphaeales to proto-Alismatales is not very likely. They suggest that many of the similarities between the Alismatales and Nymphaeales are the result of convergent evolution caused by the selection pressures which result from life in an aquatic environment. Tomlinson (1982) also expresses reservations about the idea of the Alismatidae as an archaic group.

The relationship of the Potamogetonaceae to the Ruppiaceae is another area of uncertainty. C. D. K. Cook has suggested that the Ruppiaceae evolved from the Potamogetonaceae by reduction (Heywood 1978).

Evolution within the Potamogetonaceae

Les & Sheridan (1990a) have identified three theories which have been put forward to account for the current range in morphological variation in the Potamogetonaceae.

1. The ancestral species were aquatics with linear submerged leaves. Species with broad, submerged leaves and heterophyllous species (which have both submerged and floating leaves) evolved from these.

2. The ancestral species were aquatics with broad submerged leaves, having evolved from broad-leaved terrestrial plants. *Potamogeton* species with linear submerged leaves and the heterophyllous species are derived from them.

3. The ancestral species were heterophyllous. Species with only broad and those with only linear submerged leaves are derived from them.

The first hypothesis was that favoured by Hagström (1916), who regarded the genus *Groenlandia* and the Subgenus *Coleogeton* as derived at an early stage from the ancestral species (see Les & Sheridan 1990a). Haynes (1974) also suggests that the primitive species of *Potamogeton* were linear-leaved plants with numerous veins and were wind-pollinated. Les (1983), however, points out that it is difficult to accept that pondweeds arose from ancestors which were totally submerged yet characterised by wind pollination. As a result of their cladistic analysis, Les & Sheridan (1990a) suggest that the ancestors of the genus were broad-leaved homophyllous species. According to this view the species of Subgenus *Coleogeton*, far from being a separate and early diverging lineage, are a highly specialised group derived from the species in Section *Graminifolii*. There is as yet no consensus about which of the above hypotheses is the most likely to be correct, let alone any direct evidence which would allow one to be chosen with any confidence. It seems that our ignorance of evolution within the genus is as great as our ignorance of the evolution of the genus itself.

HYBRIDISATION IN *POTAMOGETON*

Evidence for hybridisation in the genus

The significance of hybridisation in the genus *Potamogeton* was not appreciated by early students of the genus. In the British Isles its importance was first realised by Fryer in 1889 and 1890 (Preston 1988a). Despite the fact that hybrids have been known for over a century, it must be admitted that almost all the evidence for their existence comes from morphological studies and from the sterility of putative hybrids. I do not know of any attempt to synthesise *Potamogeton* hybrids, and isozyme studies which will provide an additional line of evidence have only just begun. Nevertheless, the existence of hybrids is not likely to be doubted by anyone who is familiar with the morphology of the species. The hybrids between dissimilar species, such as *P. natans* and *P. berchtoldii*, *P. coloratus* and *P. berchtoldii*, or *P. crispus* and several broad-leaved species, are particularly striking. The existence of hybrids can, I believe, be taken as an accepted fact, even though the proof of their nature is not as complete as it is in genera such as *Salix* where the synthesis of hybrids is relatively straightforward. There is, however, an area of doubt about the putative parentage of a few of the hybrids recognised in the British Isles. Dandy and Taylor did not recognise any triple hybrids in the genus, nor did they ever suggest that introgression might occur. However, there is little information on the viability of the pollen of hybrids, and it would be unwise to rule out the possibility of some hybrids back-crossing with one of the parent species.

The importance of hybridisation in the genus does not lie in the number of hybrids recorded, but in the capacity of hybrids to persist and spread vegetatively once they are established. The figures below, taken from Kent (1992), show that the number of hybrids in *Potamogeton* is less than that in several other genera of similar size where the species are distinct but prone to hybridisation:

Epilobium	14 species, 42 hybrid combinations
Potamogeton	21 species, 26 hybrid combinations
Rumex	21 species, 34 hybrid combinations
Salix	22 species, 61 hybrid combinations

It is possible that the establishment of a *Potamogeton* hybrid from seed is actually rather a rare event. However, there is no doubt that many hybrids can persist and spread vegetatively once established. We have evidence that some were present in their current localities when botanists first began to take a critical interest in the genus in the 19th century, and the apparently relict distribution of *P.* × *suecicus* suggests that it may have been present in the River Wharfe and River Ure for thousands of years. There is every reason to suppose that such a hybrid might persist indefinitely if habitat conditions remain suitable.

No hybrids involving *Groenlandia* or *Ruppia* are known.

Occurrence of hybrids in the genus

The occurrence of hybrids in *Potamogeton* is summarised in Figure 1 (overleaf). This is an updated version of a figure originally published by Taylor (1949). It can be seen that, although hybrids occur within both Subgenus *Coleogeton* and Subgenus *Potamogeton*, no hybrids between the subgenera are known. It is not known whether this is because of genetic incompatibility or because of the difference in pollination biology between the two subgenera.

In Subgenus *Potamogeton*, hybrids appear to be more frequent in Section *Potamogeton* than in Section *Graminifolii*. This may be a genuine difference, perhaps resulting from the fact that reproduction in Section *Graminifolii* is often vegetative, as Fernald (1932) suggested. However, the differences between the linear-leaved species are less obvious than those between the broad-leaved species, and it is possible that we are overlooking hybrids between them or ascribing them to one or other of the parents. Hybrids are known with one parent in Section *Graminifolii* and the other in Section *Potamogeton* and between *P. crispus* of the monotypic Section *Batrachoseris* and species in both the other sections.

Map 1 (overleaf) summarises the distribution of hybrids in Britain and Ireland.

Sterility of hybrids

Only one hybrid, *P.* × *zizii*, ever produces an infructescence of numerous well-formed fruit. The fertility of *P.* × *zizii* is variable, however, and some flowering populations appear to set no fruit. Some other hybrids, including *P.* × *fluitans* and *P.* × *sudermanicus*, may produce the odd well-formed fruit in an otherwise sterile inflorescence. I do not know if these well-formed fruits are capable of germination. Many hybrids show no sign of fruiting. In her detailed investigation of *P.* × *suecicus*, Bance (1946) showed that the pollen initially develops normally but later the walls of the grains split and the contents disintegrate.

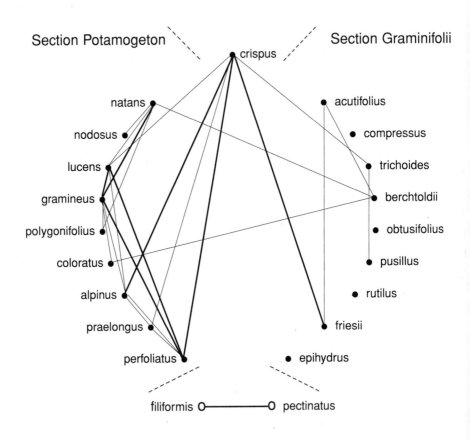

Section Batrachoseris

Section Potamogeton

Section Graminifolii

crispus

natans
nodosus
lucens
gramineus
polygonifolius
coloratus
alpinus
praelongus
perfoliatus

acutifolius
compressus
trichoides
berchtoldii
obtusifolius
pusillus
rutilus
friesii
epihydrus

filiformis O———————O pectinatus

Figure 1

The occurrence of *Potamogeton* hybrids in Britain and Ireland. The parents of widespread hybrids are linked by thick lines; those of rare or casual hybrids are linked by thin lines. Species in Subgenus *Potamogeton* are shown by solid dots (●); those in Subgenus *Coleogeton* are shown by open symbols (O).

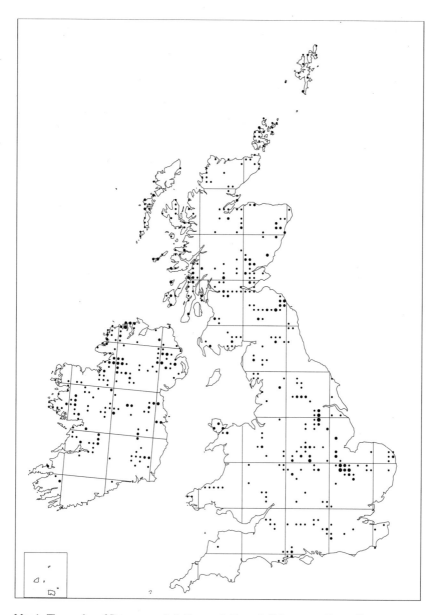

Map 1. The number of *Potamogeton* hybrids recorded in each 10-km square. Dots of increasing size indicate that 1, 2, 3, 4 or 5 hybrids have been recorded in the square. All records are included, irrespective of date.

Recognition of hybrids

Any plant with numerous well-formed fruit is unlikely to be a hybrid, especially if the possibility that it is *P.* × *zizii* can be ruled out on morphological grounds. Unfortunately, although fertility can be used to rule out the possibility of a plant being a hybrid, sterility is of little use in identifying a hybrid. Many pondweeds are only found as vegetative material. Even if a plant appears to be failing to set fruit, this could be for reasons other than hybridity. Plants of *P. pectinatus*, for example, fail to fruit when growing in rivers with a fast current (Bance 1946, van Wijk 1988). It is possible that a study of the pollen of species and hybrids might show that hybrids have a higher proportion of sterile pollen, but this would be of limited use in recognising that a plant was a hybrid unless one already suspected hybridity on morphological grounds. The inflorescences of hybrids, like those of fertile species, initially have closed tepals through which the stigmas protrude. The tepals of species then open to reveal the anthers and the carpels, but those of hybrids usually remain tightly closed. The anthers of hybrids often appear to be incompletely filled. These characters might provide supporting evidence that a plant is a hybrid, but I would not rely on them in the absence of other indications.

The unfortunate truth is that it is normally not possible to recognise that a plant is a hybrid *per se*. Hybrids are normally recognised by a combination of two mental processes. The more important is probably the fact that one becomes familiar with the appearance of individual hybrids and so comes to recognise '*Potamogeton* × *cooperi*' or '*P.* × *salicifolius*' just as one would recognise a species. It is also true that, as one learns the range of variation of the species, one is increasingly likely to recognise plants that are intermediate between two species. Because the recognition of hybrids requires some experience of the species, and preferably of the hybrids as well, beginners are likely to overlook them or to assign them to a species. It is not uncommon for hybrids to be identified not as one of the parental species but as a third species: *P.* × *nitens* and *P.* × *salicifolius* are sometimes identified as *P. praelongus*, for example, and *P.* × *bennettii* and *P.* × *lintonii* as *P. obtusifolius*.

The four hybrids of *Potamogeton crispus* with broad-leaved species, *P.* × *cadburyae*, *P.* × *olivaceus*, *P.* × *undulatus* and *P.* × *cooperi*, form a distinctive group. They can be recognised by stems which are slightly compressed or compressed with a groove running down one or both of the broader sides, truncate stipules, and leaves which are not dissimilar to those of the broad-leaved parent but have a reduced number of lateral veins. Somewhat surprisingly, the serration of the leaf margins of *P. crispus* is not a marked feature of its hybrids. The two hybrids between *P. crispus* and linear-leaved species, *P.* × *bennettii* and

P. × lintonii, resemble a linear-leaved species but have stems which tend to be grooved along one or both of the broader sides, truncate stipules, and some toothing of the margin towards the apex of the leaf. Another group of hybrids which have a distinct appearance are those of *P. natans*, i.e. *P. × schreberi*, *P. × fluitans*, *P. × sparganiifolius*, *P. × gessnacensis* and *P. × variifolius*. A characteristic feature of *P. natans* is the fact that the submerged leaves are phyllodes, and its hybrids often have phyllodes at the base of the stem but upper submerged leaves which are intermediate between the phyllodes of *P. natans* and the leaves of the other parent.

The persistence and distribution of hybrids in Britain and Ireland

The *Potamogeton* hybrids present in Britain and Ireland can be grouped into three categories. These are somewhat arbitrarily defined on the basis of their persistence and distribution.

Widespread hybrids

There are eight hybrids which are well established in the British Isles and have been recorded from 1970 onwards in at least ten 10-km squares:

> P. × cooperi (P. crispus × perfoliatus)
> P. × lintonii (P. crispus × friesii)
> P. × nitens (P. gramineus × perfoliatus)
> P. × olivaceus (P. alpinus × crispus)
> P. × salicifolius (P. lucens × perfoliatus)
> P. × sparganiifolius (P. gramineus × natans)
> P. × suecicus (P. filiformis × pectinatus)
> P. × zizii (P. gramineus × lucens)

One of the rarer hybrids in this group is *P. × olivaceus*, which is well established in four river systems from the Afon Teifi in Wales to the River Ythan in Scotland. Neither of its parents has been recorded in the Teifi. The commonest hybrid is *P. × nitens*, which is not infrequent in some areas in the north and west, where it behaves virtually as an independent species (only differing from a species in being sterile). It is not uncommon to find *P. × nitens* in water bodies in the absence of one or both of its parents. In south-east England this hybrid is much more local and it is usually found in sites from which its parents have been recorded. *P. × zizii* also has a distribution which differs from that of its parents in that it is more frequent in the less calcareous areas of western Scotland and western Ireland than *P. lucens*.

These are well-established and persistent in at least one locality, but have been recorded from 1970 onwards in fewer than ten 10-km squares. The following 13 hybrids fall into this category:

P. × bennettii (P. crispus × trichoides)
P. × billupsii (P. coloratus × gramineus)
P. × cognatus (P. perfoliatus × praelongus)
P. × fluitans (P. lucens × natans)
P. × gessnacensis (P. natans × polygonifolius)
P. × griffithii (P. alpinus × praelongus)
P. × lanceolatus (P. berchtoldii × coloratus)
P. × nericius (P. alpinus × gramineus)
P. × nerviger (P. alpinus × lucens)
P. × schreberi (P. natans × nodosus)
P. × sudermanicus (P. acutifolius × berchtoldii)
P. × undulatus (P. crispus × praelongus)
P. × variifolius (P. berchtoldii × natans)

Two examples illustrate the hybrids in this group. *P. × bennettii* was discovered with both parents in 1890 in artificial wood-storage ponds at Grangemouth, near the east end of the Forth and Clyde Canal. It was last collected from these ponds in 1937, and the ponds have since been built over. However, it was found in the western part of the canal itself in 1960, and it is now known to be widespread in the Forth and Clyde Canal in the Glasgow area. It reproduces by turions, which doubtless explains its ability to spread in the canal. It has never been recorded elsewhere. *P. × lanceolatus* is rather more widespread. It was described from the Afon Lligwy in Anglesey, where it persisted for over 150 years but has not been seen recently. It is, however, established in several calcareous streams in western Ireland, including three sites where it was first recorded in the last century. *P. coloratus* grows in one of these Irish streams, but *P. berchtoldii* has not been recorded from any of the Irish localities for the hybrid. The only other population of *P. × lanceolatus* was found with both parents in a ditch in Cambridgeshire in 1880, but the ditch became overgrown and the hybrid failed to persist. Reproduction of *P. × lanceolatus* is also by turions, which can be produced in quantity.

Casual hybrids

These are hybrids which are known from only a few localities, at which they apparently failed to persist. The best example is the distinctive *P. × cadburyae*.

A single plant was found by Miss D. A. Cadbury at Seeswood Pool, Warwickshire, in 1948. The hybrid has never been refound there, nor has it been discovered elsewhere. *P.* × *pseudofriesii*, also known from a single collection made by Miss Cadbury, and *P.* × *grovesii*, known from two collections, fall into this group, although the latter would be difficult to detect in the field and might be overlooked elsewhere. *P.* × *prussicus* and *P.* × *lanceolatifolius* may also belong here, but further fieldwork is needed before they can be placed with confidence in this rather than the last category.

The European distribution of the British and Irish hybrids

It is interesting to compare the distribution of hybrids in the British Isles with the wider distribution of the same taxa. Unfortunately, there is no recent, detailed account of the distribution of *Potamogeton* hybrids in mainland Europe. The following notes are largely based on the summaries of the distribution of hybrids published by Dandy (1975, 1980).

Six of the eight hybrids which are widespread in the British Isles are also relatively widespread in Europe. The most frequently recorded hybrids in Europe are *P.* × *nitens*, *P.* × *salicifolius* and *P.* × *zizii*, the three which are commonest in our area. As in the British Isles, *P.* × *sparganiifolius* and *P.* × *suecicus* have a predominantly northern distribution, the former being "especially frequent in Scandinavia" (Dandy 1975). *P.* × *cooperi* is more frequent in central Europe. Two of the hybrids which are widespread in our area are less frequent in Europe than one might expect: *P.* × *lintonii* is known only from Belgium, Holland and the Czech Republic, and *P.* × *olivaceus* is apparently confined to Denmark. Conversely, two of our rare established hybrids are recorded from several European countries: *P.* × *cognatus* and *P.* × *fluitans*.

Most of the remaining hybrids known in the British Isles are also found in mainland Europe, but only in a few countries. A few are particularly restricted: *P.* × *gessnacensis* to a single site in Germany, for example, and *P.* × *billupsii* to a single locality in Sweden. Many of the localities for these restricted hybrids were published in the early years of the century; it is difficult to find out from published sources whether the hybrids still grow there.

Six hybrids are only known from the British Isles; one or two of these have been reported from other European localities but these records have not been confirmed. The six hybrids include three which are listed above as rare established hybrids (*P.* × *bennettii*, *P.* × *griffithii* and *P.* × *lanceolatus*) and three of the casual hybrids which are apparently now extinct (*P.* × *cadburyae*, *P.* × *grovesii* and *P.* × *pseudofriesii*).

Only a few hybrids are known with certainty from Europe but have not been recorded in Britain or Ireland. *P. × spathulatus*, the hybrid between *P. alpinus* and *P. polygonifolius*, is perhaps the most likely one to be discovered in our area.

The fact that the distribution and frequency of hybrids in the British Isles correlates well with the situation in Europe suggests that their occurrence may be partly explicable by genetical and ecological factors and is not simply the result of chance events.

Hybrids requiring further research

I have examined fresh material and herbarium specimens of most of the hybrids described in this book. I have searched for but failed to find *P. × lanceolatifolius*, *P. × prussicus* and *P. × pseudofriesii*, and I have also been unable to study fresh material of the apparently extinct hybrids *P. × cadburyae* and *P. × grovesii*. Herbarium material of four of these hybrids has been sufficient to allow me to prepare adequate descriptions, although it would be very desirable to redescribe these plants from fresh material. In constructing the key I have assumed that *P. × cadburyae* is similar to the other hybrids of *P. crispus* in possessing stems which are compressed to some extent and grooved along the broader sides. I have only been able to see inadequate material of *P. × prussicus*, and the description I have prepared would doubtless need to be modified and could certainly be expanded if fresh material became available.

I have some reservations about the hybrid status or parentage of three of the hybrids included in this volume. The British population of *P. × nericius* is very close to *P. gramineus* in its morphology and requires further study. *P. × gessnacensis* is known from a single locality in Wales, where it has often been collected and where I have been able to study it *in situ*, and from a single collection from Scotland, which is morphologically rather different. I know of nothing to suggest that the specimens are not hybrids of *P. natans* and *P. polygonifolius*, as Dandy (1975) suggested, but I do not yet regard the evidence as absolutely compelling. The Welsh material is certainly a sterile hybrid of *P. natans*. My reservations about *P. × lintonii* are rather different. I am happy to accept that the type of *P. × lintonii* is the hybrid between *P. crispus* and *P. friesii* and that this is the parentage of many of the collections to which this hybrid binomial has been applied. However, I am not sure how a hybrid between *P. crispus* and *P. pusillus* would differ from one between *P. crispus* and *P. friesii*, and I wonder whether we might not be including some plants with the former parentage in our concept of *P. × lintonii*. This possibility has already been suggested (without any supporting morphological evidence) for an isolated population of *P.* × *lintonii* in Bedfordshire (Dony & Dony 1986).

As mentioned above, almost all the evidence for the occurrence of hybrids is based on comparative morphology. Haynes & Williams (1975) have used paper chromatography to demonstrate that the American hybrid *Potamogeton* × *longiligulatus* possesses all the phenolic compounds they identified in its putative parents *Potamogeton strictifolius* and *P. zosterifolius*. More recently P. M. Hollingsworth (unpublished) has obtained evidence from isozyme studies to confirm the hybrid origin of British *P.* × *schreberi* and *P.* × *suecicus*. There is considerable scope for extending this work, and the comparative fertility of hybrids also requires critical study.

VARIATION

Aquatic plants are notoriously variable. The species of *Potamogeton* do not, however, display the bewildering range of variation which some botanists imagine. Each species has a relatively limited range of variants, even if these variants can be very different in appearance. The appreciation of the range of variation of each species is perhaps the most important step in learning to identify the broad-leaved species. Once the pattern of variation in a species is known, it becomes an important aid, rather than a handicap, to identification.

Variation due to seasonal development

Some of the variation in *Potamogeton* is simply due to the seasonal development of the plants. The first-formed leaves are often very different from the later leaves, and plants where these are the only leaves present can therefore be puzzling to identify. In *P. natans*, *P. lucens*, *P. gramineus* and many of their hybrids the first leaves (which can remain at the base of the stem on mature plants) are phyllodes. All the submerged leaves of *P. natans* are phyllodes, but laminar submerged leaves develop later in the other two species. The first leaf is oblong in species such as *P. alpinus*, *P. perfoliatus* and *P. praelongus*. The mature leaves can show more subtle variations with age. In *P. richardsonii* (a North American species closely related to *P. perfoliatus*) the length and length:breadth ratio increases from the first mature leaves near the base of the stem to the youngest leaves near the apex (Spence & Dale 1978).

Although ontogenetic variation is most marked in the broad-leaved species, Haynes (1974) has reported seasonal variation in populations of *P. berchtoldii*, which can have obtuse leaves with a broad band of lacunae on each side of the midrib in early summer and narrower, acute leaves with narrower bands of lacunae later in the season. The first leaves on shoots of *P. pectinatus* can also be significantly broader than the mature leaves.

The heterophylly of those *Potamogeton* species which possess both submerged and floating leaves is usually too well known to cause confusion, but the submerged leaves of *P. polygonifolius* are not often seen and when found are frequently misidentified as *P. alpinus*.

Variation due to environment

The appearance of *Potamogeton* species undoubtedly varies according to their habitat, but, although well known, this feature has received little systematic study. Environmental factors which can affect the size, shape and colour of the leaves include water depth, shade, the rate of flow of the water and the composition of the substrate.

The most obvious effect of water depth is to control the balance between submerged and floating leaves. This is most clearly seen in *P. polygonifolius*, which possesses floating leaves when growing terrestrially or in shallow water but submerged leaves (with or without floating leaves) in deeper water. Plants of most species have a rather etiolated appearance when growing in very deep water, with long internodes and well separated leaves.

The reddish coloration of species such as *P. alpinus* and *P. coloratus* develops only in plants exposed to high light levels; plants which are shaded by surrounding vegetation or because they grow in deep water are green. In *P. alpinus* green plants which show no trace of a reddish tinge in the field can develop a marked reddish colour when they are dried. *P. berchtoldii* is perhaps more shade-tolerant than other linear-leaved species. Plants growing in shallow water in shaded ditches usually have leaves which are broader and darker green than those of adjacent, unshaded plants, with lacunae which are extremely well developed, especially towards the apex of the leaf. Plants growing in deep water also have rather broad leaves, but they are pale rather than dark green.

Pearsall & Hanby (1925) found that, under experimental conditions, the leaf shape of *P. perfoliatus* was particularly influenced by light intensity and duration, the calcium content of the substrate and (where calcium levels are low) the ratio of potassium to calcium ions. However, Spence & Dale (1978) emphasised the effects of light rather than substrate on the morphology of the North American *P. richardsonii*. At low light intensities their experimental plants had an upright stem with limp green leaves, whereas in stronger light the shoots were shorter and virtually prostrate, with stiff, brown-tinged leaves which were displayed edge-on to the light and became encrusted with marl. The related species *P. perfoliatus* displays a similar range of variation in Britain and Ireland, and prostrate shoots similar to those described for *P. richardsonii* can often be found in clear, shallow water.

The appearance of a plant is the result of an interaction between its ontogenetic variation and the environment in which it grows. Phyllodes or narrow submerged leaves can sometimes persist in rapidly flowing water, a habitat in which broader floating leaves can fail to develop.

Genetic variation

As mentioned above, variation in *Potamogeton* species has not received much study. In particular, there has been little attempt to assess the relative contribution of environmental and of genetic factors to the variation which is such a notable feature of many species. Traditionally, this problem has been tackled by cultivating different populations of a species in a uniform environment. The fact that much of the variation in *Potamogeton* appears to be due to environmental conditions, coupled with the difficulty of growing aquatics, perhaps explains why so little has been done to investigate genetic variation in *Potamogeton*.

Plants of *Potamogeton pectinatus* from fresh and brackish water have been cultivated in aquaria (van Wijk, van Goor & Verkley 1988). Even under controlled conditions, there was variation between populations in the production and morphology of tubers and in the mean shoot length. Populations also differed in their tolerance of salinity. This demonstrates that at least some of the variation in this species is genetically based.

There are also some less rigorous studies which suggest that some populations are genetically distinct from others of the same species. Alfred Fryer grew the Shetland population of *Potamogeton polygonifolius* which he called forma *cancellatus* and found that it remained distinct (Fryer & Bennett 1915). Pearsall & Pearsall (1921) suggested that the form of *P. berchtoldii* found in deep, clear water is also genetically distinct. Some populations of hybrids are noticeably different from others. The plants of *P. × fluitans* in the Moors River, for example, never have the fully developed coriaceous leaves usually found in the East Anglian populations, even when growing in sheltered bays at the edge of the river. *P. × salicifolius* in the Ouse Washes, Cambridgeshire, is much closer to *P. lucens* than other populations such as those in the River Tweed. The consistency of these differences may suggest that they have a genetic basis and are not simply the result of growth in different habitats, but there have been no cultivation experiments to test this possibility.

In recent years isozyme studies using electrophoretic techniques have provided a further means of assessing genetic variation. If appropriate enzymes are chosen, it is possible to measure variation without the need to cultivate plants in similar conditions. Van Wijk, van Goor & Verkley (1988) found that almost all the populations of *P. pectinatus* that they tested showed differences in their isozyme patterns. By contrast, variability within populations was very low. A further study by Hettiarachchi & Triest (1991) confirmed the variability of *P. pectinatus* and provided preliminary observations on *Groenlandia densa* and 17 other *Potamogeton* taxa.

CHROMOSOME NUMBERS[*]

The chromosome number of a plant is of interest to taxonomists for several reasons. It provides a character which might help to distinguish one species from another and which can be used to test the homogeneity of taxa arrived at by the study of macroscopic characters. If differences in chromosome number occur within a species, they can indicate breeding barriers within populations of that species. In a group in which hybrids occur, there is the additional prospect of confirming the identity of hybrids between parents of differing chromosome number. Chromosome numbers also can provide information about the affinities of species in a genus and suggest possible evolutionary relationships.

The Potamogetonaceae is by far the largest flowering plant family in the British Isles for which there are no published chromosome numbers based on native material (R. J. Gornall pers. comm.). The following unpublished counts of *Potamogeton* have been obtained from British material by P. M. Hollingsworth; full details will be published elsewhere. A single count for *Ruppia maritima* has been published from our area (Al-Bermani *et al.* 1993) and is also listed below.

Potamogeton coloratus	2n=*c*. 26
P. natans	2n=*c*. 52
P. pectinatus	2n=*c*. 78
P. perfoliatus	2n=*c*. 52
P. polygonifolius	2n=28
P. × nitens	2n=*c*. 52
P. × salicifolius	2n=*c*. 52
Ruppia maritima	2n=20

Chromosome numbers have been published for all the British and Irish species from material collected outside our area. These numbers are listed overleaf. The gametophytic chromosome number is indicated by n, the sporophytic number by 2n. For the Potamogetonaceae, the counts given in the first column are taken from Les (1983), whose criterion for inclusion was the most commonly reported number (Les & Sheridan 1990a). The number of reports on which this figure is based is given in brackets after the count. Counts in the second column

* By P. M. Hollingsworth

are deviations from those reported in Les' review, with a code letter for the reference to the source of the deviant count. The code letters are explained below the list. *Potamogeton berchtoldii* and *P. pusillus* are regarded as synonymous by Les (1983) and *Groenlandia densa* is not included within the scope of his paper; counts for these species are taken from Palmgren (1939). There do not appear to be any published counts of the *Potamogeton* hybrids which are recorded in Britain and Ireland. The counts for the Ruppiaceae are taken from Reese (1962), van Vierssen, van Wijk & van der Zee (1981) and Talavera, García-Murillo & Herrera (1993). Earlier counts of *Ruppia* species are omitted as the nomenclatural and taxonomic complications make them particularly difficult to interpret.

Potamogeton

Subgenus Potamogeton

Section Potamogeton

P. natans	2n=52 (8)	n=21 (A), 2n=*c*. 42 (B)
P. nodosus	2n=52 (3)	
P. lucens	2n=52 (2)	
P. gramineus	2n=52 (8)	
P. polygonifolius	2n=52 (2)	n=13 (C), 2n=26 (D), 2n=28 (E)
P. coloratus	2n=26 (1)	
P. alpinus	2n=52 (6)	2n=26 (F)
P. praelongus	2n=52 (6)	
P. perfoliatus	2n=52 (12)	n=7 (G), n=*c*. 24 (H), 2n=26 (B), 2n=*c*. 40 (B), 2n=78 (I, J)

Section Graminifolii

P. epihydrus	2n=26 (2)	
P. friesii	2n=26 (2)	
P. rutilus	2n=26 (1)	
P. pusillus	2n=26	2n=28 (K)
P. obtusifolius	2n=26 (1)	
P. berchtoldii	2n=26	
P. trichoides	2n=26 (3)	
P. compressus	2n=26 (3)	
P. acutifolius	2n=26 (2)	

Section Batrachoseris

P. crispus	2n=52 (9)	2n=26 (L, M), 2n=50, 56 (N), 2n=52, some cells 36 (O), 2n=78, some cells 72(O)

Subgenus Coleogeton

P. filiformis	2n=78 (6)	2n=c. 66 (C)
P. pectinatus	2n=78 (9)	2n=42 (N), 2n=c. 66 (J), 2n=70, 71, 73, 74, 75, 76, 77, 79, 80, 81, 82, 83, 84, 85, 86, 87 (P), 2n=86 (Q)

Groenlandia

G. densa	2n=30

Ruppia

R. maritima	2n=20, 2n=40
R. cirrhosa	2n=40, 2n=60

Key to reference codes: A: Stern (1961); B: Probatova & Sokolovskaya (1984); C: Palmgren (1939); D: Ficini *et al.* (1980); E: Hollingsworth (see above); F: Löve & Kjellqvist (1973); G: Takusagawa (1939); H: Wisniewska (1931); I: Arohonka (1982); J: Probatova & Sokolovskaya (1986); K: Harada (1956); L: Bhattacharya & Ghosh (1978); M: Ghosh & Bhattacharya (1980); N: Misra (1972); O: Sharma & Chatterjee (1967); P: Kalkman & van Wijk (1984); Q: Yurtsev *et al.* (1975).

All chromosome counts of *Potamogeton* should be treated with some caution. *Potamogeton* chromosomes are difficult to work with. They vary in size from small to very small and usually lack any distinguishing morphological characters; this not only means that they are difficult to count but also makes it difficult to distinguish 'A-chromosomes' (which are included in the chromosome number) from 'B-chromosomes' (traditionally excluded) (Kalkman & van Wijk 1984). Obtaining accurate karyotype data is fraught with difficulty, partly because of the lack of morphological features on the chromosomes.

The technical difficulties of counting *Potamogeton* chromosomes make it hard to discriminate between genuine cytological phenomena such as aneuploidy (the gain or loss of individual chromosomes) and cytological errors. Few students admit to the difficulties involved in *Potamogeton* cytology, and most do not indicate that there is any possibility that some counts may not be accurate. Kalkman & van Wijk (1984), however, provided useful information on the range of variation in the chromosome number of *P. pectinatus*. They reported a range of chromosome numbers in each of the 15 populations they studied, with the accepted number of the species, 2n=78, being the mode of

17 different counts. It is not clear from their paper whether the variation in chromosome counts in each population occurred within or between individuals.

There are clear differences between the three genera in the Potamogetonaceae and Ruppiaceae. The most commonly reported numbers in *Potamogeton* are multiples of 13 whereas the chromosome numbers of *Groenlandia* and *Ruppia* are multiples of 10.

Within the genus *Potamogeton*, the most frequently reported numbers correlate well with the major morphological subdivisions. The members of Subgenus *Coleogeton* have the same base number as those in Subgenus *Potamogeton*, but at a higher ploidy level. The lack of consistent interspecific variation in chromosome numbers within sections reduces the possibility of obtaining useful cytological evidence on the identity of putative hybrids.

There is evidence for geographical variation in chromosome number in *Ruppia*. Counts of 2n=20 have been published for material of *Ruppia maritima* from at least three areas in north-west Europe (England, Schleswig-Holstein and Texel). Detailed studies in Schleswig-Holstein revealed a consistent difference between *R. maritima* (2n=20) and *R. cirrhosa* (2n=40, 60) in that area. However, in southern Europe *R. maritima* occurs as two cytological races, with 2n=20 (Sardinia, Spain) and 2n=40 (Camargue, Corsica, Sardinia, Spain).

The use of chromosome numbers to interpret the possible evolutionary history of the species of *Potamogeton* is bedevilled both by uncertainties about the accuracy of many counts and by the difficulties posed by aneuploidy. Aneuploidy has almost certainly occurred in the genus and can be used to construct any number of scenarios to link numbers based on multiples of 7, 13 and (for *Groenlandia*) 15. Les (1983) reviewed the chromosome numbers of all species and suggested that the diploid number for the genus is 2n=14. This number has very rarely been reported from the genus, but five species characterised (on Les' criterion) as tetraploids with 2n=28 occur in eastern Asia and two are found in North America. The latter number has also been found recently for a British population of *P. polygonifolius*. Les interpreted species with chromosome numbers which are multiples of 13 as derived from plants with 2n=14 by aneuploidy, giving 2n=13, followed by polyploidy. This reduction from 14 to 13 may have happened only once or may have occurred on several occasions independently. The interpretation put forward by Les (1983) has been challenged by Wiegleb (1988b), who regarded the ancestral chromosome number as 2n=26. Les & Sheridan (1990a) argue that phylogeny should be used to clarify chromosomal trends rather than *vice versa*, but at the moment there seems little prospect that either can be clarified without a lot of basic research.

STRUCTURE

The plants covered by this book have a rather simple structure. The equipment needed to examine pondweeds is described below, and the approach which I have adopted to naming the different parts explained. The parts of the plant are then outlined, with as much detail as is needed to allow the reader to follow the keys and the taxonomic descriptions.

Equipment

In the field it is useful to have a ×20 lens to examine material. At home it is helpful to have a binocular microscope to check the identification of broad-leaved species and essential to have one to determine the structure of the sheaths and stipules of the narrow-leaved species by the simple dissection methods outlined below. A cheap microscope is adequate for this and for most other botanical purposes. Many botanists are curiously reluctant to buy a binocular microscope. When challenged they tend to cite the cost, but in most cases they are prepared to spend far more on peripheral activities such as photography than they would need to spend on an adequate microscope. It is one of those pieces of equipment which, once bought, seems absolutely indispensable. The only other items needed are slides, fine tweezers and sharp razor blades. Double-edged razor blades are finer and easier to work with than those with a single edge. Replace them regularly as they soon become blunt, and blunt blades tear rather than cut tissue. When visiting herbaria it is worth taking your own dissection equipment rather than relying on the rusty ironmongery usually supplied to visitors by these institutions.

Naming of parts

The simplicity of the Potamogetonaceae and Ruppiaceae is presumably the result of evolutionary reduction from more complex ancestors. The origin of several organs is unclear and has been the subject of varying interpretations. Morphologists tend to name the parts of a plant according to their supposed origin; where theories of the origin of an organ differ, that organ is likely to be known by different names. There are, for example, four structures in the

Potamogeton flower which appear to the uninitiated to be perianth segments, but which are adnate to the base of the stamens. These are known as tepals to authors such as Cronquist (1981) who regard them as similar in origin to the tepals of other monocots, but as sepaloid connectives to those who, like Fernald (1932), think that the *Potamogeton* flower has no true perianth and that these structures are outgrowths of the stamen connective. In this book I have tried to use simple terms for the different organs and I use them without any implications about the origin of the part or its homology with similarly named structures in other groups. Readers who want a detailed account of the morphology of the Potamogetonaceae *sensu lato* should consult Tomlinson (1982).

Rhizomes

The *Potamogeton* rhizome is quite distinct from the stem (Figure 2). It lies horizontally in the substrate; there are usually several roots at every node and erect stems arising from every second node. It is white or cream in colour, sometimes with a pinkish tinge and often marked with rust-coloured flecks; if exposed above the surface, it develops a greenish coloration. In the larger *Potamogeton* species it can be very robust, exceeding 10 mm in diameter. The rhizome is sympodial, i.e. the apical bud grows into an aerial shoot and the rhizome is continued by a lateral bud from its base (Tomlinson 1982).

Many of the broad-leaved species of *Potamogeton* perennate by the rhizome. In some species (e.g. *P. natans*) the rhizome does not change in appearance during the winter, but in others (e.g. *P. perfoliatus*) it develops a beaded appearance as the internodes swell (Tomlinson 1982). *P. alpinus* overwinters as buds formed on the rhizome rather than as the rhizome itself (Brux *et al.* 1988). The species of Subgenus *Coleogeton* produce numerous small tubers resembling miniature potatoes on side branches of the rhizome. Paired tubers are regularly found in some populations of *P. pectinatus* in the Netherlands, and chains of five tubers have been found in Egypt (van Wijk 1989a) and North America (Yeo 1965).

The rhizomes of *Groenlandia* are similar to those of *Potamogeton*. They are, however, less well differentiated from the stem (Figure 2). They often lie on or just below the surface and are white when buried but have a greenish tinge when exposed to light. *Ruppia* has rhizomes which are white or brownish in colour when buried and tinged with green when exposed; they extend from below the surface of the mud into the water and are poorly differentiated from the stem (Figure 2). They tend to have one or two roots and a shoot at each node. They are monopodial, i.e. the rhizome continues to grow from the apical bud and the leafy stems are formed from lateral buds.

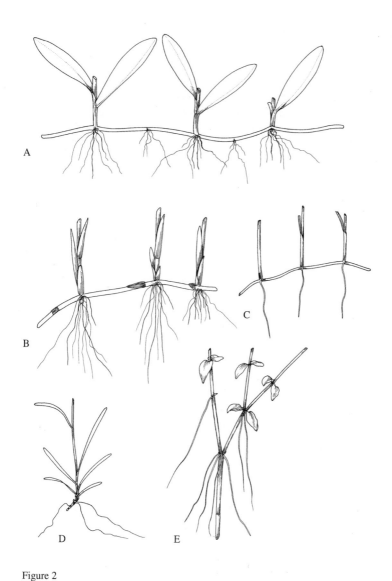

Figure 2

Rhizomes and roots. A: rhizome of *Potamogeton alpinus*; B: rhizome of *Potamogeton pectinatus*; C: rhizome of *Ruppia maritima*; D: stem of *Potamogeton obtusifolius* arising from a turion; E: rhizome of *Groenlandia densa*. Drawn by M.T.

Stems

The length and branching of the stem are of use in distinguishing *Potamogeton* species, although both can be influenced by environmental factors such as water depth. A more constant feature is the compression of the stem (Figure 3). Stems range from terete to flattened. (These terms are used in a quantitative sense and are defined in the glossary.) *Potamogeton crispus* and its hybrids have stems which when well-developed have a groove running down both of the broader

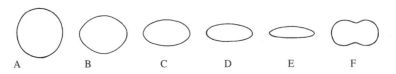

Figure 3

Shapes of stems in cross-section. A: terete; B: slightly compressed; C: compressed; D: strongly compressed; E: flattened; F: compressed, with a groove running down both of the broader sides. Drawn by M.T.

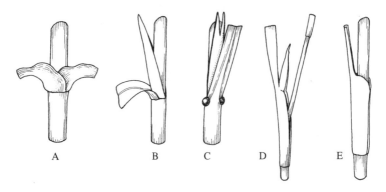

Figure 4

Nodes. A: *Groenlandia densa*, with bases of opposite leaves; B: *Potamogeton gramineus*, with leaf base and stipule; C: *Potamogeton friesii*, with nodal glands, leaf base and a stipule which has begun to split at apex; D: *Potamogeton pectinatus*, with sheath, ligule and base of leaf (the stem bent to the right to show the sheath and ligule); E: *Ruppia cirrhosa*, with sheath and base of leaf. Drawn by M.T.

sides, and these are therefore sometimes described as bicanaliculate. Slender stems sometimes show this groove down only one of the broader sides. Some linear-leaved species of *Potamogeton* have a small swelling on the stem on each side of the base of the leaf (Figure 4). These 'nodal glands' vary in shape and pigmentation: they can be smooth and green (as in *P. friesii*) or rather irregularly shaped and reddish brown (as in *P. obtusifolius*). The extent to which they are developed varies from species to species and also between populations of a particular species. They are often described as oil glands, but they have received little attention from morphologists and their functional significance is uncertain.

The internal anatomy of the stem has been used by taxonomists both for distinguishing species and for grouping the species within the genus. The importance of such characters has recently been reassessed by Wiegleb (1990a). I have not included anatomical characters in the species descriptions as I have limited the scope of this work to macroscopic characters.

Phyllodes

The lowest leaves on the stems of *Potamogeton gramineus* and *P. lucens* and all the submerged leaves of *P. natans* are reduced to phyllodes. These are equivalent to the petiole of a leaf, and in battered material it is difficult to distinguish a phyllode from a floating leaf with the lamina broken off. Phyllodes are filiform or linear in shape and are dark green and opaque; in cross-section they have a flat or shallowly concave upper side and a convex lower side.

Leaves which are intermediate between phyllodes and laminar leaves can be found in *P. lucens* and *P. gramineus* and in many of the hybrids which have a species with phyllodes as one parent. They are described as "partially reduced to phyllodes" in the species accounts.

Floating leaves

In taxonomic descriptions of pondweeds, floating leaves are usually distinguished from submerged leaves. Floating leaves are petiolate leaves with an opaque and coriaceous lamina; they have stomata on the upper surface. As their name suggests, they usually float on the surface of the water but they can be found beneath the surface on plants that have been inundated by rising water levels. In addition to the morphological differences between floating and submerged leaves, there are also significant biochemical differences (Les & Sheridan 1990b).

The capacity to produce floating leaves is an important taxonomic character. The presence of floating leaves is more significant than their absence, as a species which can produce floating leaves may only do so in certain environmental conditions. The floating leaves of different species are more similar to each other than the submerged leaves and are therefore less useful in identification. They are, for example, always entire. Most of the characters which can be derived from them are self-explanatory, but two are worth mentioning. The lateral veins of *Potamogeton natans* are translucent when held up to the light, and this gives the leaf a quite distinct appearance compared to those of other species which have lateral veins which are similar in colour to the rest of the lamina or darker. This only applies to leaves which are actually floating on the water; when *P. natans* grows terrestrially, the veins can lose their translucency. The second character is also a feature of *P. natans*. This species often has a discoloured and flexible section of petiole immediately below the lamina of the leaf. This remains visible on herbarium specimens, as it shrinks and becomes narrower than the rest of the petiole. This flexible junction allows the leaves of *P. natans* to point in any direction and thus fill any available space on the water surface. The base of the petiole of *P. natans* is also swollen and flexible at the junction with the stem. As water levels rise or fall, the floating leaves remain on the surface as the petioles articulate at this node.

The stipules associated with the floating leaves are similar to those of the submerged leaves of the same species. They are discussed in the next section, and they are covered by the descriptions of stipules in the species accounts. The stipules of leaves which subtend inflorescences are, however, often rather larger than those of other leaves and are not included in the description of stipules.

Submerged leaves and stipules

There are two types of submerged leaf in the plants covered by this book, which, rather surprisingly, cut across the generic divisions (Figures 4 and 5). It is convenient to deal with these two types of leaf separately.

Groenlandia and *Potamogeton* Subgenus *Potamogeton*

The submerged leaves of *Groenlandia* and *Potamogeton* Subgenus *Potamogeton* are joined directly to the node. Important characters of the submerged leaves include leaf shape, the nature of the apex and base, the presence or absence of teeth on the margin, the presence of lacunae along the midrib, and the number of lateral veins. The submerged leaves provide the most important characters for the identification of the broad-leaved species of *Potamogeton*, and many of these can be identified (although not necessarily separated from their hybrids) on the basis of a single submerged leaf.

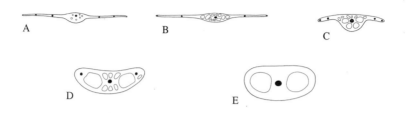

Figure 5

Sections of leaves. A: *Groenlandia densa*; B: *Potamogeton obtusifolius*; C: *Potamogeton trichoides*; D: *Potamogeton pectinatus*; E: *Ruppia cirrhosa*. Drawn by M.T.

Leaf shape and venation

The terms used to describe leaf shape are given in the glossary. It is normally easy to tell whether the leaf is sessile or petiolate at the base, although the petioles of *P. lucens* are short so that inexperienced observers sometimes conclude that the leaf is sessile. In some sessile leaves the leaf base completely embraces the stem; these are said to be amplexicaul. If the leaf base only partly clasps the stem, the base is described as semi-amplexicaul. It sometimes requires careful observation to distinguish leaves which are rounded but not amplexicaul at the base from those that are slightly amplexicaul. This is an important distinction between *P. gramineus* and variants of *P.* × *nitens* which approach this parent. The leaf base of *Groenlandia* differs from that of *Potamogeton* in its distinctly hyaline cells, which contrast with the green cells of the rest of the lamina.

The shape of the leaf apex is important in both linear- and broad-leaved species. Some of the broad-leaved taxa have a hooded apex which splits when the leaf is pressed. It is often suggested that *P. berchtoldii* and *P. pusillus* differ in the venation at the apex of the leaf, and successive editions of Clapham, Tutin & Warburg (1952) even italicise this feature as an important distinguishing character. However, I have systematically examined numerous leaves and have found that the veins at the apex cannot be used to distinguish these species. Any identifications based on this character should be disregarded.

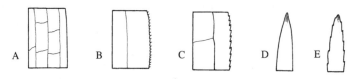

Figure 6

Margins of leaves and leaf apices. A: entire margin; B: denticulate margin; C: serrate margin; D: entire apex; E: denticulate apex. Drawn by M.T.

Leaf margin

The leaves of *Groenlandia* and of some broad-leaved species in Section *Potamogeton* have tiny teeth along the border (Figure 6). These teeth usually can be seen in the field if the margin of a fresh leaf is held against the light and examined with a ×20 lens. It is often necessary to check the leaf margin under the binocular microscope, as the teeth can be difficult to see with a lens (especially if the plant is a hybrid between a species with entire leaves and one with denticulate leaves). Teeth are more conspicuous on fresh than on dried material, and it is sometimes useful to rehydrate a portion of dried leaf before looking for them. They can be completely obscured on herbarium specimens which are mounted on a film of glue. The teeth tend to be eroded away on older leaves but are more persistent in some species than in others. Examination under a high-power microscope shows that the margin of toothed leaves is composed of long, narrow cells; each tooth projects from this and is largely composed of a single cell. The teeth of the mature leaves of *P. crispus* in the monotypic Section *Batrachoseris* are much more conspicuous than those of the species in Section *Potamogeton*, as they tend to be at the apex of a small projection of the lamina. Immature leaves of *P. crispus* and the leaves of its hybrids are often rather inconspicuously toothed but teeth can always be found towards the apex of some leaves.

All the members of Section *Graminifolii* have entire leaves. Some species have a thickened strand forming the edge of the leaf which resembles one of the veins in the lamina. This is referred to as a marginal vein in the descriptions. It is not included when the number of veins on each side of the midrib is counted.

Lacunae

Lacunae appear as pale bands on each side of the midrib; the bands are usually broader towards the base of the leaf and taper towards the apex. They sometimes line some of the lateral veins as well, and this makes these veins more prominent than those which have fewer or no lacunae bordering them. Those species which lack lacunae tend to have lateral veins which are equally prominent. The structure of lacunae does not appear to have been investigated by morphologists, and they are scarcely mentioned in Tomlinson's (1982) account of the genus. They appear to be virtually empty cells or air spaces resulting from the breakdown of cell walls.

Stipules

The stipules in most of the broad-leaved species of *Potamogeton* Section *Potamogeton* are conspicuous structures. They are of some taxonomic importance, and differences between species are much greater in dried than in fresh material. The texture of the stipules seems to be governed primarily by the appearance and density of the veins. The dried stipules of species like *P. natans* and *P. praelongus* are opaque as they have closely set veins which are slightly raised and opaque when dry. These coarse veins tend to remain as fibrous

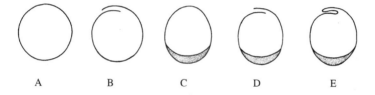

A   B   C   D   E

Figure 7   .

Sections of stipules and sheaths. A: tubular stipule; B: open and convolute stipule; C: tubular sheath; D: open and convolute sheath; E: tubular sheath with a fold in sheath. Drawn by M.T.

strands after the rest of the stipule tissue has eroded away. Other species such as *P. polygonifolius* and *P. perfoliatus* have stipules which are translucent when dry; in these the veins are more widely spaced and less prominent and they do not persist. In most of the broad-leaved species two of the veins are more prominent than the others (the extent to which this is so varying from species to species) and in *P. lucens* these veins are winged on the abaxial side. All species in Section *Potamogeton* have stipules which are open rather than tubular at the base.

The stipules of the narrow-leaved species in Section *Graminifolii* are smaller and often more delicate than those of the broad-leaved species but are of crucial importance in identifying the species (Figure 7). When young, the stipules enfold the stem above the node. They are either closed and tubular like a drainpipe or the ends are free but overlapping like a piece of paper which has been rolled into a cylinder. The latter type is described as open and convolute. Closed stipules split with age and it is therefore essential to examine young stipules to establish the structure. Fresh material is, perhaps, the easiest to work with, but it is also possible to dissect the stipules of herbarium specimens if shoot tips are removed and soaked in water until rehydrated.

To establish the structure of the stipule, choose a suitable young shoot and place a node complete with leaf and stipule in a drop of water on a microscope slide. Under the microscope cut through the stem and the surrounding stipule just above the node with a sharp razor. The node with the attached leaf can then be discarded, leaving the stipule around the stem. There are then two ways of examining the stipule. The first is to make another cut immediately above the first. This will give a cross-section of the stem and stipule; the stem can be poked out and the stipule examined in cross-section. This is perhaps the better procedure, especially for stipules which are tubular only at the extreme base. A second method is to pull the stipule lengthwise off the stem as one would pull a Wellington boot off a foot. The cut end of the stipule can then be turned up towards the microscope and examined. It is important to check the stipule carefully, as the two free ends of a convolute stipule can stick together, especially if the material has been pressed and then rehydrated. A few pokes with the end of a needle or a pair of forceps sometimes help to separate free ends which have been pressed together. Tubular stipules sometimes appear to be open and convolute if the stipule is not completely circular in section but is partly folded in towards the stem. I usually dissect two or three stipules to make absolutely sure that I have interpreted the structure correctly.

If it is not possible to examine the stipules of a linear-leaved pondweed as soon as it is collected, it is better to press the plant and then rehydrate it (or even to dry the specimen without pressing) than to leave it sitting in a saucer on a window ledge for a week or two until the opportunity to examine it (or present it to an expert) arises. Fresh material left in water like this soon decays, leaving only turions.

The colour and texture of the stipules of linear-leaved pondweeds also provide useful characters. In many species two veins, one along each edge if the stipule is compressed, are stronger than the others. These veins are sometimes green and are conspicuous when the rest of the stipule is hyaline. This hyaline tissue between strong veins tends to tear, leaving the veins as a V-shaped remnant. The veins between the two stronger veins are known as the intercostal veins; in open stipules they should be counted along the closed side of the stipule.

The stipules of *Groenlandia densa* are quite different from those of the *Potamogeton* species. They are described in the account of that species.

Potamogeton Subgenus *Coleogeton* and *Ruppia*

As described above, these leaves have a superficial resemblance to those of grasses, as they have a sheath above the node, with a free lamina arising from the top of the sheath. The lamina is circular, semicircular, elliptical or canaliculate in cross-section and there are one or more air channels on each side of the inconspicuous midrib (Figure 5). The air channels run along the length of the leaf and are easily seen in section. They are quite distinct from the much smaller lacunae which line the midrib of some members of Subgenus *Potamogeton*.

The leaves of *Potamogeton* Subgenus *Coleogeton* differ from those of *Ruppia* in the presence of a ligule at the junction of the sheath and the lamina and in their entire apex. The leaves of *Ruppia* are distinctly toothed at the apex (Figure 6), but the teeth are small and are much more easily seen in fresh or rehydrated than in dry material.

The sheath of *Potamogeton filiformis* is closed and tubular towards the base whereas that of *P. pectinatus* is open and convolute throughout (Figure 7). This difference is similar to that between the stipules of the linear-leaved species in Subgenus *Potamogeton* and can be ascertained by similar procedures to those described above. Tubular sheaths tend to split from the top of the tubular portion downwards, so the base of a young sheath should always be examined. Tubular sheaths which, in section, are partly folded in towards the stem are not uncommon, especially in *P.* × *suecicus* (Figure 7E); the older sheaths split along the line of the fold.

Turions and other vegetative propagules

Many different terms are used to describe the vegetative propagules of *Potamogeton* species. I use the word turion to describe the morphologically specialised propagules produced in the leaf axils and at the stem apices of certain species. These are modified short stems which usually have a thickened axis and which bear reduced leaves. They are a means of vegetative spread and of perennation during the winter. In some species they are produced for much of the summer but in others they only develop towards the end of the season. Other authors often refer to these turions as hibernacula or winter-buds.

Turions are produced by all the British and Irish species in *Potamogeton*

Figure 8

Turions and other vegetative propagules. A: turion of *Potamogeton trichoides*; B: turions of *P. crispus*, including one shown in leaf axil; C: turions of *P.* × *lintonii*, including one shown in leaf axil; D: tubers of *P. pectinatus*; E: axillary shoot of *P.* × *nitens*; F: axillary shoot of *P. alpinus*. Drawn by M.T.

Section *Graminifolii* except for *P. epihydrus* (Figure 8). The species which produce turions lack rhizomes, so the turions are the means by which they over-winter. When the turions begin to grow, they do so from the apex (Tomlinson 1982). *P. crispus*, of the monotypic Section *Batrachoseris*, also produces turions with very reduced, toothed leaves. They are sometimes called burs in the American literature. *P. crispus* has rhizomes, and the turions are more important as a means of vegetative dispersal during the summer than as overwintering organs. They begin to grow from lateral branches (Arber 1920, Tomlinson 1982).

Less specialised propagules are produced in the leaf axils of some pondweeds. I have not included these within my definition of turions, although some authors do so. In *Potamogeton alpinus* (Figure 8F), *P. epihydrus*, *P. nodosus* and some sterile hybrids, these propagules consist of a short axis like a slender rhizome which arises in the leaf axil and is terminated by a bud or by a fascicle of reduced leaves. They are usually found towards the end of the growing season but they do not appear to be produced consistently. *P. natans* and some of its hybrids also produce short axillary branches bearing phyllodes or narrow leaves in the autumn. These are readily detached and in the hybrids they can be a significant means of vegetative reproduction. *P. pectinatus* occa-sionally produces densely branched shoot tips in the autumn; these brush-like growths become detached from the parent plant and are capable of sending out a rhizome and developing into established plants (van Wijk 1989a). Many *Potamogeton* species and hybrids can send out roots and become established from detached stem fragments.

The tubers produced on the rhizomes of the species in *Potamogeton* Subgenus *Coleogeton* are described with the rhizome above. Some populations produce similar tubers above ground, on small side branches in the leaf axils (Yeo 1965, van Wijk 1989a).

Groenlandia densa lacks turions, but small side branches may become detached. As in *Potamogeton*, such detached fragments can root and develop into established plants (Sauvageau 1893–94). Our *Ruppia* species apparently lack vegetative propagules.

Inflorescences and flowers

The inflorescences of the three genera treated here are significantly different from each other (Figure 9, overleaf), as explained in the chapter on classifica-tion. The peduncle of *Groenlandia* and *Potamogeton* Subgenus *Potamogeton* is sufficiently rigid to hold the inflorescence out of the water at anthesis. The

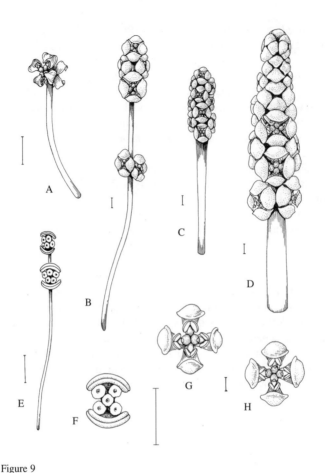

Figure 9

Inflorescences (A–E) and flowers (F–H). A: *Groenlandia densa*; B: *Potamogeton pectinatus*; C: *P. compressus*; D: *P. natans*; E: *Ruppia maritima*; F: *R. maritima*; G: *P. compressus*; H: *P. natans*. Scale bars: 1 mm. Drawn by M.T.

peduncle of *Groenlandia* bears two opposite flowers, whereas *Potamogeton* has a spike which can occasionally be reduced to only three flowers but usually has more. In *Potamogeton* Subgenus *Coleogeton* and *Ruppia* the peduncle is flexible and the flowers usually rest on the surface of the water at anthesis. *Ruppia* inflorescences bear two flowers, and as the fruits develop the carpel stalk elongates. In *Potamogeton* Subgenus *Coleogeton* the flowers are more numerous and the fruits are sessile.

Within the subgenera of *Potamogeton* the inflorescences and flowers can differ from species to species in features such as the size of the inflorescence, the number of flowers in it, the size of the tepals, the size and colour of the carpels, and the length and compression of the peduncle. Most of these characters are too variable, or the differences are too slight, for them to be particularly useful for diagnostic purposes. It is useful to know that some broad-leaved species have peduncles which are of more or less uniform diameter throughout their length whereas in others (particularly *P. lucens* and *P. gramineus*) they are broader and distinctly spongy towards the inflorescence. Almost all the *Potamogeton* species in Britain and Ireland have four carpels in the majority of their flowers. It is not unusual to find flowers in an inflorescence which depart from this number, although this fact has only recently been recognised in the literature (Charlton & Poluszny 1991). The uppermost flowers in an inflorescence often have more or less than the normal number of carpels and may have fewer perianth segments than normal. Of more critical importance is the number of carpels in the flower of some narrow-leaved species. *P. berchtoldii* has a marked tendency to have five carpels in some flowers. Three species are characterised by a reduction in the number of carpels in the flower. *P. compressus* usually has two carpels per flower, and *P. acutifolius* and *P. trichoides* usually have only one.

Potamogeton filiformis differs from *P. pectinatus* in having stigmas which are virtually sessile rather than carried on a short style. This character is not usually needed to separate the species, as the structure of the sheath and the size of the fruits are more easily observed, but it can be very important in identifying hybrids which possess a combination of the parental characters.

The length of the peduncle is the crucial feature which distinguishes the two *Ruppia* species. This length can be given in absolute terms but is often more usefully expressed as a multiple of the length of the longest fruit stalk. As the fruit stalk elongates after anthesis, it is important to measure an inflorescence in mature fruit.

Fruits

Many different terms have been used for the *Potamogeton* fruit: these include drupe, drupelet, achene, nut and nutlet. They are reviewed briefly by Haynes (1974), who suggests that none are satisfactory; Haynes himself simply calls them fruits and I have no hesitation in following his example. The body of the fruit can be distinguished from the beak, which is formed by the persistent remains of the style and stigma.

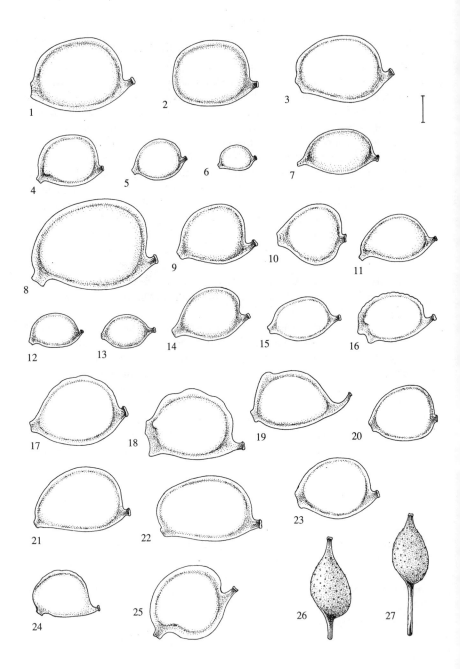

There is a widespread belief that many *Potamogeton* species can only be identified if ripe fruits are available. Many people who have brought me pondweed specimens to identify in the last few years have apologised for the absence of fruit, but most of our pondweed species and hybrids can be identified unequivocally on the basis of good vegetative material. This is just as well, as many species are more frequently found as vegetative or flowering shoots than they are with mature fruit, and of course most hybrids do not produce any fruits at all.

Although fruits are not normally essential for identification, they can certainly provide helpful characters (Figure 10). A fruiting specimen can often be identified more rapidly than vegetative material, if only because the possibility of a hybrid can often be eliminated. It is certainly easier to separate *P. acutifolius* from *P. compressus* and *P. filiformis* from *P. pectinatus* if fruits are available, and without fruits some specimens referable to *P. coloratus* or *P. polygonifolius* cannot be identified. The length of the fruits is the most important single character. The measurements of fruits in the species accounts have been made on dried material and the lengths include the beak. The length of the beak itself and its position can also be important. The beak is either apical or ventral, i.e. at the apex of the fruit or continuing the line of the lower edge. Other useful characters of the fruit include colour, texture and the presence of teeth along the dorsal or ventral edge.

Subfossil *Potamogeton* fruits can be found in lake sediments. A guide to their identification has been produced by Aalto (1970). It is rather humbling to realise that botanists who undertake studies of Quaternary sediments can apparently identify a species of *Potamogeton* on the basis of a single decayed fruit.

Figure 10 (facing)

Fruits. 1: *Potamogeton natans*; 2: *P. nodosus*; 3: *P. lucens*; 4: *P. gramineus*; 5: *P. polygonifolius*; 6: *P. coloratus*; 7: *P. alpinus*; 8: *P. praelongus*; 9: *P. perfoliatus*; 10: *P. epihydrus*; 11: *P. friesii*; 12: *P. rutilus*; 13: *P. pusillus*; 14: *P. obtusifolius*; 15: *P. berchtoldii*; 16: *P. trichoides*; 17: *P. compressus*; 18: *P. acutifolius*; 19: *P. crispus*; 20: *P. filiformis*; 21: *P. pectinatus*; 22: *P.* × *fluitans*; 23: *P.* × *zizii*; 24: *P.* × *sudermanicus*; 25: *Groenlandia densa*; 26: *Ruppia maritima*; 27: *R. cirrhosa*. Scale bar: 1 mm. Drawn by M.T.

LIFE HISTORY

Life-forms of species

All the members of *Potamogeton* Section *Graminifolii* except for *P. epihydrus* are annuals. The mature plants die down in autumn and regrow in the spring from seeds or, more frequently, from turions. Some species such as *P. acuti-folius* fruit freely; others only fruit rarely. All have the capacity to produce turi-ons and often do so in abundance. *Groenlandia densa* and the remaining species of *Potamogeton* are rhizomatous perennials. Most have leafy shoots which die down in the autumn to buds which develop on the rhizome or to the rhizome itself. The shoots regrow in spring. However, a number of species retain rather short leafy shoots through the winter: these include *Groenlandia densa*, *Potamogeton coloratus*, *P. crispus*, *P. praelongus* and some populations of *P. pectinatus*. *P. natans* neither dies down in autumn nor remains green but the old shoots persist and decay gradually as the winter progresses.

Colonies of *P. alpinus* in flowing water often fail to reappear in the same place from one year to the next, as the rhizome buds are washed away. However, they may reappear subsequently if buds are washed down from other colonies growing upstream (Brux, Todeskino & Wiegleb 1987, Brux *et al.* 1988).

Some of the perennial *Potamogeton* species can behave as annuals in certain ecological situations. In the Netherlands, van Wijk (1988, 1989a) found that in a large and exposed freshwater lake, the Veluwemeer, the *P. pectinatus* popula-tion was strictly annual, dying back to tubers in the winter. Plants flowered spar-ingly and those fruits that were produced were washed away into a reed-bed, so that a seed bank never built up in the substrate. In cultivation, plants began to produce tubers at an early stage in their growth. By contrast, a population of *P. pectinatus* in a sheltered brackish pool at Yerseke was perennial, overwinter-ing as rhizomes with leafy shoots as well as by tubers. The plants flowered freely and there was a persistent seed bank in the substrate. In cultivation, plants from this population did not produce tubers as rapidly as those from Veluwemeer. Other populations in standing water fell between these two extremes, and at some sites the species behaved as a perennial in sheltered, deeper water and as an annual in the more exposed shallows. Plants in running water were annual, persisting as tubers. Flowers began to develop in these populations but did not reach maturity, so no seed was set.

Ruppia maritima can also behave either as an annual or as a perennial (Verhoeven 1979). In favourable circumstances plants in the Netherlands over-winter as quiescent vegetative stems, but in other sites the plant persists as seeds, which germinate in spring. *R. cirrhosa* persists through the winter as stems which suddenly begin rapid growth when temperatures rise in spring. After the plants flower, the stems decay and break away as floating masses. The tops of these stems send out roots and can become established as new plants. Reproduction by seed is of little importance in maintaining colonies of this species. British *Ruppia* populations have not been studied in winter, but they are likely to behave in a similar way to Dutch plants. However, *R. maritima* has been found flowering in January in Cardiganshire, suggesting that it is not always quiescent in the winter in our more oceanic areas.

The definition of annual adopted here is a functional rather than a genetic one. In genetical terms there is a clear distinction between reproduction by seed, which gives rise to a new individual, and reproduction by vegetative propagules, which perpetuates the same genotype. The difficulties of applying the geneti-cally defined terms to aquatic plants which produce both seeds and vegetative propagules are discussed by van Wijk (1988).

Life-forms of hybrids

Most hybrids arise between parents of similar life-form. Where one parent dies down during the winter and the other is winter-green, the hybrid can be inter-mediate in its behaviour. Thus Taylor & Sledge (1944) found that *P. × cognatus* in Lincolnshire persisted as leafy stems until the end of December, whereas the shoots of *P. perfoliatus* died down during the autumn and *P. praelongus* con-tinued to grow slowly throughout the winter.

Some hybrids between dissimilar parents have a life-form which differs sig-nificantly from that of either parent and enables them to grow in a habitat which neither parent can occupy (Preston 1993). The best example is *P. × lanceolatus*, a hybrid with a rhizome and narrow submerged leaves which is found in several rapidly flowing calcareous streams in western Ireland. One parent, *P. berch-toldii*, lacks a rhizome and has never been recorded in the Irish sites for the hybrid. The other parent, *P. coloratus*, has a rhizome but its leaves are very broad. When *P. coloratus* grows in the same stream as the hybrid, it is restricted to quiet bays. The competitive ability of *P. × lanceolatus* is presumably enhanced by its capacity to produce narrow submerged leaves in more rapidly flowing water and broader leaves where the flow is gentler. The rarer hybrid *P. × variifolius* provides another example of the same phenomenon.

Survival through periods of drought

Potamogeton polygonifolius is unique amongst the British and Irish pondweeds in the fact that it is frequently found as aerial shoots growing in bogs, flushes or shallow ditches. Other pondweeds are only found as terrestrial plants when they are exposed by a falling water level. Species react to such desiccation in different ways. When plants which are capable of producing floating leaves are exposed, they usually produce short aerial shoots with a rosette of coriaceous leaves. Such shoots can send out stolons and thus spread vegetatively, but never flower. Plants which can persist for a period in this form include *P. alpinus*, *P. natans* and *P. gramineus* and their hybrids *P. × fluitans*, *P. × sparganiifolius*, *P. × zizii*, *P. × billupsii* and *P. × nitens*. *P. coloratus* also produces similar shoots, although even the aerial leaves of this species are membranous and translucent. Descriptions of the land-forms of *P. coloratus* and most of the other taxa which produce them are given by Fryer (1887d) and Fryer & Bennett (1915). Populations of *P. alpinus* also produce an increased number of buds on the rhizomes in response to drought (Brux, Todeskino & Wiegleb 1987).

The species which are unable to produce floating leaves simply dry up if exposed above the water. Those species which are rhizomatous can survive as rhizomes, rhizome buds or tubers for a period, although these organs have limited tolerance to desiccation. Species without rhizomes are killed outright by drought and the survival of the population must rely on seeds.

Pollination

The aerial inflorescences of *Potamogeton* Subgenus *Potamogeton* are wind-pollinated (Cook 1988). The flowers are protogynous and at first the receptive stigmas protrude through closed perianth segments. The concave tepals then open and the anthers dehisce; Cook (1988) suggests that the lowest tepal catches falling pollen and holds it until it is blown into the airstream. Stigmas which have not already been pollinated by other plants are likely to be self-pollinated at this stage. Some species such as *P. epihydrus* are self-compatible, and this fail-safe selfing results in almost all carpels developing into fruits. Other species, including *P. berchtoldii*, are apparently self-incompatible and the pollen falling on stigmas of the same plant does not germinate (Philbrick 1983).

Some species of *Potamogeton* always have aerial inflorescences; these include *P. epihydrus*, *P. natans* and *P. nodosus* (Philbrick 1983, Guo & Cook 1989). *P. lucens* is usually pollinated above the water, but under experimental conditions it can be pollinated by pollen floating on the water surface (Guo &

Cook 1989). This may happen in the wild to plants growing in rapidly flowing water, if the inflorescences are drawn beneath the surface of the water by strong currents and then rise into the air again. Other species of *Potamogeton* can set seed even if the flower never emerges above the surface of the water. Some species regularly flower and fruit under water, and the American *P. spirullus* has dimorphic flowers, with aerial flowers larger than submerged ones. I have seen plants of some British species fruiting in unusually deep water, where the inflorescence could not reach the surface, and the ability of submerged flowers to set seed has also been demonstrated in controlled conditions. The precise sequence of events which leads to pollination under water has been studied in only a few species. In America, Philbrick (1983) reports that *P. berchtoldii* regularly flowers under water. Flowers which open under water are pollinated by bubble pollination. When the anthers of submerged flowers dehisce, a gas bubble is formed and pollen collects on its surface. The bubble gradually increases in size until it comes into contact with the stigma of the same flower, and pollen is then deposited on the stigma (Philbrick & Anderson 1987, Philbrick 1988). In self-compatible species seed is set under water as a result of self-pollination; in *P. berchtoldii*, which is self-incompatible, any seed set is presumably the result of fertilisation by pollen which has drifted away from the gas bubble around the anthers of other plants. Philbrick (1988) suggests that bubble pollination could have been an important intermediate stage in the evolution of mechanisms of underwater pollination from aerial pollination.

The peduncles of the species in *Potamogeton* Subgenus *Coleogeton* are not sufficiently rigid to hold the inflorescences above the water surface. The flowers normally float on the surface at anthesis. The pollen also floats after it is released from the anthers and is thus carried on the water surface to the stigma (Yeo 1965, van Wijk 1989a). However, *P. pectinatus* can certainly set fruit if the flowers are completely submerged, and I suspect (from field observations) that the same is true of *P. filiformis*. Guo & Cook (1989) found that much less fruit was set on submerged than on floating inflorescences of *P. pectinatus*. In submerged flowers, pollen was transferred from the anther to the stigmas of the same flower, or between a pair of flowers at the same node, by bubble pollination.

Groenlandia densa can be pollinated in a variety of ways (Guo & Cook 1990). In still water the inflorescences are held above the surface of the water, and the stigmas receive dry pollen released by the anthers. In flowing water the inflorescences may be drawn down below the water, and the stigmas collect pollen from the water surface as they pass through it. Submerged inflorescences are self-pollinated by bubble pollination. Both aerial and submerged inflorescences are likely to be self-pollinated, but the flowers are protogynous and cross-pollination could occur if the stigmas are fertilised by pollen floating on the water surface.

The pollination of both *Ruppia* species has been studied by Verhoeven (1979). In *Ruppia maritima* the peduncles are short. The stamens dehisce under water and as each one bursts an air bubble appears. The dehisced stamen and the bubble remain attached to the inflorescence for several hours. The air bubble is connected to the internal air supply of the plant: if most of the bubble floats away the small bubble that remains gradually enlarges again. Pollen is transferred from the anthers to the stigma on the surface of the bubble, as in *Potamogeton* species. This mechanism of self-fertilisation is efficient and *R. maritima* usually sets large quantities of seed. In *R. cirrhosa* the stamens are released and rise to the surface, where they dehisce. *Ruppia* pollen is boomerang-shaped and the grains of *R. cirrhosa* link up as chain-like strings on the surface of the water (Les 1988). When the stamens are released, the peduncle elongates until the flowers float on the surface of the water. Two air bubbles appear in the flower as the stamens are released, and these act as buoys, assisting the inflorescence to float to the surface. Cross-pollination is usual in this species. Seed set is often low, especially in large, turbulent waters. Occasionally flowers of *R. cirrhosa* fail to reach the water surface; these are pollinated by a mechanism similar to that of *R. maritima*. Similarly, the odd flower of *R. maritima* that reaches the surface can be pollinated in the same way as *R. cirrhosa*.

Germination of seeds

Guppy (1894, 1897) found that seeds of six *Potamogeton* species which were placed in water or on wet mud after they were collected failed to germinate in the year of collection but emerged at intervals over the next two to five years. Seed of *P. polygonifolius*, for example, germinated in the two years after collection, whereas seed of *P.lucens* germinated gradually over a period of five years. Almost all the seeds in one batch of *Groenlandia densa* germinated in the year following collection, but germination of the second batch was spread over three years. Guppy suggested that, in the wild, germination might be accelerated if seeds were eaten by waterfowl. He bought 13 wild duck in a London market and recovered some *Potamogeton* fruits from the stomach and intestines of three. These fruits germinated within four months of being sown. Guppy also mixed a large number of *Potamogeton natans* fruits into the food of a domestic duck and recovered many intact fruits from its droppings. Some 60% of these had germinated by the next spring, compared to only 1% of fruits recovered from food which the duck had not eaten. Fruits of *Groenlandia densa* were able to withstand drying for 11 weeks but not for 17 months; those of *P. natans* withstood drying for four but not for 30 months, whereas those of *P. crispus* germinated in quantity after drying for 18 months.

Subsequent experiments have confirmed the broad conclusions reached by Guppy (1897). Freshly collected seed shows low percentage germination, which is due to the impermeability of the fruit coat. The deliberate rupture of the fruit coat causes germination, and treatments which have the same effect (such as swirling seeds in abrasive sand or treating them with sulphuric acid) also enhance germination to some extent. The ability of *Potamogeton* fruits to pass through the digestive tract of ducks has been confirmed, as has their limited tolerance of drying. Smits, van Ruremonde & van der Velde (1989) also showed that pondweed fruits could pass through the digestive tract of carp with only superficial damage, but only fish deprived of fish food for five days were prepared to eat them! There is, however, a great deal of variation in the detailed results obtained in different germination experiments, and some authors have failed to confirm even the broad conclusions outlined here. It is not clear whether this variation reflects genetic differences between populations or whether it is caused by the conditions under which the seeds matured. For further details of germination experiments, see the papers by Crocker (1907), Lohammar (1954), Moore (1913), Muenscher (1936), Spence *et al.* (1971), Teltscherová & Hejny (1973), van Wijk (1989a), Vlaming & Proctor (1968) and Yeo (1965).

There is some evidence that viable *Potamogeton* seeds can accumulate in lake sediments. Haag (1983) collected sediment from Lake Wabamun in Canada and found that the most frequent seedlings which germinated from his samples were those of *P. pectinatus* and *P. pusillus* (presumably *sensu lato*).

There is little direct evidence on the importance of reproduction by seed in populations of *Potamogeton*. Until 1994, when I found a single seedling of *P. alpinus* growing in deep water in Lough Leane, Killarney, I had never seen a seedling pondweed in the wild. It is difficult to know if reproduction by seed is genuinely rare or if seedlings are overlooked because seeds germinate in deep water or are dispersed and then come up as inconspicuous singletons rather than in swards. Brux, Todeskino & Wiegleb (1987) have emphasised the importance of vegetative reproduction for *P. alpinus*. They found that plants very rarely become established from seed in the wild, even at sites where seeds are produced in quantity. After detailed studies of *P. pectinatus* populations, van Wijk (1989a) also concluded that maintenance of populations from year to year was almost entirely due to vegetative persistence or reproduction; the main function of seeds was in dispersal and long-term survival during unfavourable periods. Reproduction by turions is usually thought to be more important in maintaining populations of the annual species in Section *Graminifolii*, although there have not been many critical studies of the life history of these species.

The germination of *Ruppia* has been studied experimentally by van Vierssen, van Kessel & van der Zee (1984). Germination of *R. maritima* is stimulated by cold temperature pretreatments, such as 4°C for two months under experimental conditions, and seeds therefore germinate in the spring. Very few seeds of *R. cirrhosa* germinated under the same experimental conditions that stimulated germination of *R. maritima*, and attempts to enhance germination in other ways have failed, so nothing can be said about the conditions that this species requires for germination.

Formation and 'germination' of turions and tubers

P. crispus is the only rhizomatous perennial pondweed which reproduces vegetatively by turions. In this species the turions are vegetative propagules rather than a means of overwintering. Populations of *P. crispus* produce turions from late spring to summer, but the onset of turion formation and the number of turions produced varies from population to population and from plant to plant. A single turion of *P. crispus* planted at the start of the season in California grew into a plant which produced 23,520 turions by the end of the year (Yeo 1966). Experimental studies show that turion formation is triggered by a combination of high temperature (16°C and above) and long days (Chambers, Spence & Weeks 1985). Turions germinate in autumn.

The turions of species in Section *Graminifolii* are produced in autumn and their production is probably triggered by short days. Studies of a population of *P. trichoides* in a pool in the Netherlands showed that plants overwintered as turions, which germinated in May. These plants grew during the summer and produced turions from early August onwards. By early October many turions had been formed and the parent plants had almost completely disappeared. Under experimental conditions freshly collected turions germinated at high temperatures, which implies that *P. trichoides* might be capable of passing through two 'generations' in a season. A short cold treatment inhibited germination, but this dormancy could be broken by a more prolonged cold treatment of 10 weeks at 4°C; after this, turions are able to germinate at relatively low temperatures (van Wijk & Trompenaars 1985).

The tubers formed on the rhizomes of *P. pectinatus* have been studied by van Wijk (1989a). They are produced by all populations of the species. In some populations they begin to be produced in May but in others they do not develop until later in the season. A single large tuber planted by Yeo (1965) gave rise to 2,380 tubers by the end of the season. The germination of tubers is stimulated by a cold treatment and can begin in March, although shoots are not sent out as early as this. Most tubers of *P. pectinatus* are killed by a period of two months' desiccation.

Dispersal

Pondweeds, like some other aquatic plants, appear to have remarkably effective powers of dispersal. This is shown by the appearance of plants in isolated ponds and even in water tanks, buckets and cattle troughs, by the rapid colonisation of new habitats such as gravel pits, and by the rich pondweed flora of offshore islands such as the Outer Hebrides. New populations of plants can arise from the dispersal of morphologically unspecialised fragments, of specialised organs such as turions or tubers, or of fruits.

Unspecialised plant fragments and specialised propagules can be detached by waves or water currents and carried around a lake or downstream in flowing waters. When rivers flood, plant material can be carried over the floodplain to otherwise isolated streams, ponds and ditches. The size of fragments dispersed by water can range from a few centimetres of stem drifting gently down a canal to large masses of material, complete with rhizomes and roots, torn up by a river in spate and deposited some distance downstream. When these fragments end up in congenial situations they can root and become established. The dispersal of stems and fruits is probably aided by their buoyancy. Stems and branches of *Potamogeton* float when they are first detached. Guppy (1906) found that the fruits of *Groenlandia densa*, *Potamogeton crispus*, *P. obtusifolius* and '*P. pusillus*' floated for less than a week, but those of *P. perfoliatus* could float for one to six months, those of *P. lucens* and *P. polygonifolius* for six to 12 months and those of *P. natans* for over 12 months. Praeger (1913) found that the fruits of '*Potamogeton pusillus*' and *Ruppia maritima* floated for 12–24 hours, those of *P. alpinus*, *P. coloratus* and *P. polygonifolius* for 24–36 hours and those of *P. filiformis* and *P. pectinatus* for 48–60 hours. The reasons for the discrepancies in these results are not clear. The buoyancy of the fruits of *P. filiformis*, *P. natans* and *P. pectinatus* can probably be attributed to their fleshy mesocarp with large air spaces (Aalto 1970).

Turions and other plant fragments may also be transported by waterfowl. Woodruffe-Peacock (1917) once saw a Mallard flying towards an isolated dewpond with a necklace of *Potamogeton perfoliatus* about three feet long around its neck. On another occasion he shot a bird which was accidentally carrying a piece of *P. crispus*. It is difficult to assess how important these occasional events are. The transport of seed in the guts of birds is probably more significant. Pondweed fruits are often eaten by waterfowl and, although many are doubtless completely digested, a proportion are still viable when they are egested and, as discussed above, the abrasion they receive can actually promote germination.

ECOLOGY

The major constraints of life in water

It is difficult for us, as terrestrial animals, to appreciate the environment in which aquatic plants grow. Water is, as Wetzel (1988) comments, an acutely hostile medium for plant growth. The supply of light, carbon and other nutrients to the plant can all limit its growth, and plants can also be affected by water turbulence. There are, however, some compensations. Changes in temperature are buffered, so that the aquatic environment is not marked by extremes of heat or cold. Vegetative reproduction is easy, as propagules in the water are protected from desiccation and can be carried in moving water to new sites.

Light

Most aquatic plants grow in shaded conditions. The amount of light reaching the surface of water is the same as that falling on the land, but a proportion of it is reflected back, especially if the surface is turbulent or if sunlight is striking the water at a low angle. Up to one third of light reaching the surface can be reflected. The light entering the water is absorbed or scattered by inorganic molecules, particles of silt suspended in the water, microscopic phytoplankton, or macrophytes and their epiphytes. The water thus becomes progressively more shaded as it deepens, and it also changes in quality as certain wavelengths are selectively absorbed. The wavelengths absorbed depend on the nature of the dissolved and suspended matter in a particular water body. Where there is a high concentration of phytoplankton, light will become depleted in the wavelengths absorbed by chlorophyll. Spence (1975) showed that in Loch Croispol, a calcareous but nutrient-poor lake in Sutherland, 43% of the photosynthetically active light entering the water was available to a leaf of *Potamogeton crispus* held horizontally 1 m below the surface. In the eutrophic Loch Leven, Fife, only 5% was available at the same depth during a moderate plankton bloom.

Carbon dioxide

Carbon dioxide (CO_2) is, with light, essential for photosynthesis. It is a soluble gas, and the total amount of CO_2 is directly proportional to that in the atmosphere when, as is usually the case, the CO_2 in the water is in equilibrium with that in the air above. However, it is only in very acid waters (with a pH below 5) that it is predominantly found as the free, dissolved CO_2 molecule. At higher pH, CO_2 hydrates to carbonic acid (H_2CO_3), which dissociates to hydrogen (H^+) and bicarbonate ions (HCO_3^-). In waters where the pH is between 7 and 10, the majority of dissolved CO_2 is present in this form. At exceptionally high pH, a significant proportion is present as the carbonate ion (CO_3^{2-}). Submerged plants must obtain their carbon dioxide from one of these sources. Free CO_2 is the form which is most easily used. The supply of CO_2 can limit photosynthesis, especially in water with a high pH. The slow diffusion of CO_2 in water is also significant in reducing the available supply, especially as there is a stagnant layer at the surface of the leaf which is only reduced in thickness, not eliminated, in turbulent water. CO_2 is also produced in respiration and can be captured and recycled. In view of the lower availability of dissolved CO_2 at high pH, the presence of bicarbonate ions is significant as a potential extra source of carbon. Aquatic plants vary in the extent to which they can make use of bicarbonate ions: Allen & Spence (1981) showed that *Potamogeton crispus* had a higher affinity for HCO_3^- than *P. polygonifolius*. All plants which exploit bicarbonate ions as a source of CO_2 must use energy in transporting the ion across membranes and removing and excreting the OH^- ion. There is little evidence that any macrophytes can utilise CO_2 from the carbonate ion.

Oxygen

Oxygen is also required by aquatic plants. This is, however, a by-product of photosynthesis and, in the light, most aquatic plants produce more oxygen from photosynthesis than they need for respiration. Like carbon dioxide, oxygen diffuses very much more slowly in water than in air, and the respiration of submerged aquatic plants in the dark may be limited by the rate at which oxygen diffuses from water into the cells of the plant. Submerged sediments are usually anoxic; plants which root in them must be able to supply the roots with oxygen. The roots of many aquatic plants have an extensive network of air spaces through which oxygen can diffuse from the stems above. Another problem with which aquatic plants have to cope is the presence in sediments of toxic chemicals, such as hydrogen sulphide, which are produced by anaerobic bacteria.

Inorganic nutrients

Aquatic plants must also obtain inorganic nutrients such as calcium, potassium, magnesium, nitrogen and phosphorus. Even the most eutrophic water has a very low concentration of dissolved nutrients compared to most terrestrial soils. Concentrations in the water in the sediment in which the plants are rooted are usually higher than those in the water above. Plants with aerial or floating leaves absorb nutrients from the sediment by the roots and transport them to the leaves in the internal circulation of solutes driven by the loss of water to the atmosphere in transpiration. Plants which are entirely submerged can also actively absorb nutrients from the sediment; water movements in these species are likely to be osmotically driven (Raven 1984). Some absorption through the foliage is possible, but this can be limited by the diffusion across the boundary layer of water which surrounds the leaf and by the presence on many surfaces of algal epiphytes. Nitrogen and phosphorus are particularly significant nutrients, and, as nitrogen is very mobile and is washed into waters from terrestrial sources, phosphorus is often the nutrient which limits growth.

Competition with algae

All submerged vascular plants face competition with algae. Phytoplankton absorbs light and competes for nutrients, and algal epiphytes colonise leaf surfaces, thus intercepting more light. The complex interaction between phytoplankton, the zooplankton which preys on them and the aquatic macrophytes is of crucial importance in determining the vegetation of a water body, and any changes which shift the balance in favour of one of these groups can have profound effects.

Turbulence

Turbulence, including the effects of water flow in streams and rivers and of waves in lakes, is clearly potentially damaging to leaves and can also uproot entire plants. In exposed lakes, pondweeds are often restricted to sheltered bays, which are protected from the prevailing winds, and they are sometimes confined to the edges of fast-flowing rivers. In flowing water the build up of plant material can itself impede the flow of water.

Water chemistry as a determinant of pondweed distribution

Water chemistry is of major importance in determining the aquatic flora found at a particular site. At least four aspects of water chemistry are potentially significant. The first is the concentration of plant nutrients in the water. The 'trophic status' of a water body is a term which refers to the concentration of limiting nutrients. The terms dystrophic, oligotrophic, mesotrophic and eutrophic are used rather loosely for waters with very low, low, moderate and high concentrations of nutrients. The remaining aspects of water chemistry are the individual concentrations of specific nutrients. They are the alkalinity of the water (defined as the amount of carbonate or bicarbonate ions dissolved in it), the concentration of calcium in the water, and the salinity, which is in effect the concentration of sodium chloride.

There is a broad correlation between the trophic status of British and Irish waters, their alkalinity and their calcium content. Waters of low alkalinity usually have low levels of calcium and other plant nutrients; many of the rivers and lakes over the acid rocks of the north and west exemplify this condition. Similarly, high alkalinity often goes hand-in-hand with high levels of calcium and other nutrients, as in many water bodies in the south and east. This correlation does not always hold. Some unpolluted, and exceptionally interesting, waters over limestone have high alkalinity coupled with low levels of nutrients other than calcium. Some lakes are not calcareous but nevertheless have a high alkalinity: this is the result of calcium carbonate precipitating out at very high pH, leaving the more soluble carbonates of magnesium, sodium and potassium in solution. Spence (1967) reported on such non-calcareous but highly alkaline lakes in Caithness.

The salinity of a water is usually determined by its distance from the sea and the extent to which it is exposed to winds which deposit salt spray. There is, therefore, little correlation between salinity and other aspects of water chemistry. There are only a few British water bodies which are saline because they receive drainage from inland salt deposits.

Although the effect of water chemistry on aquatic plant distribution is obvious to anyone who studies a range of different waters, it is very difficult to quantify. This may partly reflect the fact that the chemistry of a water body may vary from hour to hour, day to day, season to season and year to year. A single water analysis is thus of limited use. Secondly, some of the most popular measures of water chemistry integrate the effects of more than one of the factors outlined above. Thus, water conductivity, which measures the total concentration of electrolytes, can be high because water is alkaline or because it is saline. Another measure, pH, can be high in both calcareous waters and in non-calcareous but alkaline waters. A final reason for the difficulty of quantifying the relationship between water chemistry and flora is that the effects of water chemistry often operate indirectly, for example through their effects on algae.

Despite the difficulties of disentangling the various aspects of water chemistry which affect the distribution of pondweeds, there have been a number of attempts to classify species according to the chemistry of the water in which they grow. Spence (1967) listed *P. lucens* as a species which in Scottish lakes was confined to water with high alkalinity and high calcium levels; *P. filiformis*, *P. pectinatus* and *P. praelongus* were confined to lakes which were at least moderately alkaline and often slightly saline, but not necessarily calcareous. In contrast to these species, *P. gramineus* and *P. perfoliatus* were ubiquitous.

Trophic requirements

The aquatic plants of standing waters in Britain have been ranked according to their trophic requirements by Palmer, Bell & Butterfield (1992). These rankings were based on the pattern of occurrence of the species in a sample of 1124 sites. As the nitrogen and phosphorus concentrations at the sites were not known, the trophic status of each site was assessed by a consideration of pH, conductivity and alkalinity. This approach relies on the broad but imperfect correlation between trophic status and the other variables; it provides an approximate measure of trophic requirements but might be expected to misclassify any species which are particularly frequent in waters where this correlation does not hold. A similar ranking of the species in flowing water has been published by Holmes & Newbold (1984).

The trophic requirements of the *Potamogeton* species, as set out by Palmer, Bell & Butterfield (1992) for standing water, are listed below. The trophic levels in brackets are assigned to the species with less confidence than those which are not bracketed. The comments after the species are mine. As the list shows, most *Potamogeton* species are found in mesotrophic or eutrophic water.

(Dystrophic)–oligotrophic

  P. polygonifolius

Oligotrophic–mesotrophic

  P. alpinus
  Although it was not listed by Palmer, Bell & Butterfield, *P. epihydrus* probably falls into this category.

Oligotrophic–mesotrophic–(eutrophic)

  P. natans

(Oligotrophic)–mesotrophic–eutrophic

P. berchtoldii
P. gramineus
P. obtusifolius
P. perfoliatus
P. praelongus

Few of these species are tolerant of very eutrophic water. In particular, *P. gramineus* and *P. praelongus* appear to be absent from the more eutrophic sites.

Mesotrophic–eutrophic

P. crispus
P. pusillus

Eutrophic

P. filiformis
P. friesii
P. lucens
P. pectinatus
P. trichoides

P. lucens is less tolerant of eutrophic water than the other members of this group. Its preference for alkaline water of high pH may have led to an overestimation of its trophic requirements. *P. nodosus* is restricted to a few rivers in Britain but probably belongs to the eutrophic group.

Changes in the nutrient levels in a water body can have profound effects on the aquatic flora. These are discussed later.

Salinity

The tolerance of salinity of the British and Irish pondweeds is easily summarised. *Potamogeton filiformis* and *P. pectinatus* are the only species of *Potamogeton* which are frequent in brackish water, although *P. pusillus* can also be found by the coast in brackish pools and ditches. *Ruppia cirrhosa* and *R. maritima* are confined to more or less brackish sites. *R. cirrhosa* is the most salt-tolerant of our species. Verhoeven (1980a) reported that this species completely replaces *P. pectinatus* in lagoons where the chloride concentration exceeds 9‰, whereas *P. pectinatus* is the only species present at concentrations below 4‰. The two species grow together at intermediate salinities.

THE MAJOR PONDWEED HABITATS

The major habitats for pondweeds in Britain and Ireland are dealt with below. Although the treatment of each is necessarily brief, I have tried to give references to more detailed treatments where these are available.

A phytosociological description of the vegetation in which pondweeds grow is outside the scope of this book. Spence's (1964) detailed account of the vegetation of Scottish lakes is the most useful study in our area and contains a wealth of information on the northern *Potamogeton* species. The subterrestrial habitat of *P. polygonifolius* is described in accounts of mires in the Scottish Highlands (McVean & Ratcliffe 1962) and in Britain as a whole (Rodwell 1991). A volume dealing with aquatic habitats was published in the National Vegetation Classification series in 1995, after this Handbook went to press (Rodwell 1995). Continental botanists have studied aquatic vegetation in more detail, and it is unfortunate that the National Vegetation Classification does not attempt to place our vegetation into the categories which they recognise. Passarge's (1992, 1994) account of aquatic plant communities in central Europe provides a lead into the continental literature.

Lakes

Lakes are most frequent in the north and west of Britain and Ireland; in the Outer Hebrides "thair is infinite number of fresh water Lochis", as Dean Munro aptly commented in 1549 (Waterston & Lyster 1979). However, these areas where lakes are most numerous are regions of acid rocks and peaty soils. In such country, lakes are characteristically oligotrophic, and their pondweed flora is normally limited to the two common species *Potamogeton natans* and *P. polygonifolius*, which often grow together in shallow water round the edge. In addition, *P. polygonifolius* can usually be found in flushes and streams leading down to the edge of the lake.

The more diverse pondweed communities of the north and west are found in water which is enriched by base-rich rocks or sediments. The presence of an outcrop of a rock such as basalt in the catchment can be reflected in the presence in a lake of species such as *P. perfoliatus* and *P. praelongus*. A more significant enrichment is found in lakes over limestone or those which are influenced by calcareous sand. Lakes over limestone are rare: those at Durness on the north coast of Scotland and on the island of Lismore are particularly fine examples. *Potamogeton filiformis* can be found over the highly calcareous substrate in shallow water at the edge of these Scottish lochs, often growing with *Chara aspera* in a community described by Spence (1964). In deeper water there are stands of the broad-leaved pondweeds *P. perfoliatus* and *P. praelongus*, often mixed with *P. pectinatus*. A characteristic plant of limestone lakes in northern England and central Ireland is *Potamogeton lucens*. In addition to the interest of their flora, limestone lakes are particularly attractive because of the clarity of the water. They are, however, vulnerable to eutrophication.

Coastal lakes at the junction of acidic rock and calcareous dune sand are a feature of the west coast of Scotland and Ireland; they are sometimes known as machair lochs. They often have a range of water chemistry, with the calcareous and saline influences gradually increasing from the landward side to the coastal edge. The range of aquatics which they can support is correspondingly rich; their pondweed species can include *P. gramineus* and *P. praelongus* in the more mesotrophic areas, *P. crispus*, *P. filiformis*, *P. pectinatus* and *P. pusillus* towards the sea, and *Ruppia maritima* or *R. cirrhosa* where the water is particularly saline. These lochs are the usual habitat of the rare *P. rutilus* in the Hebrides.

In lowland areas of Britain and Ireland lakes are usually eutrophic. Characteristic pondweeds of lowland lakes include *P. crispus*, *P. friesii*, *P. pectinatus*, *P. perfoliatus* and *P. pusillus*. Lowland lakes in populous or intensively farmed areas are particularly vulnerable to excessive eutrophication, and unpolluted examples are very rare.

Whereas the flora of a lake is to a large extent determined by the water chemistry, the distribution of the plants within the lake is usually governed by other factors, of which exposure, substrate and depth are perhaps the most important. Exposure and substrate are intimately related. In considering exposure, the 'wave-mixed zone' at the edge of the lake is particularly important. This is the zone where the depth of water is less than half the wavelength of the waves. Its extent depends on the wavelength of the waves, which is in turn governed by the aspect of the shore and the size of the lake. In small lakes the zone may be completely absent, at least on the more sheltered shores. Within the wave-mixed zone erosion is more important than deposition, and the substrate is usually reduced to bare rock, boulders or coarse sand or gravel. The plant cover within the wave-mixed zone is low, and few *Potamogeton* species grow within it. Characteristic species of this zone where the substrates are rocky or formed from boulders are isoetids such as *Isoetes*, *Littorella* and *Lobelia*. A somewhat richer flora can be found over sand and this can include *Potamogeton filiformis*, a rhizomatous species with linear leaves. Even the vigour of this species is considerably reduced by exposure: in Loch Leven Jupp & Spence

(1977b) found that the biomass of stands on an exposed shore was only 15% of that in a sheltered area. Below the wave-mixed zone deposition is more important than erosion and sediments are finer. Plant cover is usually high in that portion of a lake which lies below the wave-mixed zone and above the point at which increasing shade prohibits macrophyte growth.

The broad-leaved *Potamogeton* species which can produce floating leaves, such as *P. gramineus*, *P. natans* and *P. polygonifolius*, are usually found in shallower water than those like *P. perfoliatus* and *P. praelongus* which only have submerged leaves. *P. alpinus*, in which submerged leaves predominate but which can produce a few floating leaves, is intermediate both morphologically and in its depth requirements. Spence (1982) recorded *P. natans* at depths down to 4 m; he never found *P. praelongus* in water shallower than 1.5 m and both *P. perfoliatus* and *P. praelongus* descend to 6.5 m in the clear waters of Loch Borralie. The narrow-leaved species of *Potamogeton* which occur in lakes appear to be able to grow at a range of depths. Plants like *P. berchtoldii*, *P. obtusifolius* and *P. pusillus* can be found in very shallow water provided that it is sheltered, but they have little tolerance of exposure, as they lack a rhizome and are easily uprooted from the sediment. They can descend to depths of 4 m or more. Like many other plants, *P. obtusifolius* can adapt to different light levels physiologically, and its leaves have a larger area per unit of dry weight when growing in the shade (Spence & Chrystal 1970b).

The most detailed investigation of the distribution of pondweeds in lakes in relation to the substrate is that of Pearsall (1920). He found that in the Lake District both linear-leaved species (*Potamogeton berchtoldii*, *P. obtusifolius*, *P. pusillus*) and species with broad, submerged leaves such as *P. perfoliatus* and *P. praelongus* were confined to the areas where the silt was particularly abundant and fine-grained. *P. alpinus* was the species which grew in areas where silt was most abundant. By contrast, *P. natans* was usually found away from silt sources and *P. gramineus* also occurred in areas of coarser substrate. Pearsall (1920) concluded that the distribution of the aquatic plants he studied was "primarily governed by the nature of the substratum". This conclusion underestimates the intimate relationship which exists between depth, exposure and substrate, which is discussed in detail by Spence (1982).

Unstable substrates can limit pondweed growth even if other conditions are favourable. In Loch Borralie, for example, the gently sloping sediments support dense beds of vascular plants, including *Potamogeton perfoliatus* and *P. praelongus*, with an understorey of charophytes. In the neighbouring Loch Croispol the lake bed slopes steeply and the unstable sediments only support a thin canopy of *P. perfoliatus* at comparable depths (Spence 1982).

An outline classification of the standing waters of Great Britain is provided by Palmer, Bell & Butterfield (1992), and a detailed description of the vegetation in Scottish lakes is provided by Spence (1964). The factors controlling the distribution of plants in lakes, including the reasons for the zonation of aquatic plants within a lake, are discussed by Spence (1967, 1982). A summary of the flora of Welsh lakes is provided by Seddon (1972), who outlines the range of water chemistry tolerated by the main species. Lakes in Northern Ireland have been surveyed in detail recently; an inventory of sites has been published (Smith *et al.* 1991) and summaries of the survey results may appear in print in due course.

Reservoirs

Some reservoirs are built specially, whereas others are natural lakes which have been converted into reservoirs by damming and controlling the outflow. The crucial factor which determines the flora of reservoirs is the frequency and extent of the fluctuations in water level. Where fluctuations are small or infrequent, the flora can be similar to that of lakes, but *Potamogeton* species or hybrids which can persist for a period as a land-form (e.g. *P. gramineus*, *P. × nitens*) sometimes appear to be particularly frequent. Reservoirs where there are large fluctuations in water level are usually devoid of macrophytes. An example cited by Smith, Maitland & Pennock (1987) is Loch an Daimh, where a dense cover of vegetation including *Potamogeton gramineus* and *P. natans* was eliminated when the natural lake was converted to a hydro-electric reservoir.

Ponds

Few areas in Britain or Ireland lack ponds, and in many areas they are the only standing waters. Some ponds are natural features of the landscape, but many are flooded clay or marl pits or were deliberately constructed as watering places for stock. Ponds are important as sites for the commonest pondweeds, but they are rarely notable for harbouring a diverse range of *Potamogeton* species or for the presence of rare species or hybrids. *Potamogeton natans* is the most characteristic pond species. In a survey of 153 ponds in a single Cheshire parish, *P. natans* was found in 61 sites; the only other species recorded were *P. berchtoldii* and *P. obtusifolius*, each of which was found in only one pond (Brian *et al.*, 1987). In areas where the water is acidic and oligotrophic *P. polygonifolius* replaces *P. natans* as the predominant pond species, and in saltmarshes brackish pools can harbour *Ruppia maritima*.

Rivers and streams

Rivers and streams are found in most parts of Britain and Ireland. Pondweeds favour those with slow or moderate flow, fine substrates and mesotrophic or eutrophic water. They are rarely found where the flow is very rapid or the water is shallow and therefore turbulent, where the substrates are rocky or consist of boulders or coarse stones, or where the water is oligotrophic. For all these reasons they tend to be plants of broad streams and mature rivers in the lowlands.

The ability of species to survive in turbulent water is governed to some extent by their life form. Most species in Section *Potamogeton* have a rhizome but possess broad leaves, which are easily damaged. Those in Section *Graminifolii* lack a rhizome and are easily uprooted. Only *P. crispus* in Section *Batrachoseris* and the species in Subgenus *Coleogeton* have a combination of a rhizomatous habit and narrow leaves which might be expected to be of selective advantage in rivers and streams. *P. crispus*, *P. pectinatus* and the hybrid *P.* × *suecicus* can be found in relatively rapidly flowing streams and rivers over gravelly substrates. In these situations both *P. pectinatus* and *P.* × *suecicus* tend to be rooted under large stones and boulders or under masonry at the foot of bridges. As mentioned above, the hybrids *P.* × *lanceolatus* and *P.* × *variifolius* have more or less linear leaves and a rhizome and can be found in shallow streams of fairly rapid flow.

An excellent classification of the plant communities in British rivers was published by Holmes (1983). He divided the communities in rivers into four major groups, labelled A–D. The first set of communities (Group A) is found in lowland rivers with very shallow slope and nutrient-rich and often calcareous water. They are found over a range of substrates including clay, silt, sand and gravel. These communities are virtually restricted to England, where they are most frequent in the south and east, with only a few outlying occurrences in Scotland and Wales. In the rivers surveyed by Holmes a number of species of pondweed are only found in these communities, including *P. friesii*, *P. nodosus*, *P. pusillus* and *P. lucens*, the latter being particularly characteristic of this group. Group A includes the plant communities of rivers and streams flowing from a chalk aquifer, which tend to have clear water with a stable flow and a gravel substrate. *Potamogeton* species are curiously rare in this habitat, but *Groenlandia densa* is one of its most characteristic species.

Group B communities are characteristic of meso-eutrophic rivers over sandstone or Carboniferous limestone and include those in the large areas of Britain which are underlain by New Red or Old Red Sandstone. Most of these rivers have stretches where the substrate is fine sand and silt, often combined with stretches where the flow is more rapid and the substrate coarser. Group B rivers are found in eastern Scotland, northern and western England and Wales. The only pondweed in Holmes' survey which is confined to these rivers is *P. gramineus*. There is, however, a sizeable group of pondweeds which occur in both Group A and Group B communities: *Potamogeton alpinus*, *P. berchtoldii*, *P. crispus*, *P. perfoliatus* and *P.* × *salicifolius*. The rivers with group B communities include those with the richest assemblages of pondweeds in Britain, including the R. Don (Aberdeenshire), R. Tweed and R. Wharfe. Although Irish rivers were not included in Holmes' survey, the outstanding Irish pondweed river, the Boyne, would probably fall into this group too. These rich rivers not only have a range of species but usually have persistent populations of hybrids as well. In addition to *P.* × *salicifolius*, these hybrids can include *P.* × *cooperi*, *P.* × *olivaceus*, *P.* × *nitens* and *P.* × *suecicus*.

Holmes' Group C communities are found in oligo-mesotrophic or mesotrophic waters which flow over hard rocks. Group D communities are those of truly oligotrophic water; many rivers have a group D flora in their headwaters and group C communities downstream. These rivers are typically fast-flowing and dominated by bryophytes; their substrates are either rocky or consist of unstable gravel, stones or boulders. Rivers with group C and D communities are found in Scotland, northern England, Wales and south-west England, with isolated outliers in areas of acidic geology elsewhere. Both community types are poor in pondweeds: Holmes only lists *P. natans* and *P. polygonifolius* as occurring in his samples. *P. polygonifolius* is confined to these two groups but *P. natans* is found in all the major communities from the calcareous rivers of Group A to the oligotrophic rivers of Group D.

The ecological distinction between the riparian species of *Potamogeton* and *Ranunculus* is of interest. Like the pondweeds, the species and hybrids in *Ranunculus* Subgenus *Batrachium* are characteristically found in the plant communities in Groups A and B; the only one of the larger riparian *Ranunculus* species which is listed for Holmes' Group C is *R. penicillatus* subsp. *penicillatus*. The *Ranunculus* species are less tolerant of very eutrophic conditions than the pondweeds, and there is no equivalent in that genus of *Potamogeton pectinatus*, which can be extremely abundant in eutrophic water. Where *Potamogeton* and *Ranunculus* species grow in the same river, as they do in many of the meso-eutrophic rivers in Group B, the *Ranunculus* taxa tend to dominate the shallower stretches where the river breaks into riffles and flows over a gravelly substrate, whereas the pondweeds dominate deeper, smoothly flowing stretches, where the substrate is often finer. *Ranunculus penicillatus* subsp. *pseudofluitans* is particularly characteristic of the chalk streams and rivers in which *Potamogeton* species are so scarce.

Canals

In Britain the start of the canal-building era can be dated from 1760, when the construction of the Bridgewater Canal was authorised by Act of Parliament. This canal proved to be a financial success, and in the next 70 years many canals were built and a great many more started but not completed, or planned but not started. In addition to the canals themselves, many feeder reservoirs and streams were built to supply the system with water. By 1830 there were over 2800 miles of canals in Britain. The beginning of the railway era then put an end to the period of canal construction. Some canals were actually sold to provide routes for railways, and most suffered from competition from the railway network. For over a century the canal network was in gradual decline. Although some canals remained viable, others lost all their traffic and became disused. Most canals were taken into public ownership in 1948, and the remorseless decline continued. The national fleet of narrow boats ceased operations in 1963, following losses sustained in the cold winter of 1962–63. The history of canal building in Ireland is rather different, as the canals were built with public rather than private money and in the hope of creating trade rather than to serve existing industry. The canals in the north centered on Lough Neagh, the first being the Newry Canal, opened in 1742. The Grand Canal running from Dublin to the Shannon was started in 1756 but not completed until 1805; this quiet canal with its simple Georgian bridges is one of our most pleasing waterways. The second major canal running west from Dublin, the Royal Canal, was completed in 1817. As in Britain, the rather meagre traffic attracted by these canals fell victim to the railways, although the Grand Canal retained an important secondary function as a source of water for Dublin.

Most pondweed species colonised the canal network, no doubt assisted by the fact that canals were usually connected to rivers in which aquatics already grew. As in other water bodies, water chemistry is an important determinant of the species which become established. The most surprising colonist was the American *P. epihydrus*, which was discovered in canals in the north of England long before it was found as a native in the Outer Hebrides and presumably originated from introduced American material. Three hybrids of *P. crispus* are particularly associated with canals: *P. × bennettii*, which is confined to a single canal, *P. × cooperi* and *P. × lintonii*. The only species of *Potamogeton* which have never been recorded in canals are the two rarities *P. nodosus* and *P. rutilus*, although there are very few canal records of *P. acutifolius*, *P. coloratus*, *P. filiformis* and *P. polygonifolius*. *P. natans* is less frequent in canals that one would expect from its abundance in other habitats, perhaps because its floating leaves are too readily detached by passing boats.

An example of a canal with a particularly important pondweed flora is the Montgomery arm of the Shropshire Union Canal, which has significant populations of the uncommon species *P. compressus*, *P. friesii* and *P. praelongus*. Other canals are less important in a national context but have pondweeds which are rare locally: the Exeter Canal, for instance, has populations of *P. lucens*, *P. obtusifolius* and *P. perfoliatus* at or near their south-western limit in Britain.

Although we know which pondweeds colonised canals, we have no detailed records of the flora of canals in their heyday or in the period when the system was in slow decline. There are plenty of old photographs of canals, but the submerged vegetation is out of sight. This lack of evidence is frustrating, as the boat traffic on canals has changed fundamentally in recent decades and we are now unable to compare the current flora with that of the past. Superb 19th-century herbarium specimens of *Potamogeton compressus* and *P. friesii* suggest that the canal flora was once more luxuriant than it is now, and the occasional presence of thriving pondweed populations in the backwaters of canals and navigable rivers is additional and more convincing evidence that the increase in motorised boat traffic has led to a deterioration in aquatic plant communities.

The conservation of the aquatic flora of canals presents difficult and perhaps insoluble problems. In 1950 the greatest threat to the canal flora must have appeared to be the decline in boat traffic. As the importance of canals decreased, some were abandoned and dried out and others became overgrown by emergents. However, the great boom in recreational boating in the post-war years safeguarded the future of the canals, and many have been restored by volunteer labour. Plants recolonise the newly restored canals rapidly. However, the increase in boat traffic in a canal can itself be a threat to their flora. Murphy & Eaton (1983) showed that the abundance of macrophytes in a canal was inversely proportional to the density of boat traffic once a certain critical threshold of boat traffic had been exceeded. Boats physically damage the plants and also disturb silt, which is held in suspension in the water and can then settle on the leaves of aquatic plants. The adverse effects of boating on the canal flora has sometimes led to conflict between wildlife conservationists and members of the canal restoration movement. Proposals to restore the Basingstoke Canal, in particular, have been the subject of a particularly acrimonious controversy which has yet to be resolved (Byfield 1990).

Histories of the canal-building era, and details of recent restoration projects, are given by Baldwin & Burton (1984), Delany & Delany (1966), Hadfield (1984), McCutcheon (1965) and Squires (1983). I know of no general review of the flora or vegetation of canals. There have been numerous surveys of particular canals, most of which are only available as unpublished reports.

Drainage ditches

Drainage ditches are features of landscapes which have been created by the reclamation of wetlands for agriculture. The most important ditches for aquatic plants are those in so-called 'grazing marshes'. These are areas of grassland in which the fields are separated by ditches which provide a water supply for grazing animals and act as a stock-proof barrier. They are usually unshaded and the regular maintenance they need to keep them stock-proof ensures that they do not become overgrown with emergents. Until recently this pastoral landscape was characteristic of many low-lying flatlands in England and South Wales, including the Somerset Levels, Monmouthshire/Gwent Levels, Pevensey Levels, Romney Marsh and Broadland. Smaller fragments of grazing marsh could be found in many river valleys and coastal plains. Many of the areas in which drainage ditches are found receive drainage from calcareous uplands, and therefore the water in the ditches tends to be base-rich and mesotrophic or eutrophic.

The most important pondweeds of smaller drainage ditches are the narrow-leaved species in Section *Graminifolii*. Significant populations of uncommon species such as *P. compressus*, *P. friesii* and *P. trichoides* occur in grazing marsh ditches, and these are the main British habitat for the rare *P. acutifolius*. The only area in which all these species occur is Broadland, where the hybrids *P.* × *grovesii* and *P.* × *pseudofriesii* were also recorded in their only localities. Commoner species which are often found in ditches include *Groenlandia densa*, *P. crispus*, *P. natans*, *P. pectinatus* and *P. pusillus*. The water in ditches is often too shallow to support species with large submerged leaves, but plants such as *P. lucens*, *P. perfoliatus* and some of their hybrids can be found in larger ditches or associated major drains.

In areas of non-calcareous soils *P. polygonifolius* is frequent in ditches, and many of the sites for the closely related but calcicolous *P. coloratus* in eastern England are fenland ditches.

The flora of many ditches has been impoverished in recent decades. Drainage methods have improved, and many ditches which were replaced by under-drainage systems were filled in or allowed to silt up. The loss of ditches has been particularly severe in areas where pastoral land has been converted to arable (Mountford 1994). If ditches remain in an arable landscape, they tend to become dominated by tall emergents. Even in protected grazing marshes, eutrophication has often reduced the floristic diversity of the plant communities in ditches and has led to the decline of species which require mesotrophic water.

Grazing marsh ditches have been recognised as a vulnerable habitat in recent years and have received much attention. This is particularly true in

Broadland, where the ditches retained their rich flora after the macrophytes of the broads themselves were virtually eliminated by eutrophication. The detailed studies of Broadland ditches are summarised by George (1992); studies of other areas have been published by Mountford (1994), Mountford & Sheail (1989), Palmer (1986), Wade & Edwards (1980), Williams & Hall (1987) and Wingfield & Wade (1988).

Sand and gravel pits

Sand and gravel pits are a feature of many lowland river valleys in Britain; in Ireland they are less frequent, as gravel can be obtained from glacial eskers. When the pits are being actively worked they have to be pumped to prevent them from flooding. Mineral extraction usually ceases when the gravel has been worked out, and the stratum below it is often an impermeable clay. Abandoned gravel pits soon flood. Some disused pits are managed for water sports or angling, as amenity areas or as nature reserves. However, many are transient features as they are filled with rubbish and 'restored' to agricultural or amenity use when they cease to be actively worked.

Gravel pits are often colonised by a range of pondweed species, particularly if they have expanses of shallow water as well as deeper areas. *P. crispus*, *P. pusillus* and *P. pectinatus* are perhaps the most frequent colonists, but others include some of the less common linear-leaved species (e.g. *P. friesii*, *P. trichoides*) or broad-leaved plants such as *P. lucens*, *P. natans* and *P. perfoliatus*. Some gravel pits can acquire an exceptionally rich flora. The Cambridgeshire Fenland is an area which has long been known for the diversity of its pondweeds, but the site which currently has the greatest number of species is not an area of semi-natural fenland or ancient washland but a gravel pit at Chatteris in which nine species of *Potamogeton* have been reliably recorded since 1988, along with the hybrid *P.* × *nitens* at the only locality in which it has been found in the vice-county this century.

An exceptional group of gravel pits are those which now form the Cotswold Water Park. These have been left by the extraction of highly calcareous Jurassic gravels. In recent years eight species of *Potamogeton* have been recorded from them.

I know of no general account of the aquatic flora of gravel pits, and the processes of succession in their waters have received little study. The aquatic flora of gravel pits sometimes appears to become less diverse as they mature. If this is so, I do not know whether it is the result of natural processes or merely reflects the fact that pits become managed for other purposes to the detriment of submerged plants.

PONDWEEDS AND BIRDS

Both *Potamogeton* and *Ruppia* species are significant food sources for waterfowl. This is well known in North America, where research on the life history of the genera has sometimes been motivated by the desire to enhance the populations of pondweed by management and thus to improve the environment for waterfowl. Martin, Zim & Nelson (1951) list 20 species of North American waterfowl which are thought to rely on *Potamogeton* species for at least 10% of their diet; eight species eat a similar percentage of *Ruppia*. At least 50% of the diet of the Coot and the Canvasback consists of *Potamogeton* material. *P. pectinatus* is described as "the outstanding species in this outstanding genus". According to W. L. Jepson (cited by Moore 1913) the Canvasback greedily devours the tubers of *P. pectinatus* in the autumn and they impart a fine nutty flavour to the meat. In Britain and Ireland this aspect of the ecology of *Potamogeton* has received less attention, but there is plenty of information on the diet of individual species which has been brought together in *The Birds of the Western Palearctic* (Cramp 1977, 1980). I have attempted to summarise it here.

Some waterfowl are predominantly vegetarian and subsist on the rhizomes, tubers, stems, leaves and seeds of aquatic and waterside plants. Both *Potamogeton* and *Ruppia* species can be important components of the diet of such species. *P. pectinatus* and *R. maritima* are often particularly significant, as they have tubers and rhizomes which are available in winter and they often occur in quantity near the coast, where many waterfowl winter. The vegetarian waterfowl include Bewick's, Mute and Whooper Swans, which can obtain material from up to a metre below the suface of the water. The famous swannery at Abbotsbury is totally dependent on the large quantities of *Ruppia* and *Zostera* which grow in the nearby waters of the Fleet. Wigeon and Gadwall are vegetarians which can only obtain food from shallow water, but Gadwall sometimes associate with Coot and feed off plants which are dislodged by these diving birds from depths which the Gadwall are unable to reach themselves. Many other waterfowl are omnivorous and take both animal and plant food. Those which are known to eat *Potamogeton* and *Ruppia* include Coot, Garganey, Mallard, Pintail, Pochard, Scaup, Shoveler, Teal and Tufted Duck. *Potamogeton* forms an important part of the diet of the Pochard, which is related to the American Canvasback. Olney (1968) found seeds of *P. berchtoldii*, *P. crispus*, *P. gramineus*, *P. natans* and *P. pectinatus* in the stomachs of Pochard shot at inland sites in England and Northern Ireland in the autumn and winter months, and seeds of *P. pectinatus* and *Ruppia* sp. in birds shot on the coast. Some duck, such as the Goldeneye, which usually eat animal food will sometimes take small quantities of plant material, including *Potamogeton* and *Ruppia*.

The effect of grazing by wildfowl on *Potamogeton filiformis* and *Potamogeton pectinatus* has been investigated by Jupp & Spence (1977b) at Loch Leven, a shallow eutrophic lake in Fife. Grazing Coot, Pochard and (in autumn) Whooper Swans ate the shoots of both species without dislodging the rhizomes and tubers from the clay in which they are firmly embedded at this site. Stands of the pondweeds were enclosed in mesh cages which ex.ʌuued waterfowl. In these exclosures the biomass of *P. filiformis* was 1.1–5.3 times higher than in grazed areas and that of *P. pectinatus* was 1.9–10.8 times higher. These losses from grazing were, however, much less than those caused at the same site by wave action. At Loch Leven, tuber density was not affected by grazing. In similar experiments in the Netherlands, van Wijk (1988) found that both the above-ground biomass and the biomass of tubers were reduced in beds of *P. pectinatus* which were frequently grazed by Coot, Mallard and Mute Swans.

The important rôle of birds as dispersal agents of pondweed fruits, and occasionally of vegetative fragments, has been discussed in the chapter on life history.

PONDWEEDS AND OTHER ORGANISMS

As important members of aquatic plant communities, pondweeds are significant not only to birds but to a range of other aquatic and amphibious animals. They are a source of food for both vertebrates and invertebrates (Fowler & Robson 1978, Lodge 1991, Jacobsen & Sand-Jensen 1994), and they also provide sites where animals can lay their eggs or escape from predators. These large but little-studied subjects are beyond the scope of this book. However, a few organisms which have conspicuous effects on pondweeds are mentioned here.

The floating leaves of pondweeds such as *P. natans* are often eaten by the larvae of the Brown China-mark moth, *Elophila nymphaeata* (L.). The larva initially mines a leaf and later lives in a floating case constructed from leaf fragments. When feeding, it attaches the case to the underside of a leaf with silk (Goater 1986). Fryer (1888b) noted that the floating leaves of the hybrid *P. × fluitans* were often entirely devoured by these larvae but that this stimulated the production of axillary fascicles of grass-like leaves which can then act as vegetative propagules.

Several galls are known on species of *Potamogeton* (Buhr 1965, J. Bowdrey & B. M. Spooner pers. comm.). *Rhopalosiphum nymphaeae* (L.), an aphid (Homoptera) whose primary host is *Prunus domestica* and *P. spinosa*, has *Potamogeton* and other aquatics as its secondary host; it causes inrolling of the leaf margin and is widespread in Britain. *Doassansia martianoffiana* (Thüm.) J. Schröt. is a smut fungus (Ustilaginales) recorded from various parts of Britain; its sori form small pustules on the undersides of the leaves of several species of *Potamogeton*, though to what extent these are true galls is uncertain. Another species, *D. occulta* (Hoffm.) Cornu, forms much more obvious galls, causing the fruits of various *Potamogeton* species to enlarge up to six times their normal size and become dark or blackish green. It is known from Europe and North America but has not yet been recorded from Britain or Ireland.

The fungus *Tetramyxa parasitica* Goebel (Plasmodiophorales) produces fleshy swellings on the stems and peduncles of *Ruppia maritima*. These galls are also found on *Zannichellia palustris*. For further details, see Hisinger (1887), Ivimey Cook (1933), Karling (1968) and Luther (1950).

DISTRIBUTION

In this chapter the wider distribution of the British and Irish species is described. The long history of pondweeds in these islands has been established by the study of subfossil fruits, and the picture that such studies have provided of the pondweed flora of the glacial period and its immediate aftermath is outlined. The effects of eutrophication and acidification on the distribution of the species in more recent times are then discussed. Finally, the current status of the species is assessed. The distribution in Britain and Ireland of the 21 *Potamogeton* species is summarised in Maps 2 and 3, overleaf. Maps of the individual species are provided with the species accounts.

The wider distribution of the British and Irish species

The distribution of all but one of the species included in this book is mapped for the northern hemisphere, south to the Tropic of Cancer, by Hultén & Fries (1986). The sole exception, *P. epihydrus*, is mapped by Hultén (1958). World distribution maps of several species are also available (Meusel, Jäger & Weinert 1965). It is therefore possible to classify the British and Irish species on the basis of their distribution in the northern hemisphere, despite the fact that the distribution of many species in Asia is under-recorded or masked by taxonomic uncertainty.

Eleven of our *Potamogeton* species have a circumpolar distribution, being found in Europe, Asia and North America. These are:

P. alpinus	P. obtusifolius
P. berchtoldii	P. pectinatus
P. filiformis	P. perfoliatus
P. friesii	P. praelongus
P. gramineus	P. pusillus
P. natans	

Of these, *P. alpinus*, *P. filiformis*, *P. gramineus*, *P. praelongus* and (to a lesser extent) *P. friesii* are primarily boreal species, which, if they extend into southern Europe, usually do so in upland areas. *P. berchtoldii*, *P. natans*, *P. obtusifolius*, *P. pectinatus* and *P. perfoliatus* are found in both boreal and temperate zones, and *P. pusillus* is rare in the boreal but extends from the temperate zone

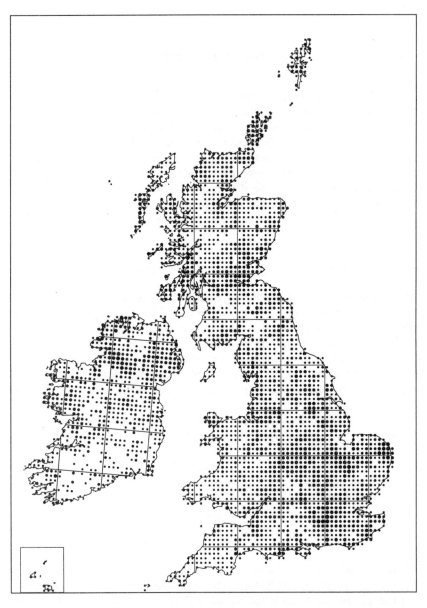

Map 2. The number of *Potamogeton* species recorded in each 10-km square. Dots of increasing size indicate that 1–3, 4–6, 7–9, 10–12 , 13–15 and 16–18 species have been recorded in the square. All records are included, irrespective of date. Areas which are well-known for their pondweed flora (such as Broadland) are clearly shown.

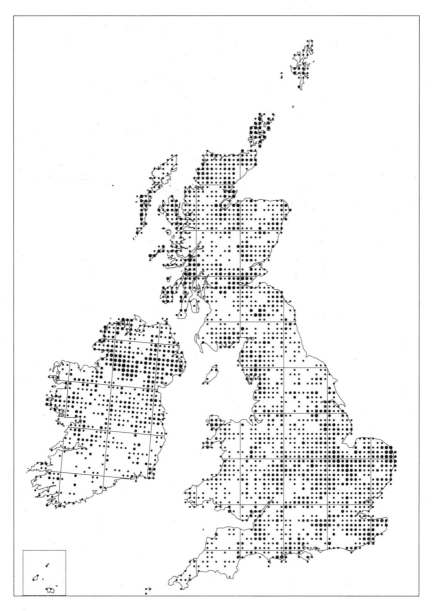

Map 3. The number of *Potamogeton* species recorded from 1970 onwards in each 10-km square. Dots of increasing size indicate that 1–3, 4–6, 7–9, 10–12, 13–15 and 16–18 species have been recorded in the square. Differences from Map 2 are likely to reflect a lack of records from 1970 onwards (as in Yorkshire) but sometimes demonstrate a loss of species (as in Surrey).

105

southwards. *P. perfoliatus* is also found in Australia and *P. pectinatus* has an almost cosmopolitan world distribution, as, in addition to its wide distribution in the northern hemisphere, it is recorded from central and southern Africa, Australasia and South America.

Both *Ruppia cirrhosa* and *R. maritima* are believed to have circumpolar distributions, but the taxonomy of *Ruppia* is very confused and the world distribution of these species is therefore uncertain.

The circumpolar *Potamogeton obtusifolius* is more frequent in Europe and eastern North America than it is elsewhere, and thus its distribution approaches that of the amphi-atlantic species. An amphi-atlantic distribution is one where the species is found in North America and in Europe, but does not extend into central or eastern Asia. True amphi-atlantic distributions are shown by two species:

P. epihydrus   P. polygonifolius

P. epihydrus is frequent in North America but in Europe it is confined to Britain. Because of this highly asymmetrical amphi-atlantic distribution, it was included by Matthews (1955) in the North American element of the British flora. By contrast, *P. polygonifolius* is widespread in western Europe and also occurs in North Africa, but in North America it is confined to Newfoundland and some nearby islands.

The following species have Eurasian distributions, being found as natives from western Europe to central or eastern Asia. *P. compressus* is replaced by the closely related species *P. zosteriformis* in North America.

P. crispus   P. lucens
P. compressus   P. nodosus

P. compressus has the most northerly distribution of the species in this group. It extends into the boreal zone, is absent from much of southern Europe and does not occur in Africa. *P. lucens* is a species of temperate areas which extends into North Africa and has an outlying locality in Uganda (Denny & Lye 1973). *P. nodosus* is a plant of even more southerly affinities, being absent from Scandinavia and extending south to Angola, Madagascar, India, Ceylon, S.E. Asia, New Caledonia, the New Hebrides, Hawaii and South America. *P. crispus* is now widely naturalised in North America and has therefore attained a circumpolar distribution; it is also widespread as an established alien in the southern hemisphere.

The final group of species comprises those with a predominantly European distribution, although some of them extend into adjacent parts of North Africa and Asia. These species are:

Groenlandia densa	P. rutilus
Potamogeton acutifolius	P. trichoides
P. coloratus	

P. rutilus is a distinctly northern plant which extends south only as far as north-west France and south-west Russia. *Groenlandia densa* and *Potamogeton acutifolius* are plants of temperate regions and *P. coloratus* is found both in the temperate zone (from Scotland southwards) and in the Mediterranean region. *P. trichoides* has a less eurocentric distribution than the others in this group as it extends south to East Africa.

Quaternary history

The pollen and fruits of *Potamogeton* are often preserved in a subfossil state in deposits laid down in lakes or river channels. Pollen can only be identified to subgenus level, but the fruits are often attributed to species. The fossil record extends back to the middle Pleistocene, but it is particularly rich from the last glacial period onwards (Godwin 1975). Even at the height of the last glacial period, some 50,000 to 15,000 years B.P., there was a diverse pondweed flora in those areas of southern and central England which lay south of the ice-sheet. The species present included those which currently have predominantly or entirely northern distributions in Britain (*P. alpinus*, *P. filiformis*, *P. gramineus*, *P. praelongus*) and those which are now widespread (*P. berchtoldii*, *P. natans*, *P. obtusifolius*, *P. perfoliatus*, *P. polygonifolius*). *Groenlandia densa* was apparently frequent then, and there are also a few records of *Potamogeton* species which now have predominantly southerly distributions, including *P. acutifolius*, *P. coloratus* and *P. trichoides*. The *P. coloratus* record came from a deposit which also contained fruits of *Damasonium alisma*. All these species must have lived in waters set in the treeless landscape of the glacial period, where the largest woody species were shrubby willows and Juniper and where Bison, Mammoth and Reindeer roamed in the open spaces. The climate was more continental than that of Britain today, with summer temperatures which were not too dissimilar to those we currently enjoy but much colder winters. The relatively warm summers may explain the presence of species with southerly affinities in glacial deposits. The rich fossil record continues through the late glacial period.

The history of *Potamogeton filiformis* is particularly interesting, as this species now has a northern distribution in Britain and Ireland. Its fruits have been found "in almost every British full Weichselian [full glacial] plant-bearing deposit" (Godwin 1975), most of which are well south of its current range. It is also frequent in the late glacial. Thereafter it must have retreated to its current range, as there are very few later records. *P. filiformis* is one of the best examples of an aquatic plant with a distribution which, within the British Isles, appears to be limited by climate. An experimental investigation of the reasons for this restriction might be rewarding.

The fact that the Quaternary records of *Potamogeton* are based on fruits means that we have no evidence about the historic distribution of hybrids. However, the history of the genus means that there must have been considerable scope for hybridisation in some regions for at least 50,000 years, and in all areas since the end of the last glacial period some 10,000 years ago. It would not be surprising if some hybrids now known from areas where their parents are absent are relicts, dating from a period when the parents grew together at the site.

Recent changes

Even in a world without man, the distribution of pondweeds would not be static. It is affected in the long term by changes in climate and in the shorter term by successional processes which modify the habitat of some water bodies and lead to the drying out of others. However, most pondweed species are lowland plants which live in the areas of Britain and Ireland which have been most heavily influenced by man. Many species have extended their range by colonising artificial habitats such as field ponds, drainage ditches, washlands, reservoirs, ornamental lakes, the Norfolk Broads, the canal network and, more recently, large sand and gravel pits in river valleys. Aquatic plants have waxed and waned in these artificial habitats as succession has progressed and as the management of the water bodies has varied. The distribution of pondweeds in 'natural' habitats has also been profoundly modified by the drainage of many natural wetlands, the eutrophication of many lowland waters, the canalisation of rivers and the lowering of the water table in some areas in recent years. The complex effects of eutrophication are dealt with in more detail below.

Effects of eutrophication and acidification

Many of the documented changes in the pondweed flora of particular sites are the result of eutrophication. The nutrient levels in many lakes and rivers have been raised in recent centuries by the discharge of sewage or other waste products, and more recently by water draining from heavily fertilised agricultural land. The effect of eutrophication is initially to favour the species which prefer eutrophic rather than mesotrophic conditions and then, as levels of nutrients continue to increase, to tip the balance in favour of algae rather than vascular macrophytes. The processes which lead to the suppression of macrophytes by phytoplankton are complex and are currently the subject of research.

The history of Rescobie Loch in Angus provides an example of a lake where a rich pondweed flora has been eliminated by eutrophication. Rescobie is a shallow, lowland lake which lies over calcareous glacial deposits. It was described in lyrical terms by Gardiner (1848): "On a clear sunny day the *Potamogetae*, flourishing at a great depth amid the transparent waters, animated by numerous members of the insect and finny races, present a delightful spectacle." No less than 14 *Potamogeton* species and three hybrids were recorded at this lake. Most were still present in 1908, when they were collected by R. H. and Mrs M. Corstorphine. However, Rescobie Loch has a large catchment which, although naturally nutrient-poor, is now intensively farmed and heavily fertilised. By the 1940s Taylor (1949) reported that *Elodea canadensis* was abundant in the lake and had largely displaced the other aquatic species. Since 1965 only *P. crispus*, *P. filiformis*, *P. pectinatus* and *P. pusillus* have been recorded. The loch now has a rich flora of blue-green algae. Spence (1964) reported that the substrate "approaches a sulphuretted or iron sulphide mud", a highly anaerobic environment in which aquatic plants could not root. Stewart, Tuckwell & May (1975) described the water as very highly eutrophic. It receives massive inputs of nitrogen by surface run-off from the catchment: some 43% of the nitrogen applied to the catchment as fertiliser was washed into the loch!

A more complex example of the effects of eutrophication is provided by the Norfolk Broads. These lakes are the flooded remains of large-scale medieval peat diggings. They lie alongside rivers, or in some cases the rivers flow through them. In their pristine state the water in the Broads was highly calcareous but inputs of nutrients were low. The water was clear and its vegetation was dominated by charophytes; the vascular plants were limited to species of nutrient-poor water and phytoplankton was virtually absent. As farmers began to increase the fertility of the surrounding land, more nutrients drained into the Broads, and the Broads downstream of Norwich also received an increased nutrient load as the city expanded and a sewerage system was established. As the nutrients in the water rose, the vegetation in the Broads became dominated by more competitive plants such as *Ceratophyllum demersum*, *Myriophyllum spicatum*, *M. verticillatum*, *Nuphar lutea*, *Nymphaea alba*, *Stratiotes aloides* and *Utricularia vulgaris*. Pondweeds which colonised some of the Broads during this period include *Potamogeton friesii*, *P. pectinatus*, *P. perfoliatus* and

P. trichoides. The transition to this vegetation took place at different times in different Broads, perhaps starting in the early 19th century downstream of Norwich but not taking place until the 1930s in more remote catchments. Despite the increased levels of nutrients, the water in the Broads remained crystal clear and teemed with fish and invertebrates. Many older botanists have happy memories of visits to the Broads in the late 1940s or early 1950s, when they were still in this state. However, as nutrient enrichment increased, the aquatic vegetation at many sites became dominated by a few species, such as *Ceratophyllum demersum* and *Myriophyllum spicatum.* Then the populations of these crashed, and the Broads became dominated by phytoplankton. Only a few beds of macrophytes survived in the now turbid water. A detailed account of this fascinating story is given in George's (1992) book on Broadland.

It seems likely that the marked decline in *Potamogeton praelongus* in southern England in recent years has been the result of eutrophication. The history of the plant in Cambridgeshire exemplifies this decline. In the 1950s it was "frequent in rivers, lodes and pits in the Fens" (Perring, Sell & Walters 1964) and superb material was collected from the River Cam just upstream of Cambridge in 1959. The plant has now gone from the Cam and has only been seen in two fenland localities in recent years. Since 1950 the nutrient levels in the large water bodies in which this species grows greatly increased as a result of run-off from heavily fertilised arable land. There is no direct evidence that this has caused its decline, but it is difficult to think of anything else which would account for it.

The effects of acidification on water bodies has recently received much attention. The waters which are most vulnerable to 'acid rain' are those in the north and west where the rocks and soils are themselves acidic and have little buffering capacity. These tend to have a rather limited, though characteristic, vascular plant flora which rarely includes any species of *Potamogeton* other than *P. natans* and *P. polygonifolius.* For this reason acidification is unlikely to be having a major influence on our pondweed flora. Some areas in eastern England have also become acidified for another reason. In these areas soils containing iron pyrites which were formerly waterlogged have been drained. When water levels are low in the summer, the soils cease to be anaerobic and the pyrites oxidises. Sulphuric acid forms as a result of this oxidation and enters the water when levels rise in the winter. At Calthorpe Broad this resulted in 1976 in a mean pH of 3.2 in the Broad itself and 4.0 in nearby ditches, a decrease of over 3 pH units compared to measurements made in 1938 (Gosling & Baker 1980). This acidification has almost certainly affected the pondweeds in some restricted areas, but it is not significant at the national scale.

Current status and future conservation

In assessing the current status of the British and Irish pondweeds it is useful to consider separately the sparsely inhabited areas in the north and west and the populous lowlands in the south and east. In the highlands and islands of Scotland, the upland areas of northern England and Wales and the western seaboard of Ireland, there are many lakes and rivers, most of which appear to retain their natural *Potamogeton* flora. There is little evidence that species have declined to any extent in these areas, although it must be admitted that our historical records from these remote regions are often rather meagre. Individual sites are, and will no doubt continue to be, subject to local threats such as fish-farming, eutrophication or tourist development. However, there is legislation to protect important botanical sites in both Britain and Ireland and, provided that this proves effective, it should be possible to safeguard those sites with a particularly rich *Potamogeton* flora. The protection of 'marl lakes' over limestone and the machair lochs of Scotland and Ireland should be an especially high priority. Two species of northern Scotland, *Potamogeton epihydrus* and *P. rutilus*, are included in the *British Red Data Book* (Perring & Farrell 1983) and therefore receive specific protection. Although their rarity makes them vulnerable to threats to their particular sites, there is no reason to worry about their future as British plants.

In the Scottish lowlands, much of southern and eastern England, lowland Wales and central and eastern Ireland the situation is rather different. In many areas natural waters have already been greatly modified by the drainage of wetlands, the canalisation of streams and rivers, and eutrophication. Even the artificial habitats which have been colonised by pondweeds have sometimes now disappeared because of redevelopment or natural processes of succession. The distribution maps indicate that many species have receded in the south and east, even if one makes allowances for the fact that some of the populations mapped as open circles may only have been transient. Most of the best remaining semi-natural habitats are now managed as nature reserves or receive some degree of protection as Sites of Special Scientific Interest, but it is difficult to insulate them from the effects of eutrophication and a falling water table. Artificial habitats such as gravel pits are vulnerable to threats such as management for water sports or angling, infilling with rubbish or infestation by Canada Geese, and the increasing use of canals for pleasure boating leads to the deterioration of their flora. Conservationists often think that gravel pits are less valuable sites than more natural sites and make no effort to protect them; if they are protected, they are often allowed to become overgrown. However, gravel pits often escape excessive eutrophication as they are fed by rain water rather than streams and rivers. Perhaps more conservation bodies should consider acquiring gravel pits and managing them specifically for water plants, especially as these can also support dragonflies and other invertebrates of interest.

Of the species in the south and east, *Potamogeton nodosus* is sufficiently rare to be included in the *British Red Data Book*, and *Groenlandia densa* is listed in the Irish counterpart (Curtis & McGough 1988). *P. nodosus* has apparently disappeared from the River Thames in recent years but is still thriving in three other rivers. *Groenlandia densa* seems to be considerably rarer than it was last century in Ireland but currently its distribution appears to be stable. I consider that the two species which are most threatened in Britain are *P. acutifolius* and *P. compressus*, neither of which are included in the *Red Data Book*. *P. acutifolius* is a plant of mesotrophic grazing marsh ditches which, for reasons which are far from clear, appears to be unable to colonise new habitats. It has decreased because of habitat destruction and, more recently, declined at some of its current sites because of eutrophication. Its continued survival in Britain is by no means assured, and this is a matter of particular concern in view of its limited world distribution. The allied *P. compressus* did colonise the canals of the Midlands but it is now extinct in many of them, and it has also been lost from some of its semi-natural sites because of habitat destruction and eutrophication. It is another species of mesotrophic water which will need determined efforts to protect it if it is going to survive in any quantity.

The hybrid pondweeds are often very localised and thus vulnerable to threats to particular sites. They receive little attention from conservationists, although some important sites may be protected because they happen to be of interest for other reasons. The recognition of the intrinsic scientific interest of these plants by conservationists and an assessment of the extent to which their habitats are protected are now overdue.

PONDWEEDS IN HORTICULTURE

Gardeners do not cherish pondweeds. In his book *The well-tempered Garden*, Christopher Lloyd (1970) describes "elodeas and potamogetons" as "rather dull and boorish manifestations of the vegetable kingdom". Although garden ponds are currently fashionable, *Potamogeton* species are rarely grown in them. Only two species, *P. crispus* and *P. natans*, are included in *The European Garden Flora* (Walters *et al.* 1986), and the flagrant inaccuracy with which they are described in that work perhaps reflects their horticultural insignificance. *P. crispus* is listed in *The Plant Finder* (Philip 1994) as being available from several sources, and this species is the one which is most frequently seen offered for sale in garden centres. *P. pectinatus* is also listed by one supplier: one wonders how many people order it. This horticultural disregard means that, unlike more ornamental species such as *Cyperus longus*, *Nymphaea* spp. and *Ranunculus lingua*, it is unusual to find pondweeds as deliberate introductions to village ponds or waters managed by anglers.

COLLECTION AND PRESERVATION OF MATERIAL

The field season

When is the best time to look for pondweeds? There is no harm in starting in May. Some linear-leaved species, including *P. berchtoldii*, are likely to be overlooked so early in the season but the fact that those species which are found will be in fresh young leaf will compensate for this. Most botanists will not be interested in pondweeds to the exclusion of all other aquatics and an early start to the season increases the chances of finding some other species, notably charophytes. The optimum time for pondweeds depends on locality and habitat: it is perhaps best to examine shallow lakes, gravel pits, ponds, ditches and canals in July (especially in the south) and larger lakes in August or early September. The general opinion that the pondweed season does not start until August is probably due in part to the erroneous belief that ripe fruits are essential for identification and in part to the fact that botanists with general interests have other things to do in the earlier part of the season.

Collecting material

Most *Potamogeton* species need to be removed from the water before they can be identified with certainty. Fortunately material can almost always be collected without threatening the continued existence of a population, and indeed adequate vouchers can occasionally be obtained simply by gathering flotsam. If it is suspected that a population may suffer from collecting, the botanist should of course exercise restraint and only gather the minimum amount of material.

For fishing plants out of small ponds and ditches an implement mounted on a strong pole is useful. Both window poles and garden rakes can be pressed into service, although they rather inconveniently lack a cutting edge. One botanist I know uses a mounted trowel with one of the shoulders sharpened to remedy this deficiency. The pondweeds in lakes can often be identified by examining fragments of stems which have been broken off and washed to the edge, and material caught up on overhanging tree branches sometimes gives clues to the plants growing in rivers. It is useful in both these habitats to use a grapnel attached to a rope to obtain plants which are otherwise out of reach. There are almost as many different designs of grapnel as there are aquatic botanists; a design for rather a superior grapnel is given by Moore (1986) in the B.S.B.I. Charophytes Handbook. Grapnels have the disadvantage that they are difficult to aim at specific stems which catch the eye, especially in dense vegetation, which soon clogs them up.

In collecting material, try to collect a sample which adequately represents the whole plant. For broad-leaved taxa, a single stem broken off at the base will usually be an adequate specimen. The lowest leaves on the stem are often significant, and it is helpful to gather stem leaves as well as branch leaves. Avoid collecting a small fragment from the upper stem or a short branch when more adequate material is available. When collecting narrow-leaved taxa, ensure that the material includes enough young shoots to permit dissection of a number of young stipules. This can be difficult to achieve with fruiting or senescent plants.

Unlike terrestrial plants, pondweeds do not deteriorate if kept for some hours in a polythene bag. Sealable bags are the most convenient, although rather more expensive than the non-sealable variants. Bags which cannot be examined at the end of the day are best kept in a cool box or fridge. Plants taken from clean, nutrient-poor water seem to deteriorate less rapidly than those from eutrophic water. If the plants are to be sent away for examination, it is usually better to press them first than to send fresh specimens, as material can deteriorate rapidly in the post. If fresh material is specially requested, it should be wrapped in damp newspaper then placed in a polythene bag inside a padded envelope. It is advisable to press and retain a subsample of the collection.

Pressing specimens

Even the greatest experts in the genus *Potamogeton* have made the occasional error of identification, and no one can expect to have their records accepted unless they are supported by voucher specimens. Not every record need be backed by herbarium material, but it is advisable to preserve specimens of a representative sample and especially important to document the more significant records and more critical taxa.

Features that are apparent only on the living plant (particularly the shape of the stem and the leaf apex) should be noted before the material is pressed. It is often helpful to establish the characters of the stipule at this stage. Broad-leaved pondweeds can be pressed like other plants, being placed directly in the flimsy and arranged to best advantage. It is useful to change the drying papers some hours later, as they will by then have soaked up a lot of superficial water, and to take advantage of the more pliant state of the specimen to straighten out any crumpled leaves. Narrow-leaved species are best 'floated out' in water. Plastic photographic trays are ideal for this purpose. After the specimens have been arranged in the water as required, a sheet of paper is slipped under them and gently lifted out of the water. As the water slides off, the specimen is left in position on the paper; if it is disturbed by the flowing water minor rearrangements can be made with fine forceps. Some botanists recommend the use of nylon mesh curtain material instead of paper, as the water drains through the mesh and leaves the specimen in perfect shape. The paper or mesh is then placed in a flimsy and pressed in the usual way. Pondweeds dry rapidly; applying artificial heat to the press is rarely necessary and risks overheating the specimens, which will then become brittle. Once dried, specimens should be labelled with details of locality (including grid reference), habitat (including water depth, if known), associated species, collector and date of collection. All these data should be included with specimens which are sent away for identification, as referees are likely to resent the time taken to establish missing details and the need to match the incomplete data sent initially with subsequent information introduces scope for confusion. Voucher specimens are best placed in an established institutional herbarium, although botanists living some distance from such a collection may find it useful to keep an additional reference collection of their own.

Reference collections

A reliably named herbarium collection is invaluable in indicating the appearance of the species and hybrids and in demonstrating their range of variation. It can also provide information on distribution, phenology and life history. A collection in which the species are unreliably named can literally be worse than useless to the inexperienced student. In general, collections can only be relied on if the identification of the specimens has been confirmed by an expert. Otherwise many specimens are likely to be misidentified, especially if the herbarium contains (as many do) material which has not been checked since it was collected in the late 19th or early 20th century.

Fortunately, there are numerous well-named collections in the British Isles. These include those at Belfast (**BEL**), Cambridge (**CGE**), Cardiff (**NMW**), Dublin (**DBN**), Edinburgh (**E**), Glasgow (**GL**), Lancaster (**LANC**), Leicester (**LTR**), Liverpool (**LIV**), London (**BM, K**), Manchester (**MANCH**), Newcastle upon Tyne (**HAMU**), Norwich (**NWH**), Oxford (**OXF**) and Reading (**RNG**). Further details of these herbaria, and of many other valuable collections, are given by Kent & Allen (1984). Most herbaria are keen that their collections should be consulted and welcome visitors with a *bona fide* interest in them.

KEYS

Two keys are provided to help identify the species and hybrids covered by this volume. Both assume that the user has access to a hand-lens (preferably with ×20 magnification) when identifying broad-leaved species and to a dissecting microscope when identifying linear-leaved species. Botanists who are unfamiliar with *Potamogeton* and allied genera should read the earlier chapter on structure, as it is important to understand the morphology of the plants before launching into the keys. In particular, it is essential to master the simple dissecting techniques used to establish the structure of the stipules of linear-leaved species (see p. 68).

Key 1 covers species and the two commonest hybrids only; Key 2 also includes the other recorded hybrids. If fruiting plants are available, Key 1 should be used, as it includes all the taxa which produce numerous well-formed fruits (although some hybrids included only in Key 2 can produce an occasional well-formed fruit on an otherwise sterile inflorescence). When deciding which key to use, remember that hybrids between linear-leaved species are very rarely recorded and that hybrids between broad-leaved species are rare or absent from many parts of the British Isles (see Map 1, p. 45).

Finally, the warning that many authors of keys include but many users ignore: *using a key is only the start of the identification process.* After keying out a plant, compare it with the description and illustration in the text. Users of Key 1 should be particularly careful to make sure that the plant tallies with the description. The account of each species lists its hybrids and draws attention to those which are most likely to be confused with that species. If, when identified, a plant appears to be a significant new record, a voucher specimen should be preserved. This can then be compared with named material or checked by an appropriate authority.

Key 1, to the species and commonest hybrids

1a   Leaf margin serrate, with teeth which are easily seen with the naked eye; beak at least half as long as the rest of the fruit   **19 P. crispus**

1b   Leaf margin entire or minutely denticulate, with teeth which are not or scarcely visible with the naked eye; beak much less than half as long as the rest of the fruit   2

2a   Some or all leaves narrowly elliptical to orbicular, with convex sides   3

2b   All leaves filiform to linear, with parallel sides   17

3a   All leaves floating or terrestrial, petiolate, usually coriaceous and opaque ('floating leaves') or submerged leaves, if present, reduced to opaque phyllodes without a distinct midrib and lamina   4

3b   Some or all leaves submerged, either sessile or petiolate, with a distinct midrib and a thin, delicate and more or less translucent lamina ('submerged leaves')   6

4a   Floating leaves often with a discoloured junction 7–25 mm long between the petiole and the lamina; stipules 40–170 mm, the veins prominent when dry; fruits 3.8–5.0 mm   **1 P. natans**

4b   Floating leaves without a discoloured junction between the petiole and the lamina; stipules 10–65 mm, the veins inconspicuous when dry; fruits 1.5–2.6 mm   5

5a   Floating leaves opaque, coriaceous, with inconspicuous secondary veins; fruits 1.9–2.6 mm, reddish brown   **5 P. polygonifolius**

5b   Floating leaves relatively translucent, not coriaceous, with conspicuous secondary veins; fruits 1.5–1.9 mm, olive-green or greenish brown, without a reddish tinge   **6 P. coloratus**

6a   All submerged leaves opposite; inflorescence capitate, with 2 opposite flowers   **48 Groenlandia densa**

6b   Submerged leaves (except for those immediately below an inflorescence) alternate; inflorescence cylindrical, with at least 12 flowers   7

7a Submerged leaves semi-amplexicaul or amplexicaul, sessile, at least on the main stems 8
7b Submerged leaves not amplexicaul, either petiolate or sessile 10

8a Submerged leaves amplexicaul; stipules hyaline when dry, fugacious; fruits 2.6–4.0 mm **9 P. perfoliatus**
8b Submerged leaves semi-amplexicaul; stipules buff to dark green when dry, persistent or subpersistent; fruits (if present) 4.5–5.5 mm 9

9a Submerged leaves lanceolate to oblong-lanceolate, entire, obtuse and broadly hooded at the apex; floating leaves absent; flowers 15–20; fruits 4.5–5.5 mm **8 P. praelongus**
9b Submerged leaves broadly elliptical to ovate-oblong, minutely denticulate, acute or, if obtuse, only shallowly hooded at the apex; floating leaves present or absent; flowers 20 or more; fruits not developing **30 P. × nitens**

10a Submerged leaves linear **10 P. epihydrus**
10b Submerged leaves linear-elliptical to oblong-elliptical 11

11a Leaves at the base of the stem not reduced to phyllodes; submerged leaves obtuse to acute at apex, but not mucronate, the margins entire or (rarely) with fugacious teeth 12
11b Leaves at the base of the stem reduced to phyllodes; submerged leaves mucronate or with the midrib excurrent, the margins minutely denticulate with persistent teeth 15

12a Submerged leaves sessile; fruits 2.6–3.7 mm, pale brown, with a shiny appearance when mature **7 P. alpinus**
12b Submerged leaves petiolate; fruits 1.5–2.6 mm, green or greenish brown, with a matt appearance 13

13a Floating leaves translucent or subcoriaceous, not markedly different in texture from the submerged leaves, truncate to cordate at base, the petioles (4–)8–45 mm, shorter than the lamina **6 P. coloratus**
13b Floating leaves coriaceous, contrasting strongly in appearance with the translucent submerged leaves, cuneate to subcordate at base, the petioles (13–)30–210(–300) mm, longer or shorter than the lamina 14

14a Submerged leaves 160–280 × 22–38 mm, 6–7.5 times as long as wide, elliptical, the margin denticulate but the teeth minute and fugacious; fruits 2.7–4.1 mm **2 P. nodosus**

14b Submerged leaves 60–160 × 2.5–24 mm, 5–15(–30) times as long as wide, linear-elliptical to narrowly elliptical, the margin entire; fruits 1.9–2.6 mm **5 P. polygonifolius**

15a Stems and main branches with petiolate submerged leaves 25–65 mm wide, the petiole 1–12(–25) mm; stipules on stems and main branches 35–80(–110) mm, with 2 parallel wings on their abaxial side extending from base for at least half the length of the stipule; fruits 3.2–4.5 mm **3 P. lucens**

15b Stems and main branches with sessile, or rarely petiolate, submerged leaves 5–25(–30) mm wide; stipules on stems and main branches 10–45(–55) mm, with 2 parallel ridges but no wings on the abaxial side, or narrowly winged at the base; fruits 2.4–3.4 mm 16

16a Stems and main branches with submerged leaves 5–12 mm wide, with 3–4 lateral veins; stipules on these stems 10–25(–35) mm; fruits 2.4–3.1 mm **4 P. gramineus**

16b Stems and main branches with submerged leaves 10–25(–30) mm wide, with 4–5(–6) lateral veins; stipules on these stems 20–45(–55) mm; fruits 2.7–3.4 mm **26 P. × zizii**

17a Leaf lamina arising directly from the node, flat in section, with a conspicuous midrib, or leaves reduced to phyllodes 18

17b Leaf lamina arising from the top of a sheath which surrounds the stem above the node (like the sheath and blade of a grass), elliptical to semicircular in section, with one large or several smaller air channels on each side of an inconspicuous midrib 28

18a Leaves reduced to opaque phyllodes, without a distinct midrib and lateral veins; stipules 40–170 mm **1 P. natans**

18b Leaves with a distinct midrib and lateral veins; stipules 4–55 mm 19

19a Stems compressed, with a shallow groove running down one or both of the broader sides; leaf margin toothed at the apex **19 P. crispus**

19b Stems terete to flattened, but, if compressed, then without a groove running down the broader sides; leaf margin entire 20

20a Stems strongly compressed to flattened; leaves with 1–2 lateral veins on each side of the midrib and many additional sclerenchymatous strands   21

20b Stems terete to strongly compressed; leaves with 1–4 lateral veins on each side of the midrib but no additional sclerenchymatous strands   22

21a Leaves with 2 lateral veins on each side of the midrib, the outer vein often faint; peduncles 28–95 mm; inflorescences with 10–20 flowers; most flowers with 2 carpels; fruits without a tooth on the ventral edge
                                                                              17 P. compressus
21b Leaves with 1 lateral vein on each side of the midrib; peduncles 5–30 mm; inflorescences with 4–6 flowers; flowers with 1 carpel; fruits often with a tooth on the ventral edge   **18 P. acutifolius**

22a Plant rhizomatous; leaves 2.5–11 mm wide, with a broad band of lacunae which towards the base of the leaf extends at least as far as the inner lateral veins; lateral veins 2–4 on each side of the midrib
                                                                              10 P. epihydrus
22b Rhizomes absent; leaves 0.5–3.5(–4) mm wide, without lacunae or with a band of lacunae on each side of the midrib which rarely reaches the inner lateral veins; lateral veins 1–2(–3) on each side of the midrib
                                                                                                   23

23a Stipules closed and tubular at the base when young   24
23b Stipules open throughout their length   26

24a Leaves 1.5–3.5(–4) mm wide; lateral veins (1–)2(–3) on each side of the midrib; leaves abruptly contracted to a mucronate apex; turions fan-shaped; fruits 2.4–3.0 mm   **11 P. friesii**
24b Leaves 0.5–1.4(–1.9) mm wide; lateral veins 1(–2) on each side of the midrib; leaves gradually tapering or rather abruptly narrowed to an acute but not mucronate apex; turions cylindrical; fruits 2.0–2.3 mm
                                                                                                   25

25a Leaf apex gradually tapering to a very fine point; stipules opaque when dry, the veins very prominent   **12 P. rutilus**
25b Leaf apex acute but not finely pointed; stipules translucent when dry, the veins not very prominent   **13 P. pusillus**

26a Leaves (1–)2.5–3.5 mm wide, often tinged pink or reddish brown
along the midrib or throughout; stipules with (8–)10–17 intercostal
veins; turions 3–5 mm wide; inflorescences with 6–8 flowers
14 P. obtusifolius

26b Leaves 0.3–1.8(–2.3) mm wide, without any pink or reddish brown
tinge; stipules with 4–8(–9) intercostal veins; turions 0.6–1.7 mm
wide; inflorescences with 2–5 flowers 27

27a Leaves flaccid, with a midrib which occupies 10–20% of the leaf
width near the base and in section has a shallowly convex lower side;
flowers with (3–)4–5(–7) carpels; dorsal edge of fruits smooth
15 P. berchtoldii

27b Leaves relatively rigid, with a midrib which occupies 30–70% of the
leaf width near the base and in section has a strongly convex lower
side; flowers with 1(–2) carpels; dorsal edge of fruits muriculate
16 P. trichoides

28a Ligule 5–15 mm long at the junction of the leaf sheath and the lamina;
leaf apex entire; inflorescences with 4–14 flowers; mature fruits sessile
29

28b Ligule absent; leaf apex minutely denticulate; inflorescences with
2 flowers; mature fruits on stalks 3–35 mm long 30

29a Leaf sheath closed and tubular at the base when young; mature fruits
2.2–3.2 mm **20 P. filiformis**

29b Leaf sheath open and convolute along its entire length; mature fruits
3.3–4.7 mm **21 P. pectinatus**

30a Peduncles 8–26 mm, 0.5–1.8 times as long as the longest fruit stalk at
maturity, rarely up to 3.3 times as long but only when peduncle is less
than 10 mm long **49 Ruppia maritima**

30b Peduncles 40–300(–770) mm, (1.6–)2–10(–30) times as long as the
longest fruit stalk at maturity **50 Ruppia cirrhosa**

Key 2, to all species and hybrids

This key first allocates the taxon to one of six groups. Keys are then provided to each of the groups.

Key to the groups

1a   Some or all leaves linear-elliptical to orbicular, with convex sides   2
1b   All leaves filiform, linear or linear-oblong, with parallel sides   5

2a   All leaves floating or terrestrial, petiolate, usually coriaceous and opaque ('floating leaves') or submerged leaves, if present, reduced to opaque phyllodes without a distinct midrib and lamina   **Group A**
2b   Some or all leaves submerged, either sessile or petiolate, with a distinct midrib and a thin, delicate and more or less translucent lamina ('submerged leaves')   3

3a   Floating leaves absent   **Group D**
3b   Floating leaves present in addition to the submerged leaves   4

4a   Submerged leaves linear, with parallel sides   **Group B**
4b   Submerged leaves linear-elliptical to broadly ovate, with convex sides   **Group C**

5a   Leaf lamina arising directly from the nodes, the leaves reduced to opaque phyllodes or flat in section with a distinct midrib   **Group E**
5b   Leaf lamina arising at the top of a sheath which surrounds the stem above the node (like the sheath and blade of a grass), elliptical to semicircular in section, with one large or several smaller air channels on each side of an inconspicuous midrib   **Group F**

Group A

Submerged leaves absent or reduced to opaque, linear phyllodes without a distinct lamina and midrib. Floating leaves present.

Two of the species included in this group often grow more or less terrestrially in fens, bogs or flushes. Terrestrial forms of other species and hybrids (particularly *P. gramineus* and *P.* × *nitens*) occur at the edge of lakes and reservoirs in places from which water has receded. They are not covered by the key.

1a   Floating leaves often with a discoloured junction 7–25 mm long between the petiole and the lamina; stipules 40–170 mm, the veins prominent when dry   **1 P. natans**
1b   Floating leaves without a discoloured junction between the petiole and the lamina; stipules 10–65 mm, the veins inconspicuous when dry   2

2a   Floating leaves opaque, coriaceous, with inconspicuous secondary veins   **5 P. polygonifolius**
2b   Floating leaves relatively translucent, with conspicuous secondary veins   **6 P. coloratus**

Group B

Submerged leaves linear, with parallel sides. Floating leaves present.

1a   Submerged leaves sessile   2
1b   Submerged leaves petiolate   4

2a   Nodal glands absent; stipules truncate or slightly emarginate at the apex; inflorescences 12–23 mm   **10 P. epihydrus**
2b   Nodal glands present; stipules rounded to obtuse at the apex but sometimes rolled so that they appear acute; inflorescences 3.5–12 mm   3

3a   Submerged leaves 0.5–0.8 mm wide; floating leaves sometimes with a discoloured section between the petiole and the lamina; petioles of floating leaves 25–155 mm   **31 P. × variifolius**
3b   Submerged leaves 1.5–5.5(–7.5) mm wide; floating leaves without a discoloured section between petiole and lamina; petioles of floating leaves 1–9 mm   **32 P. × lanceolatus**

4a   Stems sparingly to richly branched; submerged leaves 2–12 mm wide; petioles of submerged leaves not more than 55 mm
                                                      24 P. × sparganiifolius
4b   Stems unbranched; submerged leaves 1–4 mm wide; petioles of submerged leaves 45–175 mm   **25 P. × gessnacensis**

Group C

Submerged leaves narrowly oblanceolate or linear-elliptical to ovate-oblong, with convex sides. Floating leaves present.

1a	All submerged leaves petiolate	2
1b	Some or all submerged leaves sessile	8

2a	Apex of submerged leaves mucronate or with the midrib excurrent for up to 12 mm; stipules with 2 ridges which are often winged on the abaxial side	**23 P. × fluitans**
2b	Apex of submerged leaves obtuse, acute or acuminate but never mucronate or with the midrib excurrent; stipules with 2 ridges which are never winged on the abaxial side	3

3a	Margin of young submerged leaves denticulate	**2 P. nodosus**
3b	Margin of submerged leaves more or less entire	4

4a	Floating leaves relatively translucent, with conspicuous secondary veins, not markedly different from the submerged leaves	**6 P. coloratus**
4b	Floating leaves opaque, coriaceous, with inconspicuous secondary veins, markedly different from the submerged leaves	5

5a	Submerged leaves without a prominent midrib; petioles 14–80(–165) mm	**5 P. polygonifolius**
5b	Submerged leaves with a prominent midrib, appearing like phyllodes with a narrow lamina; petioles 45–350 mm	6

6a	Leaves at the base of the stem not reduced to phyllodes; submerged leaves 1–4 mm wide, with 1–2 lateral veins on each side of the midrib and no lacunae	**25 P. × gessnacensis**
6b	Leaves at the base of the stem reduced or partially reduced to phyllodes; submerged leaves 2–15 mm wide, with 1–6 lateral veins and a band of lacunae on each side of the midrib	7

7a	Petioles of submerged leaves (60–)100–350 mm	**22 P. × schreberi**
7b	Petioles of submerged leaves less than 55 mm	**24 P. × sparganiifolius**

8a	Submerged leaves on main stems slightly amplexicaul to semi-amplexicaul at base	**30 P.** × **nitens**
8b	Submerged leaves on main stems gradually or abruptly tapering to a sessile but not amplexicaul base	9

9a	Most submerged leaves more than 12 mm wide	10
9b	Most submerged leaves less than 12 mm wide	13

10a	Leaves at the base of the stem never or only partially reduced to phyllodes; margin of submerged leaves entire	11
10b	Leaves at the base of the stem usually partially or totally reduced to phyllodes; margin of submerged leaves denticulate	12

11a	Stems unbranched; leaf apex narrowly obtuse and often shallowly but not distinctly hooded	**7 P. alpinus**
11b	Stems branched; leaf apex obtuse or rounded and distinctly hooded	**35 P.** × **griffithii**

12a	Apex of submerged leaves usually mucronate; floating leaves 55–105 × 22–40 mm	**26 P.** × **zizii**
12b	Apex of submerged leaves obtuse and usually hooded; floating leaves 20–70 × 10–22 mm	**28 P.** × **billupsii**

13a	Plants with nodal glands; leaves at base of stem never reduced to phyllodes; inflorescence with 6–11 flowers	**32 P.** × **lanceolatus**
13b	Plants without nodal glands; leaves at base of stem often reduced to phyllodes; inflorescence with more than 12 flowers	14

14a	Margin of submerged leaves denticulate, the teeth small but distinct	15
14b	Margin of submerged leaves entire or remotely and obscurely denticulate	16

15a	Some submerged leaves petiolate; apex of some submerged leaves obtuse and hooded	**28 P.** × **billupsii**
15b	All submerged leaves sessile; apex of submerged leaves obtuse to acute, mucronate, never hooded	**4 P. gramineus**

16a Submerged leaves linear or narrowly oblanceolate, more than 16 times as long as wide **24 P. × sparganiifolius**
16b Submerged leaves elliptical, oblong-elliptical or narrowly oblanceo-late, not more than 16 times as long as wide 17

17a All submerged leaves sessile; submerged leaves on the main stems and branches (4.5–)6.5–8.5(–10.5) times as long as wide **29 P. × nericius**
17b Some submerged leaves petiolate; submerged leaves 9–16 times as long as wide **27 P. × lanceolatifolius**

Group D

Submerged leaves oblanceolate or linear-elliptical to broadly ovate, with convex sides. Floating leaves absent.

1a Leaves opposite; inflorescences with 2 opposite flowers
  48 Groenlandia densa
1b Leaves (except for those immediately below an inflorescence) alternate; inflorescences with at least 3 flowers 2

2a Stems terete or (very rarely) slightly compressed but not grooved along the broader sides; stipules rounded to acute at the apex 3
2b Stems slightly compressed to compressed, with a shallow groove along one or both of the broader sides; stipules truncate to emarginate at the apex 21

3a Plants with nodal glands; leaves linear or narrowly oblanceolate
  32 P. × lanceolatus
3b Plants without nodal glands; leaves linear-elliptical to broadly ovate 4

4a Most or all leaves sessile 5
4b All leaves with petioles at least 1 mm long 6

5a Leaves on the main stems amplexicaul or semi-amplexicaul 6
5b Leaves on the main stems not amplexicaul 11

6a Leaf margin entire; leaf apex markedly hooded **8 P. praelongus**
6b Leaf margin denticulate; leaf apex not hooded to markedly hooded 7

7a   Stipules fugacious, only present on the youngest leaves
9 P. perfoliatus

7b   Stipules subpersistent or persistent, remaining for a time on the mature leaves   8

8a   Leaves with 7–12 lateral veins on each side of the midrib; leaf apex markedly hooded   **37 P. × cognatus**

8b   Leaves with 3–8 lateral veins on each side of the midrib; leaf apex not or only slightly hooded   9

9a   Stipules 20–55(–70) mm, often with 2 prominent ribs which are narrowly winged towards the base on the abaxial side
34 P. × salicifolius

9b   Stipules (5.5–)10–30 mm, without 2 prominent ribs or with 2 prominent ribs which are not winged on the abaxial side   10

10a Leaf apex obtuse or subacute, never apiculate or mucronate; leaf margin obscurely denticulate; stipules flexible, not projecting from the stems at an acute angle   **36 P. × prussicus**

10b Leaf apex usually acute, sometimes apiculate or mucronate, occasionally obtuse; leaf margin distinctly denticulate; stipules flexible or rigid, often projecting from the stems at an acute angle   **30 P. × nitens**

11a Leaf margin entire   12
11b Leaf margin denticulate   13

12a Stems unbranched; leaves with an obtuse, sometimes slightly hooded but never markedly hooded apex   **7 P. alpinus**

12b Stems branched towards the apex; leaves with an obtuse or rounded and markedly hooded apex   **35 P. × griffithii**

13a Leaves on the main stems and branches 5–12 mm wide, with 3–4 lateral veins on each side of the midrib   **4 P. gramineus**

13b Leaves on the main stems and branches 10–50 mm wide, with 4–8 lateral veins on each side of the midrib   14

14a Midrib bordered at the base by a broad band of lacunae, which extends as a narrower band to the apex; upper leaves copper-coloured when dry   **33 P. × nerviger**

14b Midrib bordered at the base by a narrow band of lacunae, which ceases below the apex; upper leaves without a copper tinge when dry 15

15a Leaves at the base of the stem reduced to phyllodes; leaves narrowly elliptical, not inrolled, often recurved, with 4–5(–6) lateral veins on each side of the lamina; stipules obtuse at the apex **26 P. × zizii**
15b Leaves at the base of the stem very rarely reduced to phyllodes; leaves linear-lanceolate to elliptical or oblong, often inrolled, never recurved, with 4–8 lateral veins on each side of the midrib; stipules rounded at the apex **34 P. × salicifolius**

16a Leaves at the base of the stem reduced to phyllodes; apex of mature leaves mucronate and sometimes with an excurrent midrib; stipules with 2 strong ribs which are often winged on the abaxial side 17
16b Leaves at the base of the stem not reduced to phyllodes; apex of mature leaves obtuse or acute but not mucronate; stipules with 2 ribs which are not winged on the abaxial side 19

17a Petioles 25–70(–90) mm **23 P. × fluitans**
17b Petioles 1–12(–25) mm 18

18a All leaves petiolate; leaves on stems and main branches 25–65 mm wide, with stipules 35–80(–110) mm **3 P. lucens**
18b Some leaves sessile; leaves on stems and main branches 10–25(–30) mm wide, with stipules 20–45(–55) mm **26 P. × zizii**

19a Margin of young leaves denticulate, with minute and fugacious teeth **2 P. nodosus**
19b Margin of young leaves entire 20

20a Mature leaves linear-elliptical or narrowly elliptical, 2.5–24 mm wide, 5–15(–30) times as long as wide **5 P. polygonifolius**
20b Mature leaves elliptical or broadly elliptical, 20–50 mm wide, 2.5–6.5 times as long as wide **6 P. coloratus**

(N.B. *P. coloratus* and *P. polygonifolius* may not be separable if only submerged leaves are available.)

21a Leaf margin denticulate or serrate, especially towards the apex 22
21b Leaf margin entire or very obscurely denticulate 25

22a Leaves with 3–6 lateral veins on each side of the midrib, semi-
      amplexicaul or more or less amplexicaul at the base   **41 P. × cooperi**
22b Leaves with 1–3 lateral veins on each side of the midrib, not or only
      slightly amplexicaul at the base   23

23a Leaves with 1–2(–3) lateral veins on each side of the midrib
                                                      19 P. crispus
23b Leaves with 2–3 lateral veins on each side of the midrib   24

24a Stipules rigid, with 2 raised ridges towards the base
                                                   38 P. × cadburyae
24b Stipules flexible, without ridges towards the base   **39 P. × olivaceus**

25a Plant without a reddish brown tinge when dry; leaves abruptly
      narrowed to an auriculate or semi-amplexicaul base **40 P. × undulatus**
25b Plant often with a reddish brown tinge when dry; leaves gradually
      tapering to a slightly auriculate base   **39 P. × olivaceus**

Group E

Submerged leaves arising directly from the nodes, filiform, linear or linear-
oblong, reduced to opaque phyllodes or flat in section with a distinct midrib.
Floating leaves absent.

1a   Leaves reduced to opaque phyllodes, without a distinct midrib and
      lateral veins; stipules 40–170 mm   **1 P. natans**
1b   Leaves with a distinct midrib and lateral veins; stipules 4–55 mm   2

2a   Rhizome absent; stipules rounded to obtuse at the apex   3
2b   Rhizome present; stipules truncate to slightly emarginate at the apex
                                                                         13

3a   Stipules closed and tubular at the base when young   4
3b   Stipules open throughout their length   8

4a   Leaves with scattered sclerenchymatous strands in the lamina
                                                  45 P. × pseudofriesii
4b   Leaves without scattered sclerenchymatous strands in the lamina   5

5a   Leaves 1.5–3.5(–4) mm wide; lateral veins (1–)2(–3) on each side of
the midrib; leaves abruptly contracted to a mucronate apex; turions
fan-shaped   **11 P. friesii**

5b   Leaves 0.35–1.4(–1.9) mm wide; lateral veins 1(–2) on each side of
the midrib; leaves gradually tapering to an acute or acuminate but not
mucronate apex; turions cylindrical   6

6a   Stipules white or buff-coloured and opaque when dry, the veins
prominent   **12 P. rutilus**

6b   Stipules hyaline and translucent when dry, the veins not very
prominent   7

7a   Flowers with 1–3 carpels   **44 P. × grovesii**

7b   Flowers with 4(–5) carpels   **13 P. pusillus**

8a   Stems terete to compressed, rarely strongly compressed; leaves
without sclerenchymatous strands in the lamina   9

8b   Stems strongly compressed to flattened; leaves with sclerenchymatous
strands in the lamina   11

9a   Leaves (1–)2.5–3.5 mm wide, often tinged pink or reddish brown
along the midrib or throughout; stipules with (8–)10–17 intercostal
veins; turions 3–5 mm wide; inflorescences with 6–8 flowers
      14 P. obtusifolius

9b   Leaves 0.3–1.8(–2.3) mm wide, without any pink or reddish brown
tinge; stipules with 5–8(–9) intercostal veins; turions 0.6–1.7 mm
wide; inflorescences with 2–5 flowers   10

10a   Leaves flaccid, with a midrib which occupies 10–20% of the leaf
width near the base and in section has a shallowly convex lower side;
flowers with (3–)4–5(–7) carpels   **15 P. berchtoldii**

10b   Leaves relatively rigid, with a midrib which occupies 30–70% of the
leaf width near the base and in section has a strongly convex lower
side; flowers with 1(–2) carpels   **16 P. trichoides**

11a   Stems compressed, with nodal glands; leaves 1.1–3(–3.5) mm wide
      46 P. × sudermanicus

11b   Stems strongly compressed to flattened, without nodal glands; leaves
1.5–6 mm wide   12

12a Leaves with 2 lateral veins on each side of the midrib, the outer vein often faint; peduncles 28–95 mm; inflorescences with 10–20 flowers; most flowers with 2 carpels   **17 P. compressus**

12b Leaves with 1 lateral vein on each side of the midrib; peduncles 5–30 mm; inflorescences with 4–6 flowers; most flowers with 1 carpel
    18 P. acutifolius

13a All leaves with an entire margin   14

13b At least some leaves with a denticulate margin, at least near the apex
    15

14a Stems terete to compressed, but, if compressed, then without a groove along one or both of the broader sides   **10 P. epihydrus**

14b Stems slightly compressed to compressed, with a groove along one or both of the broader sides   18

15a Stipules closed and tubular at the base when young   **42 P. × lintonii**

15b Stipules open and convolute throughout their length   16

16a Leaves 2–5 mm wide; flowers with 2–3(–4) carpels   **43 P. × bennettii**

16b Leaves 5–12(–22) mm wide; flowers with (2–)4 carpels   17

17a Leaves with 1–2(–3) lateral veins on each side of the midrib; teeth on leaf margin usually easily seen with the naked eye; inflorescences with 3–8 flowers   **19 P. crispus**

17b Leaves with 2–4 lateral veins on each side of the midrib; teeth on leaf margin usually obscure, not visible to the naked eye; inflorescences with 10–12 flowers   18

18a Plant without a reddish brown tinge when dry; leaves abruptly narrowed to an auriculate or semi-amplexicaul base
    40 P. × undulatus

18b Plant often with a reddish brown tinge when dry; leaves gradually tapering to a slightly auriculate base   **39 P. × olivaceus**

Group F

Submerged leaves with lamina arising from the top of a sheath which surrounds the stem above the node, filiform to linear, elliptical or semicircular in section with air channels bordering an inconspicuous midrib. Floating leaves absent.

Before attempting to key down a plant in this group, make sure that it is not *Eleogiton fluitans* or the aquatic variant of *Juncus bulbosus*. *E. fluitans* lacks a ligule at the junction of the sheath and lamina and has entire leaf apices, a combination which distinguishes it both from *Potamogeton* Subgenus *Coleogeton* and from *Ruppia*. The aquatic variant of *J. bulbosus* roots from the stem nodes and usually has an untidy habit, with clusters of leaves arising at intervals from the stem. *J. bulbosus* lacks a ligule at the junction of the sheath and lamina, although the two auricles at the top of the sheath are easily mistaken for a ligule, especially on pressed material. The leaves of *J. bulbosus* are very slender; they have transverse septae (although these can be very inconspicuous) and an entire apex.

The only European species of *Potamogeton* which is absent from the British Isles, *P. vaginatus*, will key down to this group. *P. vaginatus* differs from *P. filiformis* in its open sheaths and from *P. pectinatus* in having loose and inflated lower sheaths and fruits which are only 2.5–3 mm long and have a subapical beak (Dandy 1980).

1a	Leaf apex entire; ligule 5–15 mm long present at the junction of the leaf sheath and the lamina; inflorescences with 4–14 flowers	2
1b	Leaf apex minutely denticulate; ligule absent; inflorescences with 2 flowers	5
2a	All leaf sheaths open and convolute at the base when young; stigmas borne on a distinct style	**21 P. pectinatus**
2b	At least some sheaths closed and tubular at the base when young; stigmas sessile or borne on a distinct style	3
3a	Some leaf sheaths open and convolute when young, others on the same stem closed and tubular at the base	**47 P. × suecicus**
3b	Leaf sheaths all closed and tubular at the base when young	4
4a	Stigmas sessile	**20 P. filiformis**
4b	Stigmas borne on a distinct style	**47 P. × suecicus**
5a	Peduncles at anthesis 8–26 mm	**49 Ruppia maritima**
5b	Peduncles at anthesis 40–300(–770) mm	**50 Ruppia cirrhosa**

SPECIES ACCOUNTS

Notes on the descriptions

The description starts with the scientific name of the species or hybrid. Synonyms are not given in the main text but are listed in the index. English names are also given for the species.

The descriptions should be taken as referring to fresh material unless there is an indication that they are based on dried specimens. In particular, the colours of leaves and stipules refer (unless stated) to the living plant, and the diameter of rhizomes, stems and peduncles are also taken from fresh specimens. However, measurements of fruits are based on dried material. Measurements refer to length or to length × width, unless otherwise stated.

I have based the descriptions on herbarium specimens and on fresh material collected in the wild. Unless stated, the descriptions only cover material from Britain and Ireland. The main herbarium that I have consulted is **CGE**, but I have usually examined material at **BM** and sometimes (especially for rarer taxa) specimens in **E**, **K** and other herbaria. In drawing up descriptions of fresh material I have concentrated on those features which are not apparent, or are distorted, in pressed specimens. Unfortunately, I have been unable to find living plants of *P.* × *lanceolatifolius*, *P.* × *prussicus*, *P.* × *cadburyae*, *P.* × *grovesii* and *P.* × *pseudofriesii*, and the descriptions of these hybrids have been based on a limited amount of herbarium material. Some 1000 specimens which I have collected during the work for the Handbook have been deposited in **CGE**, with duplicates of many gatherings in other herbaria.

I have used the following terms to describe the diameter of rhizomes, stems and peduncles:

very slender: up to 1 mm in diameter
slender: 1–2 mm in diameter
robust: 2–4 mm in diameter
very robust: over 4 mm in diameter

The following terms are used to describe the shape of the stems and peduncles in section:

terete: circular
slightly compressed: with the longest axis 1.1–1.5 times as long as the
    shortest

compressed: with the longest axis 1.5–2.5 times as long as the shortest

strongly compressed: with the longest axis 2.5–3.5 times as long as
    the shortest

flattened: with the longest axis at least 3.5 times as long as the shortest

The description of leaves and stipules excludes those which subtend an inflorescence. In the description of the inflorescence, the number of flowers is described as numerous if more than 20 are present. The length of the fruits includes the beak.

The descriptive paragraph may be followed by paragraphs which summarise the ecology and distribution, variation and modes of reproduction, and notes on the identification of the plant. As in the descriptions, these remarks only cover the taxa in Britain and Ireland. All the hybrids of a species are listed in a final paragraph, including those recognised from Europe by Dandy (1975) but not recorded in the British Isles. Those hybrids which are most likely to be confused with the parent under discussion are indicated.

Notes on the illustrations

The captions to the illustrations give the origins of the material used for the main habit drawing and for the drawing of the fruit. If the habit drawing was based on fresh material this is indicated by the phrase "plants from"; if the source was a herbarium specimen this is indicated by "specimen from". All the fruits were drawn from herbarium specimens. A variety of additional drawings are included to show the critical identification features of the plant; these are usually based on the same material as that used for the main habit drawing, but other material has sometimes been used and a few drawings are based on published illustrations. Scale bars are not given for most drawings, as the approximate scale will be apparent from the dimensions provided in the description and the exact scale is of little significance in such variable plants. The fruits in the plates of individual taxa are all drawn to the same scale ($\times$ 5.2). The approximate scale of the magnified drawings of leaf margins is indicated by an appropriate scale bar. The artists responsible for the individual drawings are indicated by G. L. (G. Lyell), K. D. (Karen Dracoulis), L. T. E. (L. T. Ellis), M. D. (Megan Dowlen) and M. T. (Margaret Tebbs).

Notes on the maps

The maps show the distribution of the species and some of the hybrids in Britain and Ireland. These maps have been prepared with the assistance of my colleagues in the Biological Records Centre, and particular thanks are due to Mrs J. M. Croft for undertaking much of the work needed to incorporate the available records into the B.R.C. database. The DMAP program written by Dr A. J. Morton has been used to plot the maps. The 10-km squares in which a hybrid occurs are given in the text if the taxon is not mapped.

Criteria for the acceptance of records

The current taxonomy of *Potamogeton* in the British Isles is based on the work of J. E. Dandy and G. Taylor in the 1930s. They showed that many taxa had previously been misinterpreted and that records of the linear-leaved species were particularly unreliable. I know from the specimens which have been sent to me in recent years that the linear-leaved species are still frequently misidentified. Clearly, any distribution maps based on an uncritical assemblage of ancient and modern records are likely to be misleading. The most satisfactory records are based on expertly determined herbarium specimens, which should be correctly identified and which are available for checking by later students. The following guidelines were followed when assessing other records.

1. Records of the smaller, linear-leaved specimens of *Potamogeton* (*P. berchtoldii*, *P. pusillus*, *P. rutilus*, *P. trichoides*) and of all *Potamogeton* hybrids have usually been accepted only if they are based on expertly determined material.

2. Pre-1940 records of *Potamogeton* have not been accepted unless they are supported by expertly determined herbarium specimens. Pre-1940 records of *Groenlandia* and *Ruppia* which are not supported by voucher specimens have been accepted unless there is a particular reason to suspect that they were based on misidentifications.

3. Field records or literature records made in or after 1940 by reliable observers have been accepted for *Groenlandia*, *Ruppia* and all species of *Potamogeton* except for the smaller linear-leaved species, provided that the recorder and the locality where the plant was seen are known and the record falls within the confirmed range of the species. Records without details of locality and recorder have not been accepted, as I do not believe that it is

possible to assess the reliability of such imprecise records. I have not, there-fore, accepted records collected during the fieldwork for *Atlas of the British Flora* (Perring & Walters 1962) if they are only localised to a 10-km square, whether or not the recorder is known, nor have I accepted records from modern 'tetrad' floras unless details of the recorder and locality are avail-able from the published flora or unpublished sources.

These criteria are broadly similar to those adopted when the maps of *Potamogeton* were compiled for *Atlas of the British Flora* and its *Critical Supplement* (Perring & Walters 1962, Perring & Sell 1968). The *Atlas* criteria were slightly less stringent for some of the commoner species, where records were accepted if they were localised only to a 10-km square, but more stringent for other species, which were based solely on the records from Dandy's card index.

Source of the records

The most important source of records of *Groenlandia* and *Potamogeton* is the card index compiled by J. E. Dandy and now held at **BM**. This includes details of 20,000 specimens determined by Dandy and Taylor, and latterly by Dandy alone, during the course of their studies of the genera. Dandy and Taylor systematically checked specimens and extracted records from most of the major British and Irish herbaria. Dandy did not document records of *Ruppia* in his card index, but I have extracted records from a number of herbaria (**BM, CGE, DBN, E, GL, K, LANC, LIV, NMW, OXF** and **RNG**).

Records from a wide variety of sources have been added to the basic dataset derived from herbarium specimens. The major additional sources are listed below.

1. Records received by B.R.C. since the publication of *Atlas of the British Flora*, often sent for publication in *Watsonia* or as additions to published maps. These records also include the results of the B.S.B.I. Monitoring Scheme (1987–1988).

2. Records of *Groenlandia densa*, all *Potamogeton* hybrids and all *Potamogeton* species except for five of the commonest (*P. crispus*, *P. natans*, *P. pectinatus*, *P. perfoliatus*, *P. polygonifolius*) were received from B.S.B.I. vice-county recorders in response to print-outs of records held by B.R.C. which were circulated between 1984 and 1986. Records of *Ruppia cirrhosa* and those *Potamogeton* species which were believed to be nationally scarce in Britain (*P. coloratus*, *P. compressus*, *P. filiformis*, *P. friesii*, *P. praelongus*

and *P. trichoides*) were circulated to British vice-county recorders in 1993 during the preparation of *Scarce Plants in Britain* (Stewart, Pearman & Preston 1994) and some additional records obtained.

3. Records were kindly provided by two major lake surveys. The Nature Conservancy Council's Scottish Loch Survey covered many sites in northern and western Scotland between 1984 and 1990; it was continued by Scottish Natural Heritage in 1993 and 1994. The Northern Ireland Lake Survey, financed by the Department of the Environment (Northern Ireland) and based at the Department of Agriculture (Northern Ireland), carried out an intensive study of the lakes in the province from 1988 to 1991.

4. Records made during his survey of British rivers (Holmes 1983) were kindly extracted and forwarded by N. T. H. Holmes. Records from other Nature Conservancy Council surveys have also been made available to B.R.C.

5. Records made during my own fieldwork, which has included detailed surveys of some areas (including Coll & Tiree, Lismore and Donegal) but has usually been devoted to searches for particular species and hybrids at sites where they were recorded in the past. Much of this fieldwork has been with N. F. Stewart, who has also provided records from his own fieldwork, which included visits to many Irish localities. I have also obtained many records from fresh material and specimens sent by correspondents during the period when I have been preparing the book.

6. Records of *Groenlandia densa*, *Ruppia cirrhosa* and *R. maritima* were extracted from published county and other local floras and from a number of unpublished sources. Detailed records of *Groenlandia densa* in the Republic of Ireland, where it is a protected species, were kindly provided by Dr T. G. F. Curtis of the Office of Public Works.

The records on which the maps are based are held on computer file in the B.R.C. database. Comments in this book on the British and Irish distribution and ecology of individual taxa are based solely on these records; records which do not meet the criteria for acceptance listed above have been disregarded.

Symbols on the maps

The records are plotted on the maps in the 10-km squares of the Ordnance Survey national grids for Britain and for Ireland; Channel Island records are plotted in the 10-km squares of the Universal Transverse Mercator grid. The following symbols are used on the maps:

- Record(s) of native plants made in or after 1970

○ Record(s) of native plants made before 1970; no later record available

× Record(s) of introduced plants made in or after 1970; no record of native plants available

+ Record(s) of introduced plants made before 1970; no record of native plants and no later record of introduced plants available

Interpretation of the maps

In interpreting the maps, it is important to remember that the records on which they are based are not derived from a systematic survey of Britain and Ireland but have been acquired from numerous, dissimilar sources. There will inevitably be an uneven coverage of the area: some regions have been surveyed in detail by recorders who were very familiar with aquatic plants, whereas others have been surveyed by botanists who conscientiously collected *Potamogeton* material for expert verification but may have overlooked some of the less conspicuous species and hybrids. There are also areas where the aquatic habitats have never been systematically surveyed.

The maps distinguish records made in or after 1970 from earlier records. I have chosen this cut-off date in the hope that the maps will give a reasonably representative picture of the contemporary pondweed flora. There are areas which have not been surveyed in detail since 1970 and where there are undoubtedly more pondweeds than appear on the map; in other areas some of the populations recorded since 1970 may now no longer exist.

In spite of these qualifications, I believe that the maps do give a reasonably accurate picture of the overall distribution of the taxa in Britain and Ireland. The commonest species are likely to be the most seriously under-recorded. I hope that botanists who notice deficiencies in the maps will not sit back and criticise them, but will get out into the field and attempt to fill some of the gaps!

1   Potamogeton natans L.

Broad-leaved Pondweed

Rhizomes slender to very robust. *Stems* up to 1(–5.5) m, slender to very robust, terete, unbranched or very sparingly branched; nodal glands absent. *Submerged leaves* 120–450(–610) × 0.4–3.5 mm, 75–300 times as long as wide, consisting of filiform or narrowly linear phyllodes, flat or shallowly concave on the upper side, convex on the lower side, opaque, mid green, olive-green or dark green, narrowly obtuse to acuminate at the apex which is often decayed or broken off, entire at the margin. *Floating leaves* with the lamina (35–)50–100(–140) × (7–)20–45(–80) mm, 1.4–3.5(–5.2) times as long as wide, opaque, coriaceous, pinkish brown when young, mid green, yellow-green or olive-green, often with a brownish tinge when mature, elliptical to ovate-oblong, cuneate, rounded or subcordate at the base, shortly and narrowly decurrent on the petiole, acute to obtuse at the apex and often apiculate; lateral veins (6–)8–12(–16) on each side of the midrib, translucent in the living plant, the secondary veins numerous, transverse and rather obscure; petioles 50–150(–300) mm, shorter or longer than the lamina, with a flexible, pale, slightly swollen junction with the stem and usually with a flexible, pinkish brown, discoloured section 7–25 mm long between the petiole and the lamina. *Stipules* 40–170 mm, open, rather rigid, enfolding the stem throughout their length or projecting from it at an acute angle, more or less translucent and colourless, slightly milky white or pale brown when fresh, opaque and green, brownish green or buff when dry, narrowly obtuse to subacute, slightly hooded and rolled so that the apex appears acuminate, persistent although often eroded on the older leaves; veins prominent when dry, 2 more prominent than the others and forming weak ridges along the back of the stipules. *Turions* absent. *Inflorescences* 20–60 × 4–9 mm; peduncles 40–100(–125) mm, slender to very robust, tapering slightly towards the inflorescence, spongy, terete. *Flowers* usually numerous, contiguous, with 4 carpels. *Fruits* 3.8–5.0 × 2.4–3.2 mm, olive-green or brown-green; beak 0.3–0.8 mm, ventral, straight or recurved.

Ecologically perhaps the most tolerant of our *Potamogeton* species, *P. natans* occupies a wide range of habitats including ponds, lakes, reservoirs, ditches, streams, canals and rivers. It can be found growing with *P. polygonifolius* in oligotrophic water or with *P. crispus* and *P. pectinatus* in eutrophic conditions. It most characteristically occurs in relatively shallow, still or slowly

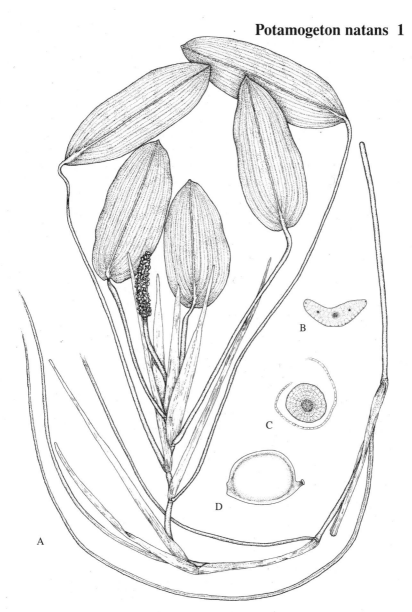

A: habit; B: section of phyllode; C: section of stem and stipule; D: fruit. Habit based on plants from experimental ditches, Monks Wood, v.c. 31, C.D.P., 1989 (Preston 89/63, **CGE**); fruit on specimen from R. Gade, Waterend, v.c. 20, J.E. Dandy, 1959 (Dandy 1379, **BM**). Drawn by L.T.E. (A–C) & M.T. (D).

flowing water and its leaves can cover the entire surface of mesotrophic ponds and ditches which do not dry out in summer. However, it can also grow in rapidly flowing streams and rivers, and up to depths of 6 m in clear, still water. It is the most familiar and conspicuous *Potamogeton* in much of low-land Britain and Ireland, though in the acidic, highland areas of the north and west *P. polygonifolius* becomes more frequent.

The phyllodes of *P. natans* are produced as the plants begin to grow in spring, and in shallow standing water they often decay in early summer. In rapidly flowing streams plants can produce numerous phyllodes, which may persist throughout the year. Spathulate leaves consisting of a long petiole terminated by a short lamina, intermediate between phyllodes and fully formed floating leaves, are sometimes produced during the transition to floating leaves. Plants in still or slowing flowing water usually fruit freely. Although *P. natans* lacks turions, plants are occasionally found with axillary fascicles of small phyl-lodes, which may act as vegetative propagules. During the winter plants of *P. natans* persist, but with rather decayed leaves.

Two features distinguish *P. natans* from all the other species which produce floating leaves: its submerged leaves are always reduced to bladeless phyllodes and there is usually (but not invariably) a discoloured flexible section between the petiole and the lamina of the floating leaves. On dried material this section can be shrunken as well as discoloured, and it remains visible even on old specimens. Plants of *P. natans* which do not have a dis-coloured section may be difficult to separate from *P. polygonifolius* if they also lack phyllodes. When living leaves of *P. natans* are held up to the light their numerous, closely set, translucent lateral veins give them a characteris-tic appearance. The lateral veins of *P. polygonifolius* are darker than the lamina, but this distinction is only reliable for floating leaves, as terrestrial or semi-terrestrial leaves of *P. natans* can also have opaque veins. The stipules of *P. natans* are quite different in texture from those of *P. polygonifolius*, having more closely set veins which give them an opaque appearance when dried. This is a crucial distinction, which can almost always be used to identify doubtful material. *P. natans* also tends to have longer stipules, and its fruits are much larger. Forms of *P. natans* without floating leaves can be puzzling, as so many other aquatic genera possess linear leaves, but the stipules indicate that they belong to *Potamogeton*.

Hybrids between *P. natans* and the following species are known from the British Isles: *P. nodosus* (*P.* × *schreberi*, **22**), *P. lucens* (*P.* × *fluitans*, **23**), *P. gramineus* (*P.* × *sparganiifolius*, **24**), *P. polygonifolius* (*P.* × *gessnacensis*, **25**) and *P. berchtoldii* (*P.* × *variifolius*, **31**). All five have submerged leaves with a distinct lamina.

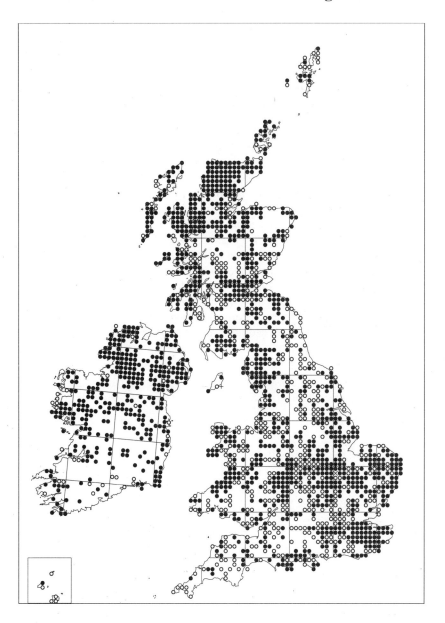

143

2   Potamogeton nodosus Poir.

Loddon Pondweed

Rhizomes robust. *Stems* up to 2.5 m, robust to very robust, terete, unbranched or sparingly branched; nodal glands absent. *Submerged leaves* with the lamina 160–280 × 22–38 mm, 6–7.5 times as long as wide, translucent, pale green when fresh, green or brownish green when dried, elliptical, gradually tapering to a petiolate base and an acute apex, denticulate at the margin, the teeth minute and fugacious; midrib bordered by a band of lacunae, the lateral veins 5–10 on each side, slightly stronger veins alternating with slightly weaker ones, the secondary veins numerous, more or less ascending, rather irregular, often wavy; petioles 70–210 mm. *Floating leaves* with the lamina 70–130 × 34–50 mm, 2–4.3 times as long as wide, opaque, coriaceous, green, broadly elliptical, rounded to cuneate at the base, obtuse at the apex and more or less apiculate; lateral veins 7–11 on each side of the midrib, opaque, darker or slightly lighter than the lamina on the living plant, the secondary veins numerous, obscure, ascending in the centre of the leaf and transverse towards the margin; petioles 30–210 mm, shorter or longer than the lamina. *Stipules* 45–125 mm, open, flexible, enfolding the stem, more or less translucent with a slight milky tinge when fresh, pale green to pale brown when dry, gradually tapering to a slightly hooded apex, fairly persistent; veins inconspicuous when dry, 2 more prominent than the others and forming ridges along the

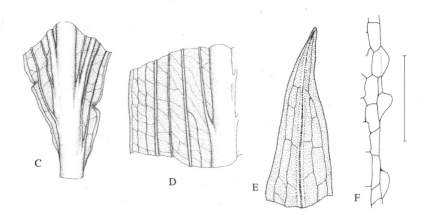

C   D   E   F

A: habit; B: submerged leaf; C, D, E, F: submerged leaf base, middle, apex and margin; G: section of stem and stipule; H: fruit. Habit based on plants from R. Loddon, Shinfield, v.c. 22, C.D.P. & N.F. Stewart, 1988 (Preston 88/287, **CGE**); fruit on specimen from pool E. of Sitera, Crete, E. Gathorne-Hardy, 1962 (**BM**). Drawn by L.T.E. (A–G) & M.T. (H). Scale bar: 0.1 mm.

145

back of the stipules. *Turions* absent. *Inflorescences* 14–70 × 4–10 mm; peduncles 45–130 mm, robust to very robust, somewhat broader and slightly spongy at the apex, terete. *Flowers* numerous, more or less contiguous, with (2–)4(–5) carpels. *Fruits* not seen in wild-collected British material; in European plants 2.7–4.1 × 2.0–3.0 mm, reddish brown or brown; beak 0.3–0.8 mm, ventral, straight or slightly recurved.

Potamogeton nodosus is usually found in slow to moderately flowing water, often with *Sagittaria sagittifolia* and *Sparganium emersum*. It is restricted to a few calcareous rivers in southern England: the R. Avon (N. Somerset, N. & S. Wiltshire and W. Gloucestershire), R. Stour (Dorset) and R. Loddon (Berkshire). It formerly grew in the R. Thames (Berkshire, Buckinghamshire and Oxfordshire), but was last collected there in 1941, and there is a single 19th-century specimen from the Warwickshire R. Stour at Alderminster. In Britain, as in the Netherlands (Coops, Zant & Doef 1993), it appears to vary in quantity from year to year. In 1988 it was planted at five sites in the R. Loddon and in the nearby R. Whitewater and Blackwater River. It is listed in the British *Red Data Book* (Perring & Farrell 1983).

Potamogeton nodosus shows little variation in the British Isles. Fruits are rarely produced in England: I have not seen any fruiting material collected in the wild but fruits have been reported by some observers, including Druce (1929b). Plants from the R. Loddon fruited when cultivated by Fryer (1899) in still water, as have plants cultivated more recently by N. T. H. Holmes in similar conditions, so the scarcity of fruit might be attributable to the restriction of *P. nodosus* to rivers in Britain. In southern Europe, *P. nodosus* grows in a much greater range of habitats including still as well as flowing water, and fruits more frequently. British plants over-winter as rhizomes bearing fusiform buds which develop in August and September. Short stolons terminating in an ovoid bud also develop in the leaf axils in late summer and probably act as a means of vegetative reproduction.

The submerged leaves of *P. nodosus* have long petioles and can therefore be distinguished from those of *P. alpinus*, which are sessile, and *P. lucens*, which have much shorter petioles. They are longer and broader than those of *P. polygonifolius* and are denticulate, at least when young. *P. coloratus* also has entire submerged leaves and its floating leaves are less opaque than those of *P. nodosus* and broader in relation to their length. *P. nodosus* can be very similar to *P. × fluitans* (*P. lucens × natans*); for the differences between them see under that hybrid.

P. nodosus × P. natans (*P. × schreberi*, **22**) is found in Dorset.

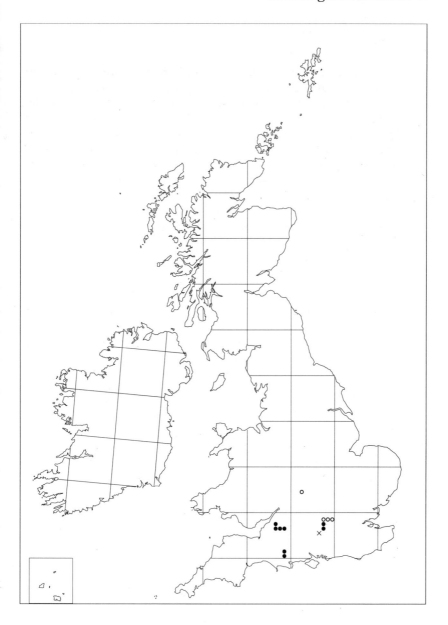

3 Potamogeton lucens L.

Shining Pondweed

Rhizomes robust to very robust. *Stems* to 2.5(–6) m, robust to very robust, terete, sparingly to richly branched; nodal glands absent. *Submerged leaves* on the lower part of the stems reduced or partially reduced to phyllodes, otherwise with the lamina 75–200(–260) × 25–65 mm on the stems, as small as 55 × 17 mm on short branches, (2–)3–6(–10) times as long as wide, translucent, usually rather glossy yellowish green, occasionally with a reddish tinge, narrowly elliptical to oblong-elliptical, gradually tapering or rather abruptly narrowed to the petiole, rounded to acuminate at the apex, which is always at least mucronate and frequently with the midrib excurrent, denticulate and minutely undulate at the margin; midrib prominent, not bordered by lacunae, the lateral veins 4–5(–6) on each side, the inner veins equally well

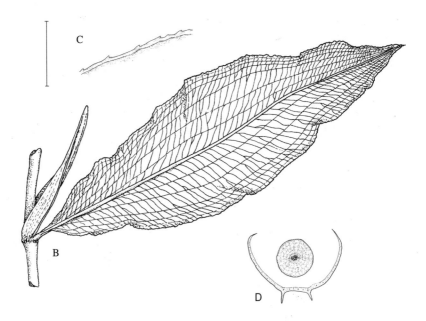

A: habit; B: leaf and stipule; C: leaf margin; D: section of stem and stipule; E: fruit. Habit based on plants from Monks Lode, Wicken, v.c. 29, J.M. Croft & C.D.P., 1987 (Preston 87/25, **CGE**); fruit on specimen from R. Nene, Upwell, v.c. 29, J.G. Dony, 1959 (**BM**). Drawn by L.T.E. (A–D) & M.T. (E). Scale bar: 1 mm.

developed, the 1–2 outer veins fainter than the others, the secondary veins frequent, ascending across the entire width of the leaf, almost as conspicuous as the laterals; petioles 1–12(–25) mm. *Floating leaves* absent. *Stipules* 35–80(–110) mm on the main stems, as short as 20 mm on short branches, open, rigid, translucent, pale green, rounded, obtuse or rarely acute at the apex, very persistent; veins inconspicuous when dry, 2 much more prominent than the others and forming conspicuous green ribs, the ribs winged on the abaxial side for at least half of the length of the stipule. *Turions* absent. *Inflorescences* 22–70 × 7–13 mm; peduncles 50–200(–270) mm, very robust, broader and spongy towards the apex, slightly compressed especially towards the base. *Flowers* numerous, contiguous, with 4–5(–6) carpels. *Fruits* 3.2–4.5 × 2.4–3.0 mm, brown; beak 0.5–0.8 mm, more or less ventral, straight.

P. lucens is a lowland species, although it reaches an altitude of 380 m at Malham Tarn. It favours relatively deep, calcareous water and is usually found in lakes, sluggish rivers, canals and major fenland drains. It is a characteristic species of low-lying regions which receive drainage from calcareous uplands, such as the Somerset Levels and the Cambridgeshire Fenland. It is still frequent in suitable habitats in England and central Ireland, but it is rare in Scotland and Wales.

The leaves vary greatly in size and shape, even on a single plant, ranging from oblong-elliptical with a mucronate apex to narrowly elliptical with a long-excurrent midrib; towards the base of the stem the lamina is usually completely absent. The stems die down during the winter, the plant persisting as rhizomes.

    P. lucens is the most robust British pondweed and once known it should not be confused with any other species, although some of its hybrids are very similar. The leaves are shortly petiolate and their conspicuous secondary veins give them a characteristic net-veined appearance, but the key to determination lies in the rigid stipules which are usually winged for at least half of their length. The winged stipules should prevent confusion with *P. nodosus* or luxuriant *P. coloratus*, which also have net-veined leaves. *P. praelongus* differs in the leaf stipule and fruit characters listed under that species.

    P. lucens × *gramineus* (*P.* × *zizii*, **26**) and *P. lucens* × *perfoliatus* (*P.* × *salicifolius*, **34**) are two widespread hybrids, both of which can resemble *P. lucens* very closely. Hybrids between *P. lucens* and *P. alpinus* (*P.* × *nerviger*, **33**), *P. crispus* (*P.* × *cadburyae*, **38**) and *P. natans* × (*P.* × *fluitans*, **24**) are much rarer.

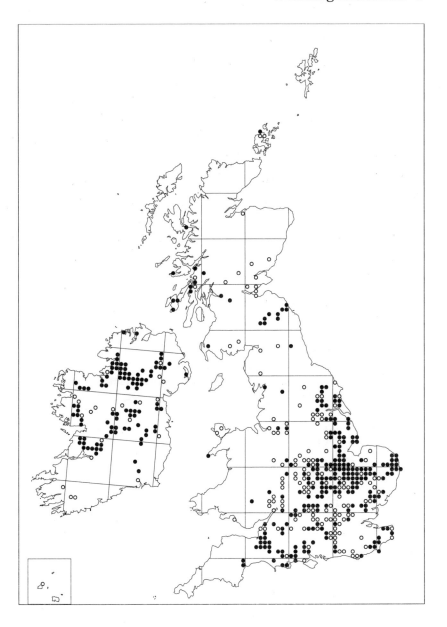

4   Potamogeton gramineus L.

Various-leaved Pondweed

Rhizomes very slender to very robust. *Stems* up to 0.8(–2.5) m, very slender to robust, terete, usually richly branched; nodal glands absent. *Submerged leaves* at the base of the stem reduced or partially reduced to phyllodes, otherwise 40–90(–140) × 5–12 mm on the main stems and branches, as small as 22 × 3 mm on short branches, 4.5–12(–20) times as long as wide, translucent, green without any pinkish tinge, narrowly elliptical or narrowly oblong-elliptical, often recurved, gradually tapering or abruptly narrowed to the base, sessile, acute to obtuse and usually mucronate at the apex, denticulate at the margin; midrib bordered by a narrow band of lacunae, the lateral veins 3–4 on each side, all equally well developed or the outermost fainter than the others, the secondary veins frequent and ascending. *Floating leaves* with the lamina 20–70(–95) × 7–34 mm, 1.3–3 times as long as wide, opaque, coriaceous, yellowish green to dark green, narrowly to broadly elliptical, oblong-elliptical or obovate, gradually tapering or abruptly narrowed to a cuneate, truncate or subcordate base, obtuse to acute and apiculate at the apex; lateral veins 5–10 on each side of the midrib, slightly lighter to slightly darker than the lamina in the living plant, the secondary veins numerous, ascending near the midrib, transverse towards the margin and rather obscure to relatively conspicuous; petioles 18–60 mm, shorter or longer than the lamina. *Stipules* 10–25(–35) mm on the main stems and branches, as short as 6.5 mm on short branches, open, rigid, sometimes (in sparingly branched forms) enfolding the stem but usually rolled and projecting from it at an acute angle, pale green to blackish green when dry, broadly obtuse and slightly hooded at the apex, persistent; veins inconspicuous when dry, 2 more prominent than the others and forming ribs towards the base on the abaxial side. *Turions* absent. *Inflorescences* 12–40 × 4–7 mm; penduncles (20–)35–100(–280) mm, slender to very robust, broader and spongy towards the apex, terete. *Flowers* usually

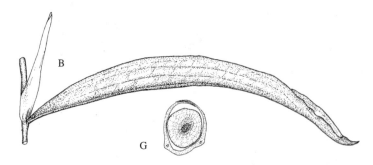

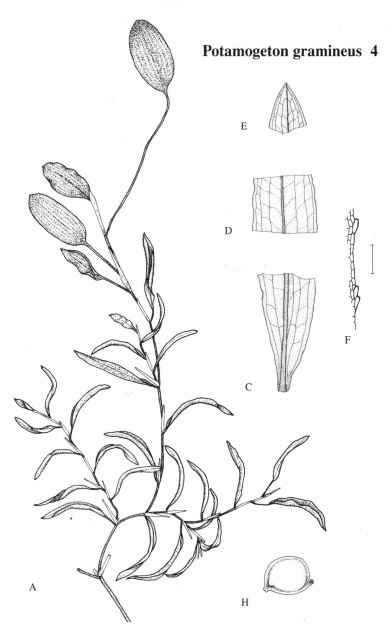

A: habit; B: submerged leaf and stipule; C, D, E, F: submerged leaf base, middle, apex and margin; G: section of stem and stipule; H: fruit. Habit based on plants from exit burn of Loch Ussie, v.c.106, C.D.P., 1988 (Preston 88/248, **CGE**); fruit on specimen from Loch Dun Mhurchaidh, Benbecula, v.c. 110, J.W. Clark, 1974 (**BM**). Drawn by L.T.E. (A–G) & M.T. (H). Scale bar: 0.1 mm.

numerous, contiguous, with (3–)4(–5) carpels. *Fruits* 2.4–3.1 × 1.6–2.1 mm, dark olive green; beak 0.2–0.4 mm, usually more or less ventral, occasionally subapical, straight.

P. gramineus grows in a wide variety of habitats. It is most often found in mesotrophic, still water 0.1–1 m deep, growing over a wide range of substrates from fine silt to stones and boulders. Although most frequent in acidic water at the edge of lakes, where associates include *Apium inundatum, Juncus bulbosus* and *Myriophyllum alterniflorum*, it is also found in highly calcareous (but not eutrophic) water in lakes over limestone or in fenland ditches, sometimes with *P. berchtoldii, P. coloratus, P. filiformis* and *Utricularia vulgaris sensu lato*. It has also been recorded from brackish water. Robust forms grow in streams and rivers; other habitats include flooded sand and gravel pits, quarries and canals. Although normally found in shallow water, plants can flower in clear still water up to 3 m deep. It is locally frequent in Scotland, northern England and much of Ireland but rare in southern England, Wales and south-west Ireland. It appears to be decreasing towards the southern edge of its British range.

Even by the standards of aquatic plants, *P. gramineus* is a highly variable species. In habitat it ranges from much-branched plants in shallow water which can be hemispherical in shape, less than 0.1 m high and with short recurved leaves, to drawn-out plants in rivers with main stems up to 1 m, fewer branches and straight leaves up to 140 mm long. Land forms occur on mud at the edge of water bodies: these have very short, condensed stems with a phyllode at the base and a group of coriaceous, short-petioled leaves similar in size and shape to the floating leaves.

Despite its variability, *P. gramineus* can be distinguished from other species by its sessile, narrowly elliptical leaves with a denticulate margin and often a mucronate apex. The short rigid stipules which often project from the stem are also characteristic. The submerged leaves of *P. coloratus* and *P. polygonifolius* are petiolate and entire; those of *P. alpinus*, though sessile, are also entire; none of these species ever have leaves with an excurrent midrib. *P. lucens* is the most closely related species but is a much more robust plant with larger leaves and fruits and winged stipules.

Hybrids of *P. gramineus* with *P. lucens* (*P.* × *zizii*, **26**) and *P. perfoliatus* (*P.* × *nitens*, **30**) are frequent and can be difficult to distinguish from it. Those with *P. alpinus* (*P.* × *nericius* **29**), *P. coloratus* (*P.* × *billupsii*, **28**), *P. natans* (*P.* × *sparganiifolius*, **24**) and *P. polygonifolius* (*P.* × *lanceolatifolius*, **27**) are scarcer.

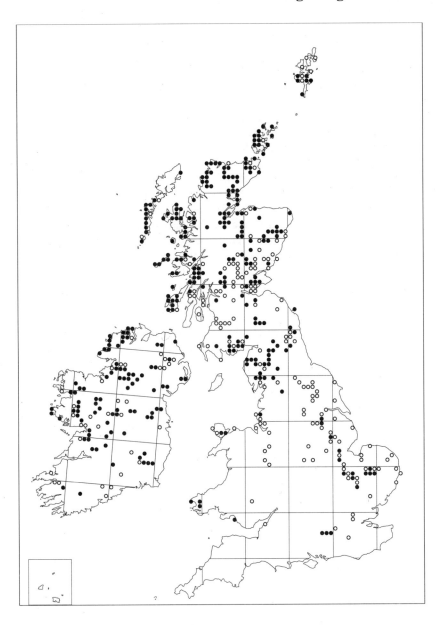

5 Potamogeton polygonifolius Pourr.

Bog Pondweed

Rhizomes slender to very robust. *Stems* up to 0.7 m, slender to very robust, terete, unbranched; nodal glands absent. *Submerged leaves* with the lamina 60–160 × 2.5–24 mm, 5–15(–30) times as long as wide, delicate, translucent, yellow-green, olive-green or pale reddish green when dry, linear-elliptical or narrowly elliptical, gradually tapering to the base and to the narrow, obtuse apex, petiolate, entire; midrib bordered by a narrow band of lacunae, the lateral veins 2–7 on each side, all more or less equally well developed, the secondary veins ascending near the midrib, more or less transverse elsewhere; petioles 14–80(–165) mm. *Floating leaves* with the lamina (15–)40–105 × (5.5–)15–70 mm, (1.1–)1.5–3.5(–4.3) times as long as wide, opaque, coriaceous, pinkish brown when young, bright green when mature, often with a strong brownish or reddish tinge, elliptical, oblong-elliptical or ovate, cuneate or rounded to subcordate at the base, shortly and narrowly decurrent on the petiole, acute to obtuse and often apiculate at the apex; lateral veins (5–)6–9(–12) on each side of the midrib, darker than the lamina in the living plant, the secondary veins numerous, transverse or more or less ascending and becoming increasingly conspicuous as the leaf ages; petioles (13–)30–150(–300) mm, shorter or longer than the lamina. *Stipules* 10–50 mm, open, flexible, translucent, hyaline, often with a strong brownish tinge, very broadly obtuse to narrowly obtuse, persistent; veins inconspicuous when dry, 2 more prominent than the others and forming distinct ridges on each side. *Turions* absent. *Inflorescences* 10–42 × 3.5–5.5 mm; peduncles 25–100(–185) mm, slender to robust, not tapered, slightly compressed near the base, more or less terete towards the apex. *Flowers* numerous, contiguous, with 4 carpels. *Fruits* 1.9–2.6 × 1.4–1.9 mm, reddish brown; beak 0.1–0.25 mm, more or less apical, straight.

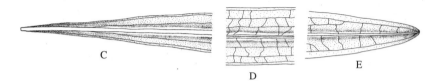

C   D   E

A: habit of aquatic plant; B: habit of subterrestrial plant; C, D, E: submerged leaf base, middle and apex; F: fruit. Fruit based on specimen from stream running from Black Loch to Widow's Loch, Straiton, v.c. 75, G. Taylor, 1949 (**BM**). Drawn by L.T.E. (A, B), K.D. (C–E) & M.T. (F).

P. polygonifolius usually grows in wet terrestrial habitats or in water less than 1.5 m deep, but it is occasionally found to a depth of 3 m. It normally behaves as a calcifuge, and typical sites include shallow water at the edge of oligotrophic lakes, lakeside pools and marshes, shallow rivers, streams and ditches (including periodically dry ditches), bog pools and peat cuttings, flushes and *Sphagnum* lawns. *Carex nigra*, *C. rostrata*, *Eleogiton fluitans*, *Eriophorum angustifolium*, *Hydrocotyle vulgaris*, *Juncus bulbosus*, *Menyanthes trifoliata*, *Potentilla palustris*, *Ranunculus flammula*, *Utricularia intermedia sensu lato* and *Sphagnum* spp. are characteristic associates. It also occurs in areas where relatively base-rich water flows over ombrotrophic bogs, including communities dominated by 'brown mosses'. It is very rarely found in highly calcareous habitats, including flushes and fenland pools. Although a common plant over peat-covered ground in the north and west, *P. polygonifolius* is decreasing in some southern counties where heaths and bogs are drying out.

An extremely variable species. The submerged leaves on young stems can be very narrow; those on more mature stems are broader. In deep or rapidly-flowing water forms occur with only submerged leaves. More frequently the submerged leaves decay early in the season, leaving only floating leaves. Terrestrial forms lack the submerged type of leaf, and can sometimes be very small. Plants with well-developed submerged leaves have been called var. *pseudofluitans* Syme and terrestrial forms var. *ericetorum* Syme, but these are simply phenotypes which develop in particular habitats. There may, however, also be some genetic variation as Fryer reported that a plant with frequent submerged leaves but very few floating leaves, which he described as forma *cancellatus*, retained its characters in cultivation (Fryer & Bennett 1915).

P. polygonifolius is closely related to *P. coloratus*. The submerged leaves of *P. polygonifolius* tend to be narrower and they are clearly differentiated from the opaque floating leaves. The fruits of *P. coloratus* are smaller than those of *P. polygonifolius* and lack any reddish tinge. These differences allow almost all specimens to be identified, although extremely small terrestrial plants without fruits can be almost impossible to name. *P. polygonifolius* is much less similar morphologically to *P. natans*, but care is needed in separating certain forms (see *P. natans*). The submerged leaves of *P. polygonifolius* are often mistaken for *P. alpinus*, but they are petiolate, not sessile.

Hybrids of *P. polygonifolius* with *P. natans* (*P.* × *gessnacensis*, **25**) and *P. gramineus* (*P.* × *lanceolatifolius*, **27**) occur in Britain, but both are rare. Hybrids with *P. alpinus*, *P. berchtoldii* and *P. pusillus* are recorded in Europe.

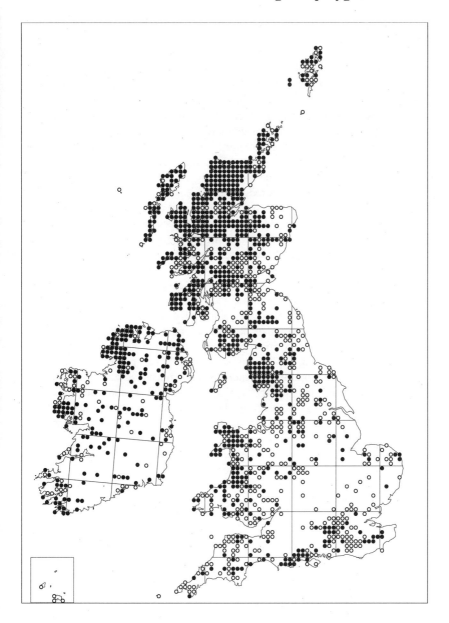

6   Potamogeton coloratus Hornem.

Fen Pondweed

Rhizomes robust. *Stems* up to 0.7 m, slender to robust, terete, unbranched or very sparingly branched; nodal glands absent. *Submerged leaves* on short over-wintering stems with the lamina 70–175 × 10–30 mm, 3–8.5 times as long as wide, oblanceolate or narrowly elliptical, very gradually tapering to the base, petiolate or rarely sessile, narrowly obtuse and hooded at the apex; on longer stems 75–150 × 20–50 mm, 2.5–6.5 times as long as wide, elliptical or broadly elliptical, tapering to an acute apex and gradually or more or less abruptly narrowed to the base, petiolate; all translucent, bright green, sometimes with a pinkish or reddish tinge especially along the veins, entire; midrib bordered on each side by a narrow band of lacunae, the lateral veins 4–8 on each side, more or less equally developed or slightly stronger veins alternating with slightly weaker ones, the secondary veins numerous, more or less ascending in the centre of the leaf and more or less transverse and rather wavy elsewhere, conspicuous; petioles (6–)20–65 mm. *Floating leaves* with the lamina (15–)25–85 × (13–)16–55 mm, 1–2 times as long as wide, more or less translucent, only rarely subcoriaceous, bright green, the older leaves often tinged reddish brown, broadly elliptical, ovate or more or less orbicular, more or less truncate or cordate at the base, more or less acute or obtuse and sometimes apiculate at the apex; lateral veins 6–10 on each side of the midrib, opaque in the living plant, the secondary veins numerous, irregularly ascending near the midrib and more or less transverse elsewhere; petioles (4–)8–45 mm, shorter than the lamina. *Stipules* 20–65 mm, open, delicate, flexible, clasping the stems throughout their length or the distal portion projecting at an acute angle from the stem, translucent when fresh, translucent or more or less opaque when dry, obtuse at the apex, persistent; veins inconspicuous when dry, 2 more prominent than the others and forming ridges along the abaxial side. *Turions* absent. *Inflorescences* 14–45 × 2–3.5 mm; peduncles (18–)30–180 mm, slender to robust, not tapered, terete. *Flowers* numerous, contiguous, with 4 carpels. *Fruits* 1.5–1.9 × 1.0–1.3 mm, olive-green or greenish brown; beak 0.2–0.3 mm, more or less apical, straight.

P. coloratus is a species of shallow, calcareous water usually less than 1 m deep. It grows in pools, runnels and damp moss carpets in calcareous fens, in drainage ditches, at the margins of lakes, in ponds and streams and occasionally in flooded clay and marl pits. It is often found with *Chara* species,

A: habit; B: submerged leaf middle; C: section of stem and stipule; D: fruit. Habit based on plants
from Sedge Fen Drove, Wicken Fen, v.c. 29, J.M. Croft & C.D.P., 1987 (Preston 87/26, **CGE**); fruit
on specimen from ditch, Burwell Fen, v.c. 29, H. & J. Groves, 1887 (**BM**). Drawn by L.T.E. (A–C)
& M.T. (D).

including *C. hispida*, *C. pedunculata* and *C. vulgaris*. At some fenland sites it is more abundant than *P. natans* in peaty ditches. Predominantly a species of eastern England and central Ireland, *P. coloratus* has a broadly similar distribution to that of some other species of calcareous wetlands, including *Carex elata*, *Chara pedunculata*, *Lathyrus palustris*, *Stellaria palustris* and the rarer *Viola persicifolia*. On the east coast it reaches its northern limit at Aberlady Bay, East Lothian, but it extends north along the west coast as far as the Monach Islands in the Outer Hebrides.

The considerable variation shown by *P. coloratus* in habit and leaf shape can be accounted for by seasonal changes and differences in habitat conditions. The species is winter-green, overwintering as short stems with narrow leaves. Flowering stems in relatively deep water bear elliptical submerged leaves: these are sometimes the only leaves present but broader floating leaves often develop towards the stem apex. Flowering stems in shallow water produce only floating leaves. Terrestrial forms found on mud or moss resemble small, condensed versions of the variants found in shallow water. Terminal buds produced on the rhizome enable the plant to survive continued periods of drought (Fryer & Bennett 1915).

Once its pattern of variation is appreciated, *P. coloratus* is a fairly easy plant to identify. The broad upper leaves are conventionally called floating leaves and distinguished from the elliptical submerged leaves, but this distinction can be rather arbitrary. All the leaves are more or less translucent, their conspicuous secondary veins giving them a characteristic reticulate venation. In water even the uppermost leaves usually float a few millimetres below the surface, so that plants have a 'drowned' look. If 'floating leaves' are present, they distinguish *P. coloratus* from *P. alpinus* and *P. polygonifolius*, which have floating leaves which contrast more strongly with the submerged leaves in appearance. Deep-water forms of *P. coloratus* must be distinguished from *P. lucens* and from forms of *P. alpinus* and *P. polygonifolius* without floating leaves. *P. lucens* differs in its denticulate leaf margin and its rigid, conspicuously 2-keeled stipules. All the leaves of *P. coloratus* are petiolate except sometimes those on short overwintering stems, whereas *P. alpinus* has sessile leaves with broader bands of lacunae along the midrib. The submerged leaves of *P. polygonifolius* tend to be narrower than those of *P. coloratus* and to have longer petioles, which sometimes exceed the length of the lamina. The two species also differ in their ecology. The fruits of *P. coloratus* are smaller than those of any other European broad-leaved species.

Hybrids of *P. coloratus* with *P. berchtoldii* (*P.* × *lanceolatus*, **32**) and *P. gramineus* (*P.* × *billupsii*, **28**) are known in the British Isles. Both are rare.

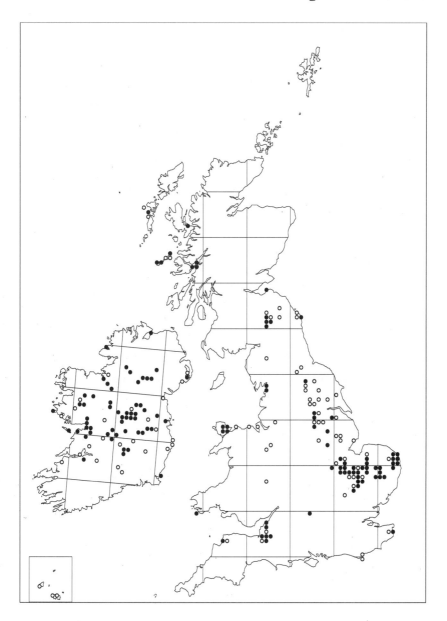

7   Potamogeton alpinus Balb.

Red Pondweed

Rhizomes slender to robust. *Stems* up to 2.8 m, usually robust, rarely slender, terete, unbranched; nodal glands absent. *Submerged leaves* 70–180(–220) × (6.5–)10–25(–33) mm, (4–)5–10(–17) times as long as wide, translucent, clear green, sometimes with a reddish or brownish tinge when fresh and usually developing a strong reddish tinge when dried, especially in the upper leaves and along the veins, narrowly elliptical to oblong-elliptical, gradually tapering to the base and to a narrow, obtuse and often slightly hooded apex, sessile, entire and shallowly undulate at the margin; midrib bordered on each side by a broad band of lacunae which occupies over half the width of the leaf base, the lateral veins 4–7 on each side, one usually more prominent than the others, the secondary veins ascending in the centre of the leaf and more or less transverse towards the margins. *Floating leaves* with the lamina 45–90 × 9–25 mm, 2–6.5 times as long as wide, opaque, subcoriaceous, green or yellow-green when fresh with a pinkish tinge especially along the veins, green, with a strong pinkish red tinge to reddish brown when dry, narrowly elliptical to oblong-elliptical or obovate, gradually tapering to the base, obtuse at the apex; lateral veins 4–9 on each side of the midrib, similar in colour or darker than the lamina in the living plant, the secondary veins numerous, ascending near the midrib, transverse elsewhere and rather obscure; petioles 10–35 mm, shorter than the lamina. *Stipules* 20–45 mm, open, delicate, flexible, clasping the stem along their entire length,

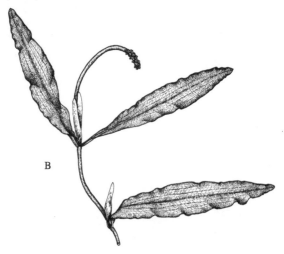

B

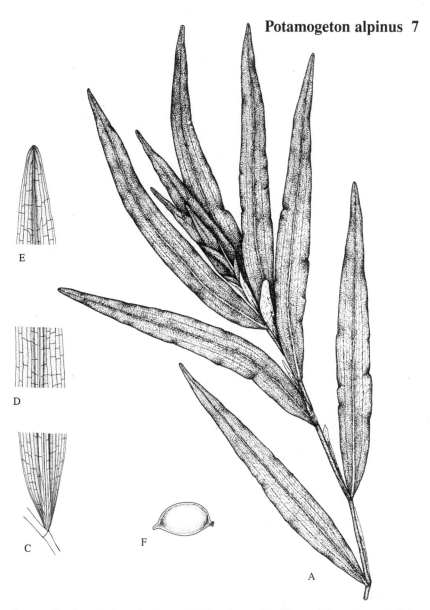

A: vegetative shoot; B: flowering shoot; C, D, E: submerged leaf base, middle and apex; F: fruit. Habit based on specimen from Loch of Clunie, v.c. 89, J.E. Lousley, 1932 (**BM**); fruit on specimen from Gartmorn Dam, v.c. 87, G. Taylor, 1948 (**BM**). Drawn by L.T.E. (A, B), K.D. (C–E) & M.T. (F).

translucent, hyaline, often with a pinkish tinge, obtuse or rounded at the apex, often lost on the older leaves or only a basal, non-fibrous portion remaining; veins inconspicuous when dry, 2 somewhat more prominent than the others but not forming distinct ridges. *Turions* absent. *Inflorescences* 15–32 × 4–8 mm; peduncles 30–150(–310) mm, robust, not or scarcely tapered, terete or slightly compressed. *Flowers* numerous, contiguous, with 4 carpels. *Fruits* 2.6–3.7 × 1.6–2.3 mm, pale brown, often with a reddish tinge, shiny; beak *c*. 0.5 mm, more or less apical, often hooked at tip.

A plant of still or flowing, usually neutral or mildly acidic water over a relatively deep silty or peaty substrate. It usually grows in water less than 1.5 m deep, somewhat shallower than that favoured by *P. lucens*, *P. perfoliatus* or *P. praelongus*: this correlates with its relatively short, erect and unbranched stems which have the capacity to produce floating leaves. *P. alpinus* is most frequent in northern England and Scotland, where it is characteristically found in sheltered bays at the edge of lakes, in ditches leading into lakes or in rivers. In Highland rivers it grows in eddies or pools where the flow rate is reduced and silt accumulates. It reaches an altitude of 950 m on Meall nan Tarmachan. In southern England it has been recorded from rivers, streams, canals, ditches, lakes, pools and flooded clay, gravel, marl and sand pits, but it is now extinct in many of its lowland sites.

Potamogeton alpinus is not a very polymorphic species, although it does show considerable variation in leaf shape. Broad-leaved forms from southern England have been named var. *palmeri* Druce, but do not merit taxonomic recognition. Very narrow-leaved plants have recently been collected from lakes in Easterness and Sutherland. Short stolons terminated by hard, ovoid buds are sometimes produced in the lower leaf axils, usually in late summer. The species overwinters as buds which develop on the rhizome in autumn.

   P. alpinus is characterised by unbranched stems, sessile (but not amplexicaul) leaves with entire margins and obtuse apices, hyaline stipules with inconspicuous veins and by its reddish tinge when dried. The very broad bands of lacunae along the midrib are also a useful character. The submerged leaves of *P. polygonifolius* are often confused with those of *P. alpinus* but they are petiolate, not sessile.

   P. alpinus × *crispus* (*P.* × *olivaceus*, **39**) is a scarce hybrid which might be confused with *P. alpinus*. The other 4 recorded hybrids, with *P. gramineus* (*P.* × *nericius*, **29**), *P. lucens* (*P.* × *nerviger*, **33**), *P. perfoliatus* (*P.* × *prussicus*, **36**), and *P. praelongus* (*P.* × *griffithii*, **35**), are exceedingly rare. A hybrid with *P. polygonifolius* is known in Europe.

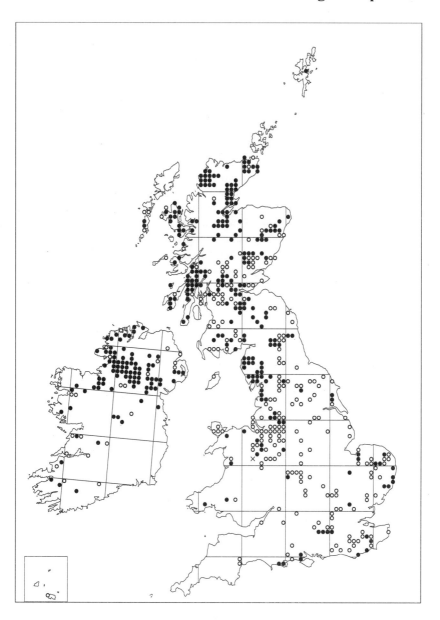

167

8   Potamogeton praelongus Wulfen

Long-stalked Pondweed

Rhizomes robust to very robust. *Stems* up to 3 m, robust to very robust, terete, unbranched or sparingly to richly branched; nodal glands absent. *Submerged leaves* (45–)60–150(–220) × 14–40 mm, (2.5–)3–6.5(–15) times as long as wide, translucent, clear green with an oily sheen when young, becoming dark green with age, sometimes tinged pink along the midrib and principal lateral veins, very rarely with a brownish red tinge throughout when dry, lanceolate or oblong-lanceolate, rarely linear-lanceolate or oblong, sessile, semi-amplexicaul at the base, obtuse and broadly hooded at the apex and often splitting when pressed, entire, plane or shallowly undulate at the margin; midrib bordered on each side by a narrow band of lacunae which occupies less than a third of the width of the leaf base, the lateral veins 5–9 on each side, 1–2 of which are usually more strongly developed than the others, the secondary veins numerous and more or less transverse. *Floating leaves* absent. *Stipules* 10–80 mm, open, flexible, the entire stipule or the proximal half enfolding the stem, milky white with a slight pinkish tinge and more or less translucent when fresh, buff-coloured, opaque and conspicuous when dry, obtuse at the apex; persistent but becoming eroded to fibrous remnants with age; veins prominent when dry, 2 slightly stronger than the others but not forming distinct ribs. *Turions* absent. *Inflorescences* 25–55 × 5–8 mm; peduncles (50–)80–200(–350) mm, robust, of uniform diameter throughout their

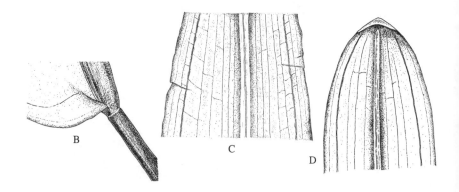

B

C

D

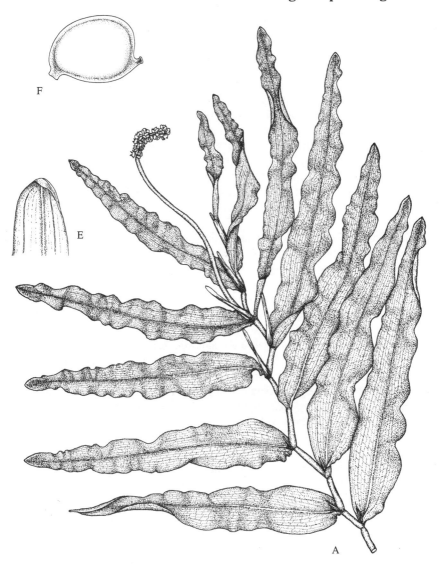

A: habit; B, C: leaf base and middle; D, E: leaf apex; F: fruit. Habit based on plants from Tarff Water S. of High Bridge of Tarff, v.c. 73, C.D.P. & O.M. Stewart, 1989 (Preston 89/287, **CGE**); fruit on specimen from Hickling, v.c. 27, T.A. Cotton, 1890 (**BM**). Drawn by L.T.E. (A), G.L. (B–E) & M.T. (F).

length or becoming broader towards the apex, slightly compressed towards the base, more or less terete towards the apex. *Flowers* 15–20, more or less contiguous, with (2–)4 carpels. *Fruits* 4.5–5.5 × 2.5–3.6 mm, dark brownish green; beak 0.6–0.9 mm, ventral, straight.

P. praelongus usually grows in larger water bodies, particularly lakes, rivers, canals and major fenland drains. In Scottish and Irish lakes it is characteristic of relatively deep (over 1.5 m), clear, mesotrophic waters, often associated with basalt, limestone or marl. In the clear water of Loch Borralie, a marl loch on the Durness limestone in Sutherland, it grows down to a depth of 6.5 m (Spence, Barclay & Allen 1984). Its ecological requirements overlap with those of *P. perfoliatus*, with which it sometimes grows, but in lakes it tends to grow in deeper water, where the silt is finer. It is apparently much rarer than formerly in lowland areas and has, for example, disappeared from many of its Cambridgeshire sites since 1950.

The length of the internodes and the shape of the leaves are the most variable features of a not very variable species. In forms with short internodes the stems often have a zigzag form and the stipules exceed the internodes in length. When the internodes are longer the stems tend to be straighter and the stipules are shorter than the corresponding internodes. *P. praelongus* grows vegetatively throughout the winter, and it is one of the earliest pondweeds to flower (Fryer 1890a, Taylor & Sledge 1944).

The fruits of *P. praelongus* are diagnostic, being larger than those of any other British broad-leaved species. Vegetative material is also distinctive, but it is occasionally confused with *P. alpinus*, *P. perfoliatus* or *P.* × *salicifolius*. Specimens of *P. perfoliatus* which approach *P. praelongus* in leaf-shape are best distinguished by their stipules, which are usually fugacious but even if present differ from those of *P. praelongus* in being translucent when dry, with inconspicuous veins. *P. alpinus* also has translucent stipules with inconspicuous veins, and its leaves are sessile but not amplexicaul, have broader bands of lacunae towards the base of the midrib and are usually reddish in colour when dried. *P.* × *salicifolius* has acute or mucronate leaves with a denticulate margin, and stipules which towards the base are rather rigid and usually keeled like those of *P. lucens*. The frequency with which *P. praelongus* has been confused with this hybrid is surprising in view of the differences between them.

Hybrids with *P. alpinus* (*P.* × *griffithii*, **35**), *P. crispus* (*P.* × *undulatus*, **40**) and *P. perfoliatus* (*P.* × *cognatus*, **37**) are recorded, but only rarely. All might be confused with *P. praelongus*.

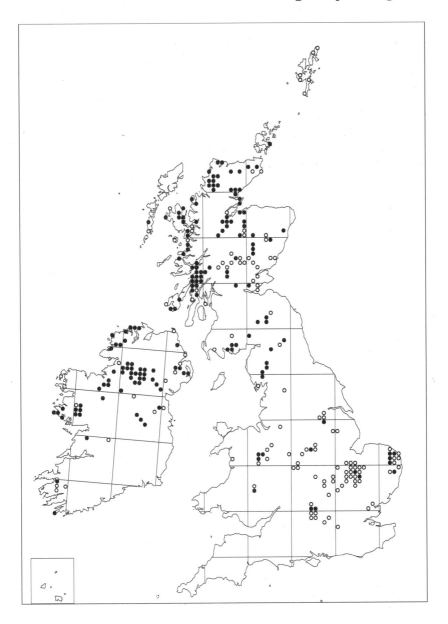

9 · Potamogeton perfoliatus L.

Perfoliate Pondweed

Rhizomes robust to very robust. *Stems* up to 3 m, exceptionally up to 8 m (West 1905), robust to very robust, terete, unbranched or sparingly to richly branched; nodal glands absent. *Submerged leaves* 20–115 × 7–42 mm, 1.3–10 times as long as wide, translucent, bright green, dark green, yellowish green, olive-green or brownish green, sometimes tinged pink along the midrib and principal lateral veins, narrowly lanceolate to broadly ovate, amplexicaul at the base, the edges sometimes overlapping on the far side of the stem, sessile, rounded to obtuse or more or less acute and often slightly hooded at the apex, denticulate and sometimes minutely undulate on the margin; midrib bordered on each side by a narrow band of lacunae, the lateral veins 5–12 on each side, 1–3 of which are usually more prominent than the others, the secondary veins numerous and more or less transverse. *Floating leaves* absent. *Stipules* 3–22 mm, open, delicate, translucent and hyaline when fresh and dry, rounded at the apex, usually fugacious, rarely persisting on mature leaves; veins inconspicuous when dry, 2 slightly stronger than the others but not forming distinct

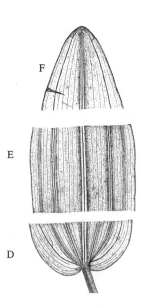

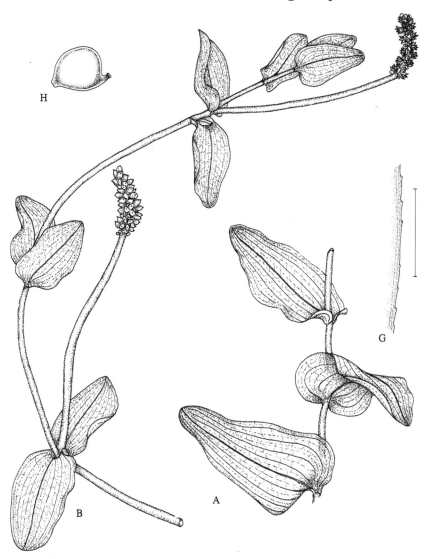

A: length of vegetative shoot; B: flowering shoot; C: stem apex with bases of leaves and stipules; D, E, F: leaf base, middle and apex; G: leaf margin; H: fruit. Habit based on plants from R. Severn, Atcham, v.c. 40, C.D.P. & T.C.G. Rich, 1987 (Preston 87/65, **CGE**); fruit on specimen from Oxford Canal, Napton-on-the-Hill, v.c. 38, D.A. Cadbury, 1947 (**BM**). Drawn by L.T.E. (A–C, G), G.L. (D–F) & M.T. (H). Scale bar: 1 mm.

ribs. *Turions* absent. *Inflorescences* 13–25 × 3–8 mm; peduncles 20–110 mm, robust, slightly broader towards the apex and slightly compressed near the base. *Flowers* 12–20, contiguous, with 4 carpels. *Fruits* 2.6–3.5(–4.0) × 1.7–2.9 mm, brownish green; beak 0.4–0.7 mm, apical, straight.

P. perfoliatus is a species of wide ecological tolerance, growing in lakes, reservoirs, canals, rivers and major fenland drains up to an altitude of 750 m. The most vigorous plants usually grow in water over 1 m deep, but smaller individuals can be found in much shallower water, although the species does not tolerate repeated desiccation. The lakes in which it grows range from almost oligotrophic to eutrophic; it is confined to meso-eutrophic or eutrophic rivers but within these it occurs in a wide variety of plant communities (Spence 1967, Seddon 1972, Holmes 1983). It is a widespread species which is still frequent in some areas of lowland England where *P. praelongus* is now rare. However, detailed studies in Romney Marsh and the Somerset Levels have revealed that it has declined in the larger drains where the water is now turbid, and disappeared from smaller ditches which are now prone to greater fluctuations in water level (Mountford 1994).

As Pearsall & Hanby (1925) remark, few submerged aquatics show greater variability of leaf-form than *P. perfoliatus*. Broad leaves are produced in response to environmental factors, in particular to high concentrations of calcium in the substrate. Broad-leaved plants are commonest in southern England, whereas plants with longer and more delicate leaves are found in the lakes of northern England and Scotland. Leaf size can differ greatly even on a single plant, small leaves on axillary branches often contrasting with the larger leaves on the stem from which they arise. The species dies down during the winter, regrowing in spring from the rhizome.

Broad-leaved forms of *P. perfoliatus* can scarcely be confused with any other British species: the broad-based, strongly amplexicaul, many-veined leaves and fugacious stipules are especially characteristic. In *Groenlandia densa*, which also has amplexicaul leaf bases which usually lack stipules, the leaves are opposite. Narrow-leaved plants might be mistaken for *P. prae-longus*: the entire leaf margins and fibrous and persistent stipules of the latter provide the best characters for separating them.

Three hybrids of *P. perfoliatus* are relatively frequent. *P. crispus × perfoliatus* (*P. × cooperi*, **41**) could easily be confused with *P. perfoliatus* but *P. gramineus × perfoliatus* (*P. × nitens*, **30**) and *P. lucens × perfoliatus* (*P. × salicifolius*, **34**) usually resemble the other parent. Two hybrids are rare: *P. alpinus × perfoliatus* (*P. × prussicus*, **36**) and *P. perfoliatus × praelongus* (*P. × cognatus*, **37**).

174

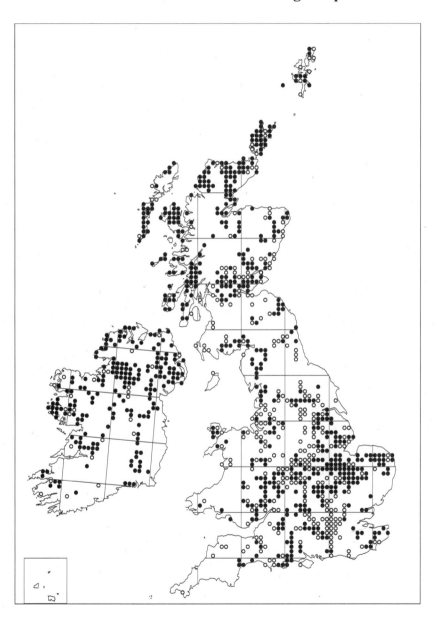

10 Potamogeton epihydrus Raf.

American Pondweed

Rhizomes slender to robust. *Stems* up to 1.9 m, very slender to robust, the vegetative stems slightly compressed to compressed or (in flowering stems) more or less terete towards the apex, unbranched or sparingly branched; nodal glands absent. *Submerged leaves* sometimes markedly distichous on the vegetative shoots, 65–240 × 2.5–11 mm, 18–30(–60) times as long as wide, delicate, translucent, pale brown, pale green or olive-green, sometimes with a pinkish tinge, linear, sessile, narrowly obtuse to more or less acute at the apex, entire, plane at the base of the leaf and plane or undulate on the margin towards the apex; midrib bordered on each side by a broad band of lacunae which towards the base of the leaf extends at least as far as the inner lateral veins and sometimes occupies the entire leaf width, narrowing above until it ceases below or reaches the apex, the lateral veins 2–4 on each side, the innermost the most prominent and the outermost often very faint, the secondary veins occasional, rather irregular, ascending, more or less transverse or descending. *Floating leaves* with the lamina 35–80 × 7–22 mm, 2.5–5 times as long as wide, opaque, coriaceous, pinkish brown when young, dark olive green when mature, elliptical to oblong-elliptical, cuneate at the base, obtuse at the apex; lateral veins 4–10 on each side of the midrib, opaque in the living plant, the secondary veins numerous, ascending and relatively conspicuous in the centre of the leaf, more or less transverse and inconspicuous towards the margin; petioles 20–60(–90) mm, usually shorter than the lamina. *Stipules* 10–45 mm, open, delicate, translucent, truncate and sometimes slightly emarginate at the apex, soon decaying; veins inconspicuous when dry, 2 more prominent than the others but not forming distinct ribs. *Turions* absent. *Inflorescences* 12–23 × 3–6 mm; peduncles 23–90 mm, slender or robust, of uniform diameter throughout their length or somewhat broader towards the apex, terete or slightly compressed. *Flowers* numerous, contiguous, with 4 carpels. *Fruits* 2.5–3.1 × 1.9–2.8 mm, olive-green or brownish green; beak 0.1–0.35 mm, ventral, straight.

A: length of stem with submerged leaves; B: floating leaves and inflorescence; C, D: submerged leaf middle and apex; E: section of lower stem; F: section of upper stem; G: fruit. Habit based on plants from lochans between East Loch Ollay and Loch Ceann a'Bhaigh, S. Uist, v.c. 110, C.D.P. *et al.*, 1987 (Preston 87/124 & 157, **CGE**); fruit on specimen from lochan adjoining Loch Ceann a'Bhaig, above Loch Eynort, S. Uist, v.c. 110, G. Taylor, 1951 (**BM**). Drawn by L.T.E. (A–F) & M.T. (G).

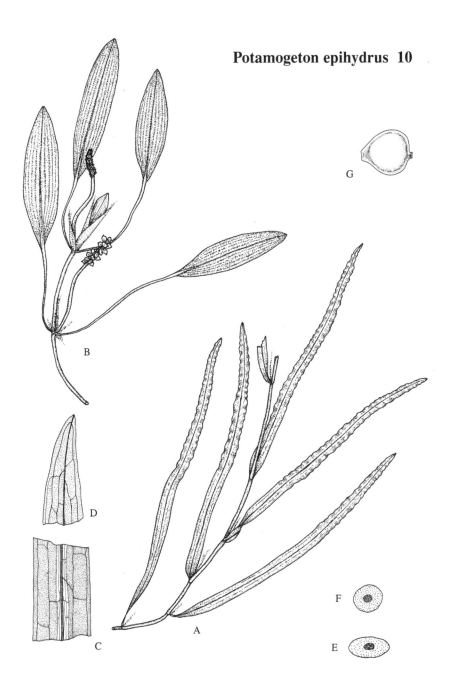

P. epihydrus is widespread in the north-eastern United States of America but in Europe is restricted as a native plant to a few otherwise unremarkable lochs and lochans in the Outer Hebrides. Here it grows in relatively shallow, oligotrophic, peaty water with species such as the aquatic form of *Juncus bulbosus, Nymphaea alba, Potamogeton natans, P. polygonifolius* and *Sparganium angustifolium*. Submerged leaves which appear to belong to this species have also been collected at the edge of a large, acidic loch in Skye, but rooted plants have not been discovered there. As it is so rare as a native plant, *P. epihydrus* is included in the British *Red Data Book* (Perring & Farrell 1983). It is also established as an introduced species in the mesotrophic Rochdale Canal and in the Calder & Hebble Navigation in S.W. Yorkshire and S. Lancashire, where it has been known since 1907. Here its associates include *Elodea nuttallii, Lemna minor, L. trisulca, Luronium natans, Potamogeton crispus* and *Sparganium emersum*. Bennett's suggestion (Fryer & Bennett 1915) that it had probably been introduced to this area with cotton was rather scornfully dismissed by Fernald (1932); the method of its introduction remains an unsolved, and probably insoluble, mystery.

Fernald (1932) divided *P. epihydrus* into two "strongly marked" varieties. Var. *ramosus* (Peck) House differs from var. *epihydrus* in having narrower submerged and floating leaves, the submerged leaves markedly distichous on the young shoots, and in its smaller fruits. In America the larger var. *epihydrus* tends to occur in richer waters. Subsequent American authors have regarded the varieties as less distinct, and some consider that they are not worth recognising. The plants from the oligotrophic waters of the Outer Hebrides are clearly referable to var. *ramosus*, whereas those from the more nutrient-rich canals of northern England are intermediate between the two varieties. *P. epihydrus* flowers and fruits freely. Short stolons bearing buds or fascicles of 5–8 narrow leaves (sometimes with rhizomes arising from their base) sometimes develop in the leaf axils in September, and are a means of vegetative reproduction.

P. epihydrus is one of the more distinctive British pondweeds. It has the compressed stem usually found in members of Sect. *Graminifolii*, but its delicate ribbon-like submerged leaves with broad central bands of lacunae and up to 4 lateral veins on each side of the midrib are unlike those of any other species, and it also produces floating leaves.

No hybrids involving *P. epihydrus* are recorded in Britain. A hybrid with *P. nodosus* is tentatively reported from North America by Ogden (1943).

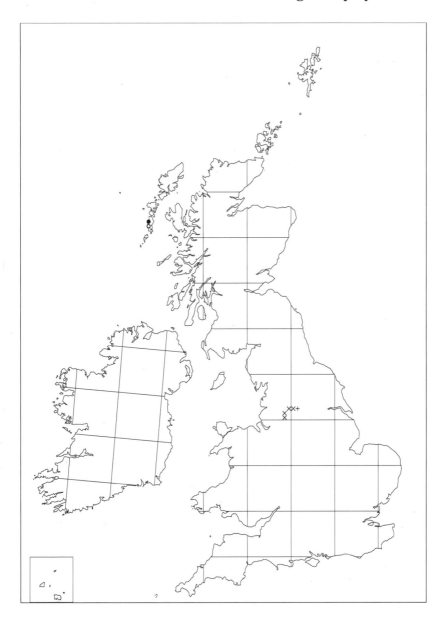

11 Potamogeton friesii Rupr.

Flat-stalked Pondweed

Rhizomes absent. *Stems* up to 1.5 m, slender to robust, compressed to strongly compressed, usually with numerous short axillary branches; nodal glands well-developed. *Submerged leaves* 35–85 (–100) × 1.5–3.5(–4) mm, 15–45 times as long as wide, firm, light green, linear, sessile, usually obtuse, rarely subacute, distinctly mucronate at the apex, entire, plane at the margin; midrib bordered on each side by a narrow band of lacunae which is restricted to the base of the leaf or extends almost to the apex, the lateral veins (1–)2(–3) on each side, distinct, the secondary veins infrequent. *Floating leaves* absent. *Stipules* 10–25 mm, tubular in the basal 2–9 mm when young but splitting with age, opaque and buff-coloured when dry, tapering to an obtuse apex, persistent but soon eroding to fibrous strands at the apex, with a strong green rib along each side which remains after the intervening tissue has decayed, the stipules eventually splitting into a V-shaped remnant; veins prominent when dry. *Turions* 12–22 × 2.5–8.5 mm, usually sessile in the leaf axils or terminal at the end of short axillary branches, occasionally terminal on the main stem or longer axillary branches, fan-shaped, composed of appressed

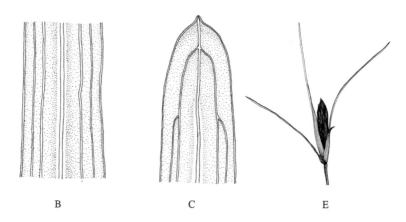

B   C   E

180

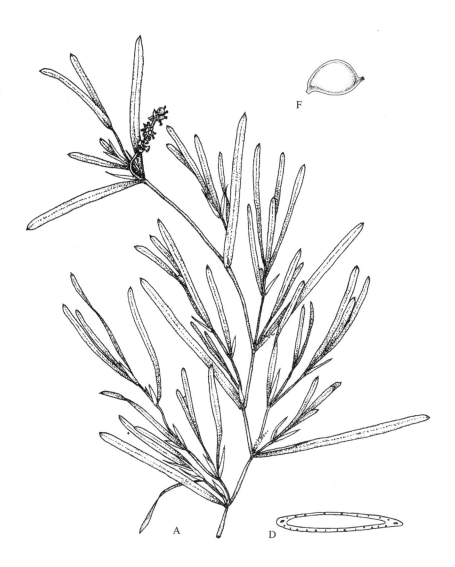

A: habit; B, C: leaf middle and apex; D: section of stipule; E: turion; F: fruit. Habit based on plants from Cantley, v.c. 27, C.D.P., 1988 (Preston 88/292, **CGE**); fruit on specimen from ditch near Ilford, v.c. 14, J.E. Lousley, 1931 (**BM**). Drawn by L.T.E. (A), K.D. (B–E) & M.T. (F).

dark green leaves enveloped in conspicuous, prominently veined, buff-coloured stipules, with 2–4 erect to erecto-patent free leaves which exceed the turions in length and are often recurved at the apex. *Inflorescences* (5–)8–13 × 2–3.5 mm; peduncles 15–30(–70) mm, very slender to slender, compressed. *Flowers* 4–8, contiguous or more or less distant, with 4 carpels. *Fruits* 2.4–3.0 × 1.3–1.9 mm, olive green; beak 0.3–0.55 mm, more or less apical, straight or recurved.

A local species, which is most frequent in southern England and central Ireland but extends north to the Outer Hebrides, Orkney and Shetland. It is particularly characteristic of ditches, drains, canals and lowland rivers but also occurs in lakes and less frequently in ponds, streams, clay pits and gravel pits. It is usually found in calcareous and often in rather eutrophic water. In the Outer Hebrides it grows in lochs at the landward fringe of the machair, where calcareous sand adjoins acidic rock. It is tolerant of a degree of disturbance in navigable waters.

P. friesii varies in leaf width. There are usually two lateral veins on each side of the midrib but in narrow-leaved plants the second vein can be short or even absent from some leaves, whereas broad-leaved plants sometimes have a third vein towards the base. It appears to fruit rather infrequently. Its usual means of reproduction is probably by turions, which may begin to develop in late June but are usually found in July and August.

 P. friesii and *P. obtusifolius* have leaves of similar size and are sometimes confused. However, well-grown plants differ in appearance, *P. obtusifolius* having rather equal branches which often give rise to a mass of leaves just below the water surface, stems and leaves which are often tinged pinkish or reddish brown, nodal glands which are rather irregular in shape, leaves with rather indistinct lateral veins and an obtuse or only obscurely mucronate apex, and a compact inflorescence. *P. friesii* tends to have a main stem with short axillary branches, lacks any brownish tinge, has neat semi-globose nodal glands, leaves with more distinct lateral veins and which taper abruptly to a distinctly mucronate apex, and a laxer inflorescence. An identification based on these characters should always be confirmed by examination of the stipules, which are tubular at the base and with very prominent veins in *P. friesii*, open and less prominently veined in *P. obtusifolius*. *P. friesii* is closer in its vegetative morphology to *P. pusillus*: the differences are outlined under that species.

 Two hybrids of *P. friesii* are known: *P.* × *lintonii* (*P. crispus* × *friesii*, **42**) and *P.* × *pseudofriesii* (*P. acutifolius* × *friesii*, **45**).

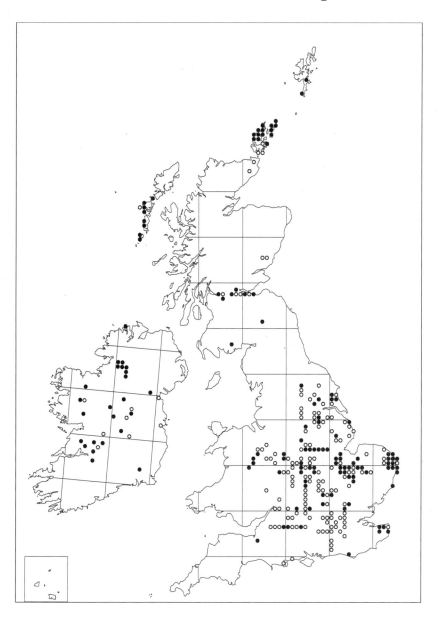

12 Potamogeton rutilus Wolfg.

Shetland Pondweed

Rhizomes absent. *Stems* to 0.45 m, very slender, compressed, unbranched or sparingly branched near the base, sometimes also with short axillary branches; nodal glands inconspicuous, sometimes absent. *Submerged leaves* 32–75 × 0.5–1.1 mm, 35–80 times as long as wide, rather rigid, bright green or brownish green, linear, sessile, gradually tapering to a very finely pointed apex, bordered by a strong marginal vein, entire and plane at the margin; midrib prominent, occupying 15–30% of the leaf width near the base, not bordered by lacunae, the lateral veins 1 on each side or occasionally 2 towards the base of the leaf, distinct, secondary veins absent. *Floating leaves* absent. *Stipules* 15–20 mm, tubular in the basal 2–3 mm when young but splitting with age, milky white and translucent when fresh, white or buff coloured and opaque when dry, tapering to an obtuse apex, persistent but the apex eroding to fibrous strands, with a colourless or green rib along each side; veins prominent when dry. *Turions* 30–75 mm, axillary, slender, cylindrical, the outermost leaves curling away from the axis, the remaining leaves appressed, the whitish prominently veined stipules conspicuous when dry. *Inflorescences* 3–7 × 2–3 mm; peduncles (3–)10–17 mm, very slender, slightly compressed to compressed. *Flowers* 6, contiguous, with (2–)4 carpels. *Fruits* not seen in British material; in European plants 2.0–2.1 × 1.1–1.3 mm, brown or olive brown; beak 0.3–0.4 mm, ventral or more or less apical, recurved.

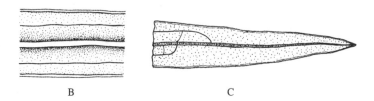

B   C

A: habit; B, C: leaf middle and apex; D: section of leaf; E: section of stem and stipule; F: turion; G: fruit. Habit based on plants from Loch Grogary, N. Uist, v.c. 110, C.D.P. & N.F. Stewart, 1987 (Preston 87/156, **CGE**); fruit on specimen from Aeremyre, Bornholm, Bergstedt, 1897 (**BM**). Drawn by L.T.E. (A, B, D), K.D. (C, E, F) & M.T. (G).

Potamogeton rutilus 12

Potamogeton rutilus grows in unpolluted mesotrophic or eutrophic lochs and adjoining streams in northern Scotland; it is sufficiently rare to be included in the British *Red Data Book* (Perring & Farrell 1983). In Shetland it grows near limestone outcrops and in the Hebrides its sites are usually situated at the junction of calcareous machair and acidic rock. The lochs where *P. rutilus* occurs tend to have a rich *Potamogeton* flora: *P. berchtoldii*, *P. filiformis*, *P. gramineus*, *P. natans*, *P.* × *nitens*, *P. pectinatus*, *P. perfoliatus*, *P. prae-longus* and *P. pusillus* are amongst the species recorded from them.

P. rutilus shows little variation in the British Isles. Although it flowers in Britain, I have not seen any fruit collected here. Reproduction is usually by axillary turions, which develop in autumn.

    P. rutilus is most likely to be confused with *P. pusillus*. It is most easily separated by the rather rigid leaves with an "almost bristle-like apex" (Dandy 1980), and by the stipules which when dry are opaque and have very prominent veins. The long turions are very different from the short, delicate turions of *P. pusillus* although both are borne in the leaf axils. The narrow leaves of *P. rutilus* are reminiscent of those of *P. trichoides* in shape but this species – and the less similar *P. berchtoldii* – differ in their stipules, which are open to the base and less prominently veined. In addition *P. trichoides* has indistinct lateral leaf veins, shorter turions, flowers with fewer than 4 carpels and a southerly distribution.

    No hybrids involving *P. rutilus* are recorded in Britain.

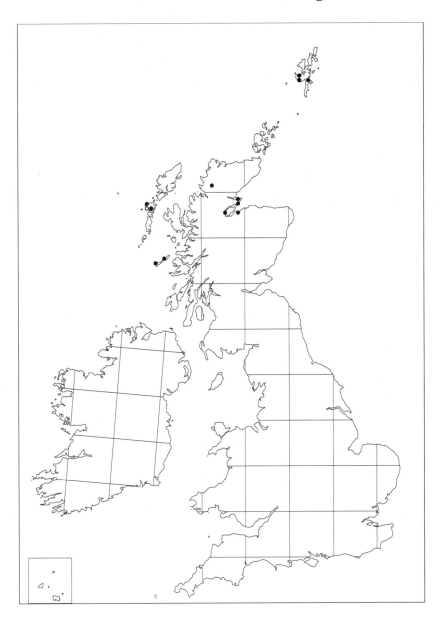

13 Potamogeton pusillus L.

Lesser Pondweed

Rhizomes absent. *Stems* up to 0.7(–1) m, very slender to slender, slightly compressed to compressed, branching sparingly near the base in deep water but richly branched in shallow water; nodal glands usually absent or poorly developed, rarely well-developed. *Submerged leaves* (15–)20–50(–100) × (0.5–)0.8–1.4(–1.9) mm, 22–50(–70) times as long as wide, flaccid or firm, mid-green or olive-green, linear, sessile, tapering or rather abruptly narrowed to an acute apex, bordered by a marginal vein, entire and plane at the margin; midrib occupying 15–35% of the leaf width at the base, not bordered by lacunae or the lacunae poorly developed and restricted to the proximal half of the leaf, rarely bordered by well-developed lacunae, the lateral veins 1(–2) on each side, distinct, secondary veins absent. *Floating leaves* absent. *Stipules* 5–17 mm, tubular for most of their length when young but splitting with age, hyaline and translucent when fresh and dry, obtuse at the apex, persistent, usually with a green rib along each side; veins inconspicuous when dry. *Turions* 10–23 × 0.6–1 mm, usually sessile and axillary but in autumn also terminal on axillary branches, narrowly cylindrical, with 1–3 erecto-patent to recurved free leaves. *Inflorescences* 6–13 × 2–4.5 mm; peduncles 10–40(–80) mm, very slender to slender, slightly compressed to compressed. *Flowers* 3–6, more or less contiguous, with 4(–5) carpels. *Fruits* 1.8–2.3 × 1.2–1.5 mm, pale olive-green; beak 0.2–0.4 mm, apical, straight.

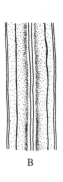

B

C

E

A: habit; B, C: leaf middle and apex; D: section of stipule; E: turion; F: fruit. Habit based on plant from pond, Goodestone Common, v.c. 28, C.D.P. & N.F. Stewart, 1990 (Preston 90/264, **CGE**); fruit on specimen from drain by Knottingley & Goole Canal, Beever's Bridge, Cowick, v.c. 63, J.M. Taylor, 1943 (**BM**). Drawn by L.T.E. (A, D), K.D. (B, C, E) & M.T. (F).

P. pusillus grows in a wide range of habitats including lakes, reservoirs, coastal lagoons, ponds, rivers, canals, streams and ditches, and in disused and flooded quarries, sand, gravel and marl pits. It is similar in its ecological requirements to *P. berchtoldii*, and occasionally the two species occur in the same water body. *P. pusillus* is, however, much more tolerant of brackish conditions than *P. berchtoldii* and it may also be more frequent in eutrophic waters. It is as common or commoner than *P. berchtoldii* in some areas of S.E. England but significantly rarer than that species in S.W. England, Wales, northern Scotland and Ireland.

P. pusillus varies in habit, leaf width and in the extent to which nodal glands and lacunae are developed. Some plants have leaves as narrow as those of *P. trichoides* and others are as broad as those of *P. berchtoldii*. The turions of *P. pusillus* are produced from July onwards. Plants frequently flower and fruit, but they probably reproduce more frequently by turions than by seed.

P. pusillus can be distinguished from both *P. berchtoldii* and *P. trichoides* by its tubular stipules. *P. friesii* differs from *P. pusillus* in having well-developed nodal glands, broader usually 5-veined leaves with a distinctly mucronate apex, opaque stipules with prominent veins, fan-shaped turions and larger fruits. Separation of these species is usually straightforward. However, variants of *P. pusillus* with rather rigid leaves with very distinct veins and discernable nodal glands can be difficult to distinguish from narrow-leaved *P. friesii* if neither turions nor fruit are available. For the distinction from *P. rutilus*, see under that species.

A hybrid between *P. pusillus* and *P. trichoides* (*P. × grovesii*, **44**) has been recorded from Britain, but it is apparently extinct. *P. polygonifolius × pusillus* was described by Dandy (1970) from the Azores.

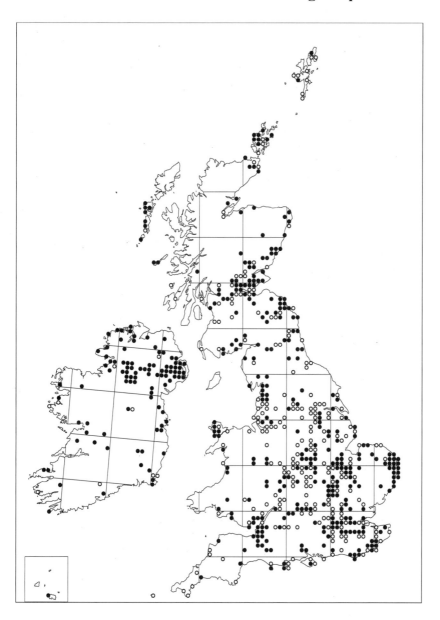

14 Potamogeton obtusifolius Mert. & W. D. J. Koch

Blunt-leaved Pondweed

Rhizomes absent. *Stems* up to 1.9 m, very slender to slender, compressed, richly branched at least above; nodal glands well-developed. *Submerged leaves* 48–85(–100) × (1–)2.5–3.5 mm, 15–30(–35) times as long as wide, flaccid, pale green, often tinged pink along the midrib or pinkish or reddish brown throughout and with an oily sheen, linear, sessile, usually rounded to obtuse, rarely subacute, and often very shortly and rather obscurely mucronate at the apex, entire and plane at the margin; midrib occupying 8–20% of the leaf width near the base, bordered on each side by a band of lacunae which is broad towards the base but narrower above and ceases just below the apex, the lateral veins 1–2 on each side, rather indistinct, the secondary veins infrequent. *Floating leaves* absent. *Stipules* 10–30 mm, open, translucent when fresh, buff-coloured and more or less opaque when dry, rounded to broadly obtuse at the apex, persistent, with a distinct green or an indistinct pale brown rib on each side and (8–)10–17 intercostal veins, the veins inconspicuous when dry. *Turions* 23–40 × 3–5 mm, terminal on short or long axillary branches, composed of appressed dark green leaves enveloped in conspicuous stipules, with 3–5 erect to erecto-patent free leaves. *Inflorescences* 4–9 × 1.5–3.5 mm; peduncles (6–)8–20(–35) mm, slender, slightly compressed or compressed. *Flowers* 6–8, contiguous, with (3–)4(–5) carpels. *Fruits* 2.6–3.2 × 1.7–2.1 mm, brownish green, the dorsal edge entire or muricate; beak 0.2–0.5 mm, more or less apical or closer to the ventral than the dorsal edge, straight.

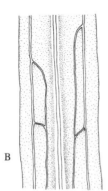

B

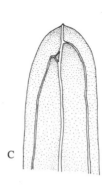

C

F

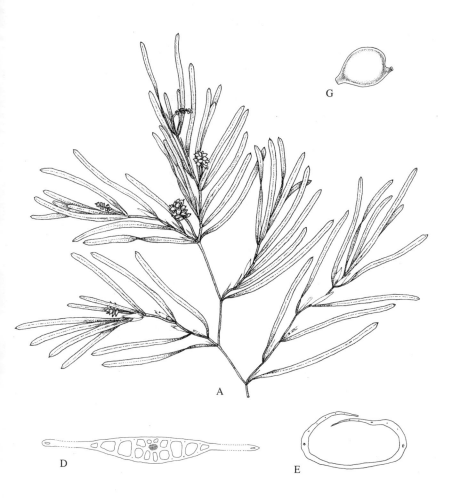

A: habit; B, C: leaf middle and apex; D: section of leaf; E: section of stipule; F: turion; G: fruit. Habit based on plants from exit burn of Loch Ussie, v.c.106, C.D.P., 1988 (Preston 88/247, **CGE**); fruit on specimen from Snipe Loch, Dalrymple, v.c. 75, G. Taylor, 1947 (**BM**). Drawn by L.T.E. (A, D, E), K.D. (B, C, F) & M.T. (G).

P. obtusifolius is a widespread species, but it has a curiously patchy distribution. Over much of its range it is characteristically found in mesotrophic, acidic or circum-neutral waters over inorganic or peaty substrates, only occasionally occurring in more eutrophic water. However, in areas such as N. Ireland it has no marked trophic preferences and is almost ubiquitous. It is predominantly a plant of ponds and lakes, where it usually grows in still, relatively shallow water; in small water bodies it can be very abundant. It also occurs in ditches, canals, the backwaters of rivers and ox-bow lakes adjacent to them, and flooded sand, gravel, marl and brick pits. Its ecological requirements have some similarities to those of *P. alpinus*, with which it sometimes grows; other plants frequently found in the same water body include *Elodea canadensis*, *Lemna minor*, *L. trisulca*, *Menyanthes trifoliata*, *Myriophyllum alterniflorum*, *Nuphar lutea*, *Potamogeton natans* and *P. pusillus*. In view of its ecological requirements, the rarity of *P. obtusifolius* in northern and western Scotland and its virtual absence from the Hebridean islands is surprising.

Short plants of *P. obtusifolius* growing in shallow water are richly branched throughout their length, whereas stems in deeper water tend to be sparingly branched below, but have more frequent branches above. *P. obtusifolius* tends to develop a mass of foliage just below the water surface. It overwinters as fruits or turions: it fruits more freely than any other linear-leaved pondweed, and produces turions from late July to November.

P. obtusifolius is a distinctive plant, characterised by its broad linear leaves, open stipules, compact inflorescences on short peduncles, and large fruits. *P. berchtoldii* is the most similar species. Fruiting plants are easily separated as *P. obtusifolius* has larger fruits, borne on less slender peduncles. Most vegetative material can be determined without difficulty: the two species differ in habit, coloration, leaf length and width and turion size. However, a small proportion of plants are difficult to identify as the vegetative distinctions between the two plants are purely quantitative. In such cases the number of veins between the ribs of the stipules can be a useful guide: (4–)5–8(–9) in *P. berchtoldii*, (8–)10–17 in *P. obtusifolius*. *P. friesii* is sometimes confused with *P. obtusifolius* but its stipules are tubular towards the base; other differences are discussed under *P. friesii*. Forms of *P. crispus* without strongly serrulate leaves and its hybrids *P.* × *bennettii* and *P.* × *lintonii* are also mistaken for *P. obtusifolius* but close inspection of these plants will reveal at least some leaves which are denticulate towards the apex. The turions of *P. crispus* and its hybrids are also distinctive.

No hybrids involving *P. obtusifolius* are recorded in the British Isles.

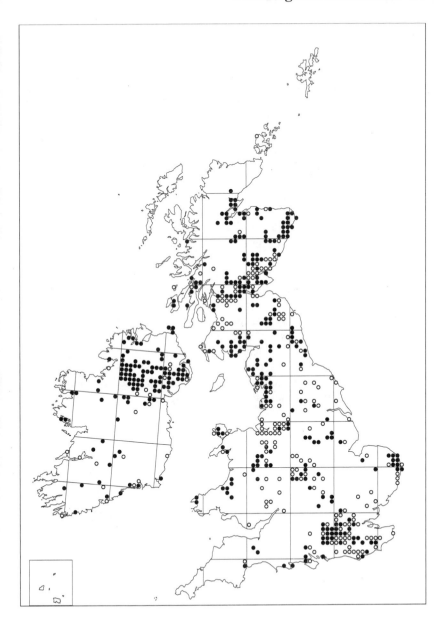

15 Potamogeton berchtoldii Fieber

Small Pondweed

Rhizomes absent. *Stems* up to 0.6(–1) m, very slender, terete to slightly compressed, sparingly or richly branched; nodal glands well-developed. *Submerged leaves* (17–)25–50(–75) × (0.5–)0.8–1.8(–2.3) mm, (15–)20–45(–55) times as long as wide, flaccid, pale green, olive green or brownish green, linear, sessile, more or less abruptly narrowed to an acute or obtuse, often slightly asymmetrical apex which is not bordered by a marginal vein, entire and plane at the margin; midrib occupying 10–20% of the leaf width near the base, bordered on each side by a band of lacunae which is sometimes narrow and confined to proximal part of the leaf but is often well-developed and extends to the apex, the lateral veins 1 on each side, distinct, rarely with a faint second vein in the proximal half, secondary veins absent. *Floating leaves* absent. *Stipules* 5–15 mm, open, hyaline or hyaline with a greenish tinge and translucent when fresh and dry, rounded to obtuse at the apex, often lost on the oldest leaves, with very weak ribs along each side which are similar in colour to the other veins and (4–)5–8(–9) intercostal veins, the veins inconspicuous when dry. *Turions* 8–24 × (0.6–)0.8–1.6 mm, terminal on the main shoots and on axillary branches, cylindrical, dark green, with 2–4 erect to erecto-patent free leaves. *Inflorescences* 4–8 × 2–3.5 mm; peduncles (7–)10–30(–45) mm, very slender, slightly compressed to compressed. *Flowers* 2–4, more or less contiguous, with (3–)4–5(–7) carpels. *Fruits* 1.8–2.7(–3.0) × 1.1–1.8 mm, olive green, the dorsal edge smooth; beak 0.2–0.7 mm, ventral to apical, recurved to straight.

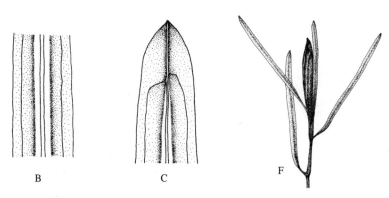

B   C   F

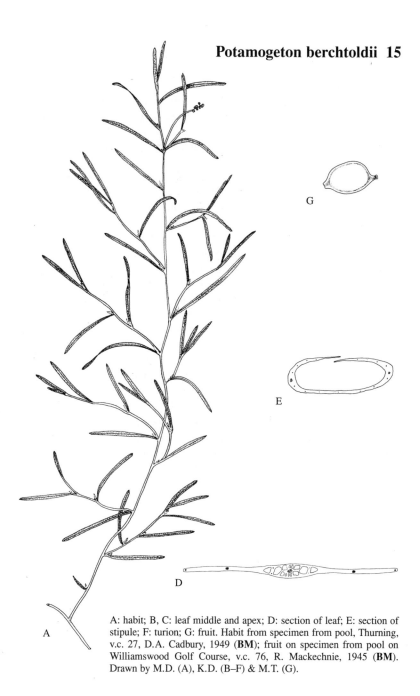

A: habit; B, C: leaf middle and apex; D: section of leaf; E: section of stipule; F: turion; G: fruit. Habit from specimen from pool, Thurning, v.c. 27, D.A. Cadbury, 1949 (**BM**); fruit on specimen from pool on Williamswood Golf Course, v.c. 76, R. Mackechnie, 1945 (**BM**). Drawn by M.D. (A), K.D. (B–F) & M.T. (G).

One of the commonest pondweeds, although one of the least conspicuous, found in still or slowly flowing water in a multiplicity of habitats including lakes, reservoirs, ponds, rivers, canals, streams, ditches, disused and flooded quarries, sand, gravel, clay and marl pits and even turning up in transient water bodies such as cattle troughs, water tanks and buckets. It tolerates a range of pH and nutrient status, although it is absent from the most oligotrophic habitats and is only rarely found in even slightly brackish conditions.

P. berchtoldii varies considerably in leaf characters, including colour, length and width, apex shape and the development of lacunae. Numerous varieties have been described in an attempt to fit this variation into a taxonomic framework, but most are doubtless based on environmental modifications and in the absence of cultivation experiments it is only feasible to regard *P. berchtoldii* as a single, very variable taxon. Plants from shaded, shallow water with relatively broad, dark green leaves with well-developed bands of lacunae which expand towards the leaf apex to occupy the entire width of the leaf are almost certainly environmentally induced phenotypes. Plants with very well developed, translucent nodal glands and delicate, pale green leaves with a very obtuse apex are found in clear, oligotrophic upland lakes and may be genetically distinct (Pearsall & Pearsall 1921). Reproduction of *P. berchtoldii* is probably usually by turions, which are regularly produced from August onwards, but the species also fruits fairly frequently.

P. berchtoldii can be distinguished from the superficially similar *P. pusillus* by its open, not tubular, stipules and its more robust turions. The separation from *P. obtusifolius* and *P. trichoides*, the other linear-leaves species with open stipules, is dealt with under those species.

Hybrids between *P. berchtoldii* and the broad-leaved species *P. natans* (*P.* × *variifolius*, **31**) and *P. coloratus* (*P.* × *lanceolatus*, **32**) and with the narrow-leaved *P. acutifolius* (*P.* × *sudermanicus*, **46**) are recorded in the British Isles, but all are rare. Additionally a hybrid with *P. polygonifolius* is reported from France.

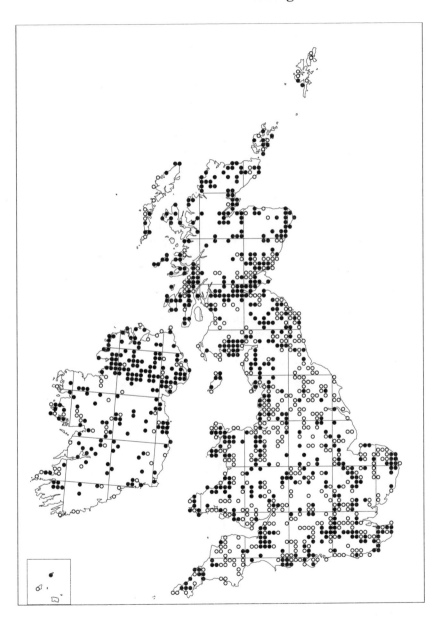

16 Potamogeton trichoides Cham. & Schltdl.

Hairlike Pondweed

Rhizomes absent. *Stems* up to 1(–2) m, very slender, more or less terete to slightly compressed, sparingly to richly branched especially towards the apex; nodal glands absent or poorly developed. *Submerged leaves* 16–80(–130) × 0.3–1(–1.8) mm, (28–)40–80(–110) times as long as wide, rigid, green, becoming dark green or brownish green with age, linear, sessile, gradually tapering to an acute or acuminate apex, not bordered by a marginal vein, entire and plane at the margin; midrib prominent, occupying 30–70% of the leaf width near the base; lacunae absent or restricted to very narrow bands at the base of the leaf, very rarely well developed and extending almost to the apex, the lateral veins 1 on each side, indistinct, secondary veins absent. *Floating leaves* absent. *Stipules* 5–30 mm, open, tightly inrolled, translucent when fresh and dry, green or hyaline with a greenish tinge, obtuse at the apex, persistent; veins inconspicuous when dry, 2 stronger than the others and sometimes forming faint ribs, the intercostal veins 4–7. *Turions* 9–22 × 0.8–1.7 mm, terminal on the main stems and axillary branches, fusiform, dark green or brownish green, with 2–3 erect to erecto-patent free leaves. *Inflorescences* 5–10 × 1.5–4 mm; peduncles 10–75 mm, very slender, terete to slightly compressed. *Flowers* 3–5, contiguous, with 1(–2) carpels. *Fruits* 2.5–3.2 × 1.8–2.1 mm, olive-green, the ventral edge often with a single tooth towards the proximal end, the dorsal edge often muriculate; beak 0.3–0.5 mm, more or less apical, straight.

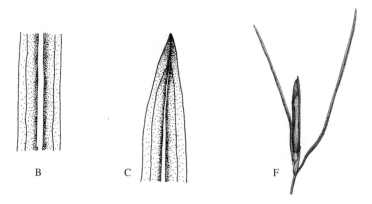

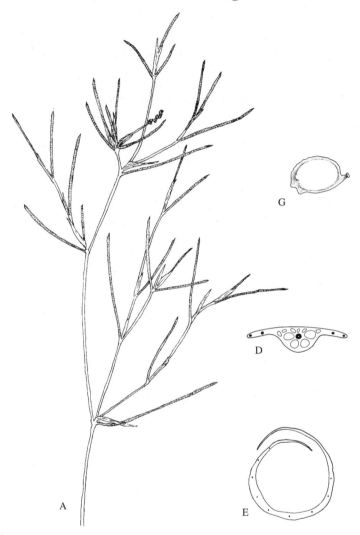

A: habit; B, C: leaf middle and apex; D: section of leaf; E: section of stipule; F: turion; G: fruit. Habit from specimen from dyke between Ingham and Palling, v.c. 27, J. Groves, 1897 (**BM**); fruit on specimen from ditch between Ilford and Lewes, v.c. 14, C.E. Salmon, 1900 (**BM**). Drawn by M.D. (A), K.D. (B, C, F), C.D.P. (E) & M.T. (D, G).

A local species, found in a range of habitats including ponds, lakes, reservoirs, drainage ditches, canals, rivers, brick pits and gravel pits. It often grows with *Elodea canadensis* or *E. nuttallii* and is frequently accompanied by *Potamogeton pusillus*. In drainage ditches it can behave as a pioneer species, appearing when ditches are cleaned out (Wade & Edwards 1980). It is tolerant of, and may even be favoured by, eutrophic water and it has apparently increased recently in some areas, such as the Somerset Levels. It is primarily a species of southern England, being rare in Wales and southern Scotland and absent from Ireland.

P. trichoides varies in habit, leaf length and leaf width. Although it usually has very narrow leaves, without or with poorly developed lacunae, some plants from canals and rivers have broader leaves with fairly well developed lacunae.

Vegetative material of *P. trichoides* is characterised by its finely pointed leaves with a broad, prominent midrib and indistinct lateral veins, and by its rather long, open, tightly rolled greenish stipules. In section the midrib has a strongly convex lower side. The flowers of *P. trichoides* have less than 4 carpels and the fruits are at least 2.5 mm long and often have a muriculate dorsal edge. This species is often overlooked or mistaken for others. *P. pusillus* can resemble *P. trichoides* in leaf shape but is distinguished by its tubular stipules. *P. berchtoldii* usually has more pronounced nodal glands and flaccid leaves with a broader, less finely tapering apex and with more extensive lacunae; its stipules are shorter, less tightly rolled and usually lack the green colour found in *P. trichoides*; its midrib is more slender than that of *P. trichoides*, the lower side being very shallowly convex in section, and most of its flowers have 4 or more carpels.

Two hybrids of *P. trichoides* are known from Britain. *P.* × *bennettii* (*P. crispus* × *trichoides*, **43**) is most unlikely to be confused with *P. trichoides*; *P.* × *grovesii* (*P. pusillus* × *trichoides*, **44**) is similar to both parents but is apparently extinct. A hybrid with *P. compressus* has been described from Denmark.

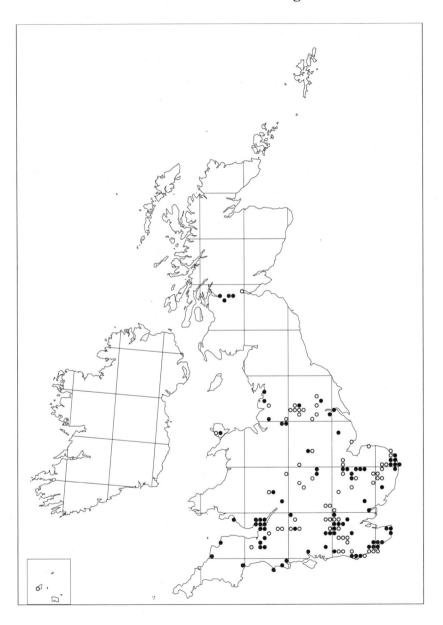

17 Potamogeton compressus L.

Grass-wrack Pondweed

Rhizomes absent. *Stems* to 0.9 m, robust or very robust, flattened, sometimes narrowly winged at the edges on one or both sides, slightly swollen just below the nodes, richly branched; nodal glands absent. *Submerged leaves* 85–240(–270) × 3–6 mm, 20–60(–90) times as long as wide, olive-green or dark green, the upper leaves sometimes with a reddish tinge especially along the midrib, linear, sessile, bordered by a strong marginal vein, truncate or rounded to acute and mucronate at the apex, strongly thickened, entire and plane at the margin; midrib bordered on each side by a band of lacunae which is variable in width at the base of the leaf and sometimes extends to the inner lateral vein but narrows rapidly until it ceases in the distal half of the leaf, sometimes well below the apex but sometimes almost reaching it, the lateral veins 2 on each side, the inner stronger than the outer, secondary veins absent; sclerenchymatous strands present in the lamina, conspicuous. *Floating leaves* absent. *Stipules* 20–55 mm, open, translucent and hyaline with a brownish tinge when fresh, opaque and buff-coloured when dry, obtuse at the apex, persistent but soon eroding to fibrous strands at the apex, with a strong green rib along each side which remains after the intervening tissue has decayed, the stipules eventually splitting into a V-shaped remnant; veins prominent when dry. *Turions* 25–45 × 3.5–8 mm, terminal at the ends of short axillary branches, composed of appressed short leaves with more or less truncate apices

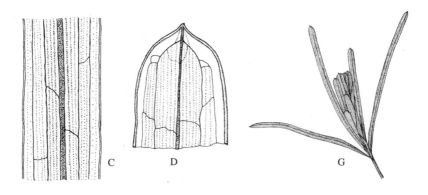

C   D   G

A: length of vegetative shoot; B: flowering shoot; C, D: leaf middle and apex; E: section of leaf; F: section of stem and stipule; G: turion; H: fruit. Habit and flowering shoot based on plants from Upton Marshes, Norfolk, v.c. 27, C. Doarks, C.D.P. & N.F. Stewart, 1989 (Preston 89/315, **CGE**); fruit on specimen from Little Tring, v.c. 20, J.E. Lousley, 1935 (**BM**). Drawn by L.T.E. (A, B, D–F), K.D. (C, G) & M.T. (H).

surrounded by conspicuous stipules, with 2–4 erecto-patent to erect leaves arising near the base. *Inflorescences* 11–25 × 2.5–4.5 mm; peduncles 28–95 mm, slender or robust, compressed. *Flowers* 10–20, more or less contiguous, with (1–)2 carpels. *Fruits* 3.4–4.0 × 2.1–3.0 mm, brown or brownish green, the ventral edge smooth, the dorsal edge smooth or muricate; beak 0.4–0.7 mm, ventral, recurved.

P. compressus is a local species with its headquarters in the English Midlands, where it is predominantly a plant of canals and the backwaters of rivers. In East Anglia it grows in species-rich drainage ditches in grazing marshes. It occasionally occurs in lakes and pools. It is apparently decreasing and there are, for instance, no recent records from the Thames valley or Cambridgeshire. It is extinct in its outlying localities in Angus, where the lakes in which it formerly grew are now very eutrophic, but it has recently been discovered in a new Scottish site, the Loch of Aboyne in S. Aberdeen.

This is not a very variable species, although the shape of the leaf apex and to a lesser extent the development of lacunae along the midrib show some variation. Even on the same stems the lower leaves can be truncate and the upper leaves acuminate.

The flattened stems and the numerous sclerenchymatous strands in the lamina of the leaf will immediately distinguish *P. compressus* from all British species except *P. acutifolius*. Because of the sclerenchymatous strands the leaf appears to have many veins, and Ray (1660) compared it to that of the grass *Elytrigia repens*. Flowering and fruiting plants of *P. compressus* can be distinguished from *P. acutifolius* by their longer peduncles, longer inflorescences, predominantly 2-carpellate rather than 1-carpellate flowers and fruits which lack a tooth on the ventral edge. Vegetative material can be much more difficult to identify. *P. compressus* is usually a larger plant with longer stipules and longer, broader leaves which tend to have a more obtuse apex and more conspicuous sclerenchymatous strands than those of *P. acutifolius*, but all these characters are too variable to be relied on for certain identification. The differences in stipule shape given in successive editions of Clapham, Tutin & Warburg (1952) are imaginary, and I have been unable to confirm the difference in the shape of the epidermal stem cells detailed by Pearsall (1934). The most reliable vegetative distinction lies in the number of lateral veins. *P. acutifolius* only has one on each side of the midrib whereas there is an additional faint vein towards each leaf margin in *P. compressus*.

No hybrids involving *P. compressus* are known in Britain, although a hybrid with *P. trichoides* is reported from Denmark.

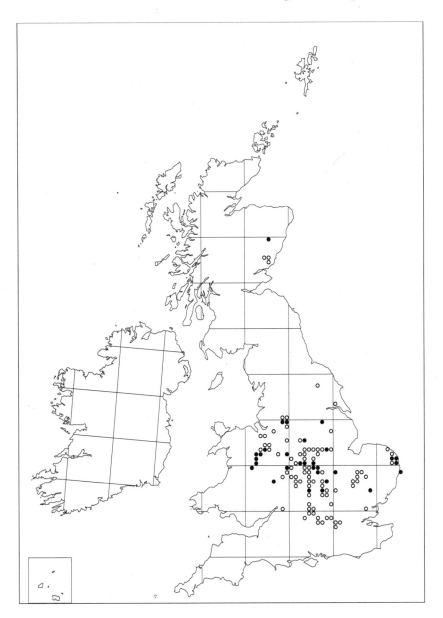

18 Potamogeton acutifolius Link

Sharp-leaved Pondweed

Rhizomes absent. *Stems* up to 1 m, slender to robust, strongly compressed to flattened, slightly swollen just below the nodes, unbranched below, richly branched above; nodal glands absent. *Submerged leaves* 35–100(–135) × 1.5–5.5 mm, 13–30(–40) times as long as wide, dark green, often with a strong brownish or reddish brown tinge, linear, sessile, bordered by a strong marginal vein, acute or more or less abruptly contracted to a distinctly mucronate apex, entire and plane at the margin; midrib bordered on each side by a band of lacunae which is broad towards the base of the leaf and usually extends to the lateral vein but narrows more or less rapidly until it ceases below the apex, the lateral veins 1 on each side, secondary veins absent; sclerenchymatous strands present in the lamina, rather inconspicuous. *Floating leaves* absent. *Stipules* 13–25(–38) mm, open, translucent and hyaline with a milky or brownish tinge when fresh, opaque and buff-coloured when dry, obtuse at the apex, persistent but soon eroding to fibrous strands at the apex, with a strong green rib along each side which remains after the intervening tissue has decayed, the stipules eventually splitting into a V-shaped remnant; veins prominent when dry. *Turions* 22–36 × 3–3.5 mm, terminal on the axillary branches, composed of appressed leaves with more or less mucronate apices, the surrounding stipules not especially conspicuous, with 2–3 erecto-patent leaves arising near the base. *Inflorescences* 2.5–5 × 1.5–2 mm; peduncles 5–20(–30) mm, slender, compressed. *Flowers* 4–6, contiguous, with 1 carpel. *Fruits* 3.0–4.0 × 2.3–3.0 mm, green, the ventral edge with a single rather blunt tooth; beak 0.4–1.1 mm, ventral, straight or recurved.

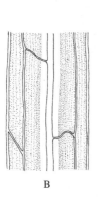
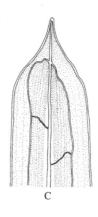

B   C   E

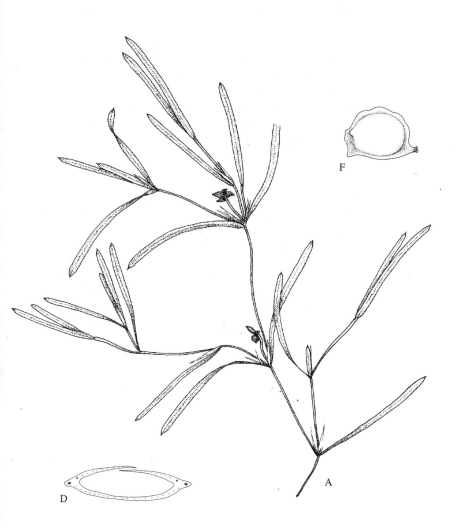

A: habit; B, C: leaf middle and apex; D: section of stipule; E: turion; F: fruit. Habit based on plant from Cantley, v.c. 27, C.D.P., 1988 (Preston 88/291, **CGE**); fruit on specimen from ditch by R. Frome above Stoborough, v.c. 9, D.A. Cadbury, 1959 (**BM**). Drawn by L.T.E. (A,D), K.D. (B, C, E) & M.T. (F).

P. acutifolius is most characteristically a species of shallow, species-rich drainage ditches in grazing marshes, where some of its typical associates are *Elodea canadensis, Hottonia palustris, Hydrocharis morsus-ranae, Lemna minor, L. trisulca, Myriophyllum verticillatum, Potamogeton natans, Ranunculus circinatus, Sagittaria sagittifolia* and *Spirodela polyrhiza*. It is now confined to a few grazing marsh localities in Dorset, Sussex, Kent and Norfolk. It has also been recorded recently in a pond in Middlesex. North of a line from Dorset to Norfolk it is recorded from a number of scattered sites, but at most of these sites it was only found once. Although there are two records from canals, it never (unlike *P. compressus*) became established in the canal system. At its northernmost localities, in Lincolnshire and Yorkshire, it has not been seen since the late 18th century.

P. acutifolius is not a variable plant. It fruits more readily than the closely related *P. compressus*. Its turions develop from August onwards. They are morphologically less specialised than those of *P. compressus* and, judging from herbarium specimens, may be produced less frequently.

The only species with which *P. acutifolius* is likely to be confused is *P. compressus*; the differences between them are outlined under that species.

The hybrids *P. acutifolius* × *berchtoldii* (*P.* × *sudermanicus*, **46**) and *P. acutifolius* × *friesii* (*P.* × *pseudofriesii*, **45**) have each been recorded in Britain from a single locality.

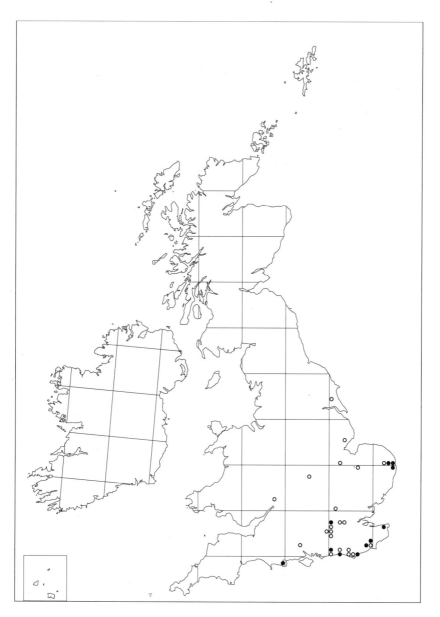

19 Potamogeton crispus L.

Curled Pondweed

Rhizomes very slender to robust. *Stems* up to 1.5 m, robust to very robust, compressed, with a shallow groove running down one or both the broader sides, contracted at the nodes, unbranched or with short branches with crowded leaves or, more rarely, long branches with distant leaves; nodal glands absent. *Submerged leaves* 25–95 × 5–12(–18) mm, 5–9(–13) times as long as wide, bright green, olive green or brownish green, often with a reddish tinge especially along the midrib, linear-oblong to oblong, sessile, the base of the broader leaves auriculate, obtuse or acute at the apex, serrate at the margin, the lower leaves often plane, the upper leaves usually strongly undulate; midrib bordered on each side by a band of lacunae which is broad at the base of the leaf but rapidly narrows above, and extends almost to the leaf apex, the lateral veins 1–2(–3) on each side, the secondary veins few, transverse to ascending. *Floating leaves* absent. *Stipules* 4–17 mm, open, delicate, translucent, hyaline with a pinkish or brownish tinge, truncate or emarginate at the apex, soon becoming torn or reduced to wispy remains, without distinct ribs; veins inconspicuous when dry. *Turions* 7–25(–50) mm, axillary, usually robust, with crowded short, broad leaves, the hardened leaf bases imbricate and completely concealing the axis, occasionally slender, with the leaves less crowded, narrow and not concealing the axis. *Inflorescences* 5–16 × 4–6 mm;

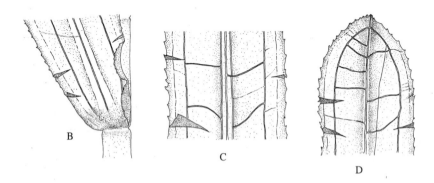

B

C

D

A: habit; B, C, D: leaf base, middle and apex; E: section of stem; F: turions; G: fruit. Habit based on plant from Vanyol Hall, v.c. 49, C.D.P. & N.F. Stewart, 1988 (Preston 88/47, **CGE**); fruit on specimen from pond, Ferrensby, v.c. 64, G. Taylor, 1945 (**BM**). Drawn by L.T.E. (A), G.L. (B–E), & M.T. (F, G).

peduncles 14–65(–125) mm, slender to robust, not tapered, slightly compressed to compressed. *Flowers* 3–8, more or less contiguous, with (2–)4 carpels. *Fruits* 4.0–6.2 × 2.0–2.5 mm, brown, the ventral edge with a single tooth at the base; beak 1.5–2.4 mm, at least half and up to four-fifths the length of the rest of the fruit, tapering from a broad base to a slender apex, more or less falcate.

P. crispus occurs in a wide range of habitats, including lakes, ponds, rivers, streams, canals, drains, ditches and even in very small water-bodies such as ornamental fountains. It is confined, however, to eutrophic or meso-eutrophic waters. In most of lowland England it is one of the commonest *Potamogeton* species, but it is much rarer in extreme S.W. England and in Wales and northern Scotland.

The leaves of *P. crispus* are typically both toothed and undulate and resemble, in Grigson's (1955) words, a wavy-edged hack-saw. Young shoots and some more mature states have plane, toothed leaves and these have been called var. *serratus*. Most recent authors regard them as environmental modifications which do not deserve taxonomic recognition. Although *P. crispus* fruits fairly freely, effective reproduction is probably more frequently accomplished by turions, which are produced from June onwards. They are a means of vegetative spread, and 'germinate' in autumn. *P. crispus* overwinters as leafy shoots.

The teeth on the leaf margins are visible with the naked eye and make this species one of the easiest to recognise. They are quite different to the minute, hyaline denticulations of broad-leaved species such as *P. lucens*, *P. perfoliatus* or *Groenlandia densa*. Plants with plane leaves and poorly developed teeth can bear a superficial resemblance to *P. obtusifolius*, especially if they are also tinged reddish, but careful inspection will reveal teeth, at least towards the apex of the leaf. Unlike *P. obtusifolius*, *P. crispus* lacks nodal glands. A character which separates *P. crispus* from all the linear-leaved species is the shallow groove which runs along the broader sides of the compressed stem; in less robust plants it can be confined to one of the broader sides but it is always present. The long-beaked fruits of *P. crispus* are unlike those of any other European species.

Hybrids with the linear-leaved species *P. friesii* (*P.* × *lintonii*, **42**) and *P. trichoides* (*P.* × *bennettii*, **43**) could be confused with *P. crispus*. Those with *P. alpinus* (*P.* × *olivaceus*, **39**), *P. lucens* (*P.* × *cadburyae*, **38**), *P. perfoliatus* (*P.* × *cooperi*, **41**) and *P. praelongus* (*P.* × *undulatus*, **40**) all bear a closer resemblance to the broad-leaved parent.

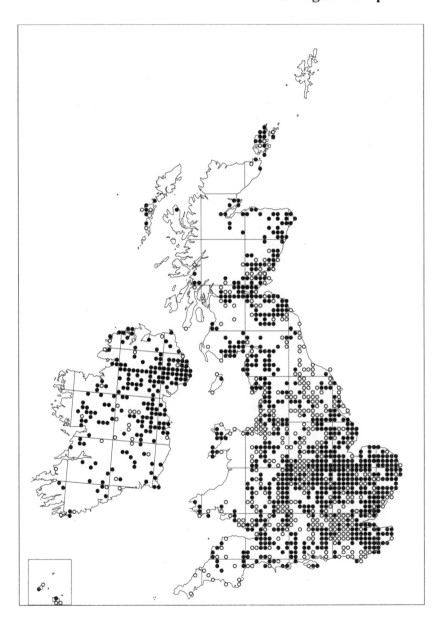

20 Potamogeton filiformis Pers.

Slender-leaved Pondweed

Rhizomes very slender to robust. *Stems* up to 0.3(–0.5) m, very slender to slender, terete, unbranched or sparingly branched; nodal glands absent. *Submerged leaves* 30–175 × 0.3–1.2 mm, (50–)100–300 times as long as wide, green, filiform, semicircular or slightly canaliculate in cross-section, sessile, obtuse or more or less acute at the apex, entire and plane at the margin; midrib bordered on each side by one large and several smaller air channels, the lateral veins 1 on each side, inconspicuous. *Floating leaves* absent. *Leaf sheaths* 8–27 mm long, the basal part closed and tubular when young, eventually splitting with age, the side from which the leaf arises green, the opposite side hyaline; ligule 5–15 mm, hyaline, obtuse to rounded or truncate and often asymmetrical at the apex. *Turions* absent. *Inflorescences* 13–75 × 2–5 mm; peduncles (25–)50–150(–220) mm, very slender, terete, flexuous. *Flowers* 5–9, in 3–5 groups of 1–2(–3), all groups distant at anthesis or the upper two more or less contiguous; carpels 4–6; stigmas sessile. *Fruits* 2.2–2.8(–3.2) × 1.4–2.0 mm, greenish brown, becoming brown with age; beak 0.2–0.3 mm, apical or subapical, straight.

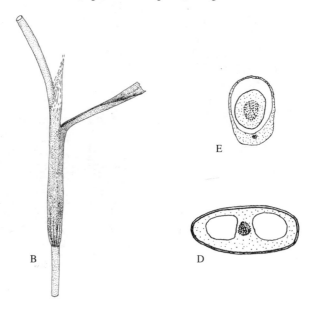

B

E

D

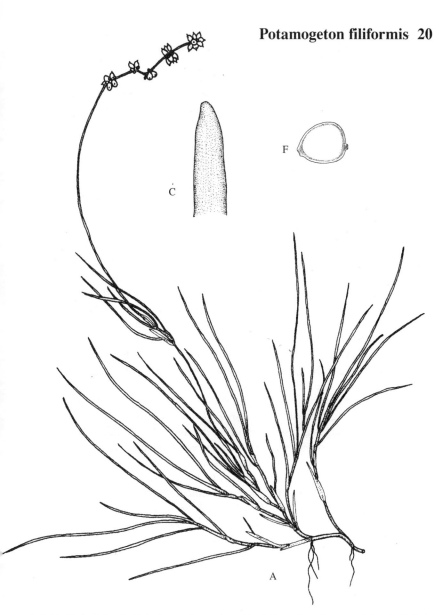

A: habit; B: leaf sheath; C: leaf apex; D: section of leaf; E: section of stem and sheath; F: fruit. Habit based on plant from Tangy Loch, v.c. 101, C.D.P. & N.F. Stewart, 1988 (Preston 88/112, **CGE**); fruit on specimen from Balgavies Loch, v.c. 90, G. Taylor, 1947 (**BM**). Drawn by L.T.E. (A, D, E), M.D. (B, C) & M.T. (F).

217

A northern and western species in Britain and Ireland, extending south to Co. Kerry and Northumberland; it has not been seen since 1826 at its outlying sites in Anglesey. *P. filiformis* usually grows in open, shallow-water communities at the edge of lowland lakes and reservoirs, often with *Chara aspera*. Characteristic habitats include sandy substrates in machair lochs, fine calcareous marl at the edge of lakes over limestone and the silty or gravelly margins of eutrophic lakes and reservoirs. It is also recorded from pools, flooded quarries, ditches, streams and rivers.

P. filiformis shows some variation in habit and leaf shape, although it is much less variable than the protean *P. pectinatus*. In many sites it flowers and fruits freely. Fruits mature early in the season; well-developed fruit can be found in June. Vegetative reproduction is by tubers on the rhizomes, which are similar but much more slender than the tubers of *P. pectinatus*.

P. filiformis and *P. pectinatus* are the two British species in Subgenus *Coleogeton*, easily distinguished from the other species by the long sheath below the point where the leaf joins the stem, the tubular leaves with air channels bordering the midrib and the flexuous peduncles. *Eleogiton fluitans* and *Ruppia* species, aquatic monocots with a similar vegetative structure, lack a ligule at the top of the leaf sheath. The aquatic form of *Juncus bulbosus* has auricles at the top of the sheath which can easily be mistaken for a ligule, but differs from *Potamogeton* in its growth habit (it lacks a rhizome but the stem nodes bear untidy clusters of leaves and roots) and the very slender leaves are transversely septate. In the field the shorter, unbranched or sparingly branched stems with tufts of upright leaves, often evenly spaced along a pioneer rhizome, help to distinguish *P. filiformis* from *P. pectinatus*; when drawn out of the water the leaves cling together like the hairs of an artist's paintbrush whereas those of *P. pectinatus* usually remain separate. Identifications based on these characters should be confirmed by examination of the leaf sheaths, which are tubular, or the fruits, which are smaller than those of *P. pectinatus* and have a sessile, apical stigma.

The hybrid between *P. filiformis* and *P. pectinatus* (*P.* × *suecicus*, **47**) is more likely to be confused with *P. pectinatus* than with *P. filiformis*.

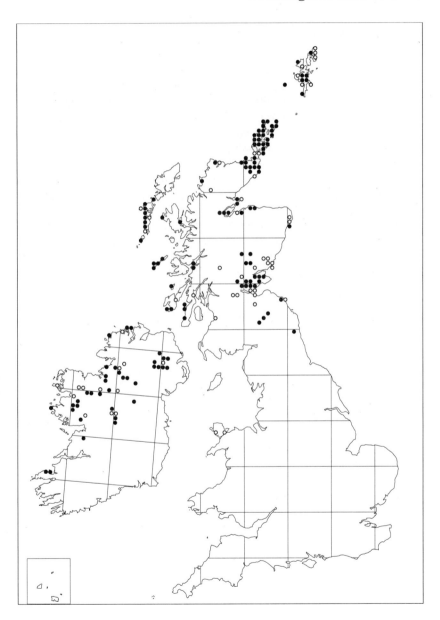

21 Potamogeton pectinatus L.

Fennel Pondweed, Sago Pondweed

Rhizomes very slender to very robust. *Stems* up to 2.3 m, very slender to robust, terete, richly branched; nodal glands absent. *Submerged leaves* 30–115 × 0.2–4 mm, 24–160(–200) times as long as wide, bright green or olive green, linear to filiform, circular, semicircular, elliptical or canaliculate in cross-section, sessile, the broader leaves with a rounded to narrowly obtuse and mucronate apex, the narrower leaves more or less acute to finely acuminate at the apex, entire and plane at margin; midrib bordered on each side by one large or 0–5 large and several small air channels, the lateral veins 1–2 on each side, inconspicuous. *Floating leaves* absent. *Leaf sheaths* 10–70 mm long, open and convolute, the side from which the leaf arises green, the free edges hyaline, often shiny; ligule 5–15 mm, hyaline or pale brown, rounded or truncate at the apex. *Turions* absent. *Inflorescences* 13–45(–60) × 3.5–7 mm; peduncles 20–90(–285) mm, usually very slender, rarely slender, terete, flexuous. *Flowers* (4–)8–14, in 2–7 groups of 1–2, all groups distant at anthesis or the upper groups more or less contiguous; carpels 4; stigmas borne on a distinct style *c.* 0.2 mm long. *Fruits* 3.3–4.7 × 2.6–3.6 mm, pale brown, becoming brown with age; beak 0.2–0.45 mm, ventral, rarely subventral, straight or recurved.

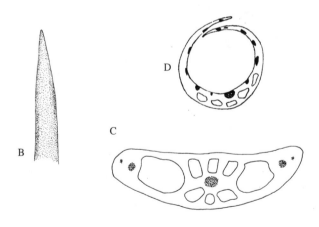

220

A: habit; B: leaf apex; C: section of leaf; D: section of sheath; E: tubers; F: fruit. Habit based on specimen from clay pits, Horseway, near Chatteris, v.c. 29, C.R. Billups, 1886 (**BM**); fruit on specimen from pool in Old Town Bog, St Mary's, Isles of Scilly, v.c. 1, W. Curnow, 1876 (**BM**). Drawn by M.D. (A, B), L.T.E. (C), K.D. (D) & M.T. (E, F).

Frequent and often abundant in eutrophic or brackish waters in a wide range of habitats, including lakes, rivers and streams, canals, ditches, ponds and flooded sand and gravel pits. *P. pectinatus* is more tolerant of pollution than other members of the genus and can be exceedingly abundant in polluted rivers. It is occasionally found in highly calcareous but nutrient-poor water bodies, but is absent from most mesotrophic and oligotrophic habitats. It is one of the most frequent species in England and eastern Ireland, but predominantly coastal further north and west.

P. pectinatus is very variable in habit and leaf shape: some of this variation is almost certainly genetic but much is environmentally induced (van Wijk, van Goor & Verkley 1988). At one extreme lie the robust plants sometimes found in rivers, which have very stout rhizomes, pioneer shoots with short, very broad, canaliculate leaves which are obtuse and mucronate at the apex and mature stems with acuminate leaves over 1 mm wide; at the other are plants from still water with slender rhizomes, scarcely differentiated pioneer shoots and a mass of very slender, acuminate leaves at the water surface. Plants with broad-leaved pioneer shoots have been separated as *P. flabellatus* but intermediate forms occur and a much deeper understanding of the variation of *P. pectinatus* is needed before a workable infraspecific taxonomy can be devised. Populations in still water usually fruit freely, but plants in flowing water only flower sparingly and often fail to set seed. Occasionally clones of *P. pectinatus* appear to be sterile, as they fail to develop fruit even when conditions appear to be suitable and neighbouring clones are fully fertile. Ovoid tubers resembling miniature potatoes are borne on the rhizomes and these are more significant than seeds in maintaining populations. Similar but smaller tubers are produced in the leaf axils of senescent plants at some Continental sites, and presumably also in the British Isles. Some populations of *P. pectinatus* survive the winter as leafy shoots whereas others persist solely as tubers. Old, detached and apparently lifeless shoots can also regenerate in spring (van Wijk 1989a).

    P. pectinatus is one of two British species in Subgenus *Coleogeton*; the differences between these species and those in Subgenus *Potamogeton* and other genera are outlined under *P. filiformis*. *P. pectinatus* differs from *P. filiformis* in its richly branched habit and the finely acuminate leaves of most variants but the critical characters are the open leaf sheaths, carpels with a distinct style rather than a sessile stigma and larger fruits.

    P. filiformis and *P. pectinatus* hybridise; their hybrid, *P.* × *suecicus* (**47**), can easily be overlooked as *P. pectinatus*.

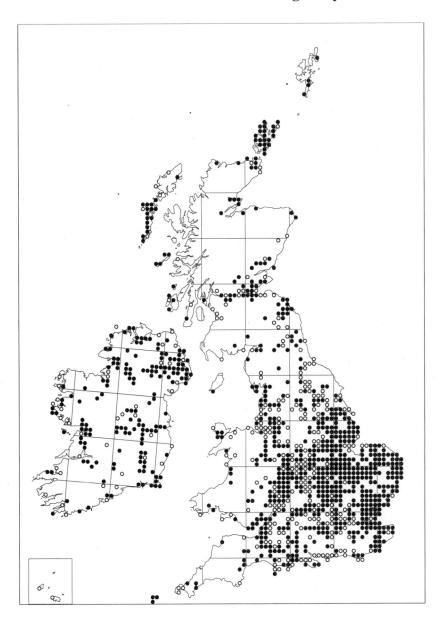

22 Potamogeton × schreberi G. Fisch.
(1 P. natans L. × 2 P. nodosus Poir.)

Rhizomes robust to very robust. *Stems* to 2 m, slender to robust, terete, unbranched; nodal glands absent. *Submerged leaves* near the base of the stem reduced to phyllodes, otherwise with the lamina 55–180 × 2.5–15 mm, (6–)10–20(–30) times as long as wide, translucent, pale brown when young, green when mature, linear-elliptical, very gradually tapering to the petiole, acute at the apex, entire; midrib bordered on each side by a band of lacunae, the lateral veins 1–4 on each side, more or less equally well developed, the secondary veins more or less transverse or ascending; petioles (60–)100–350 mm. *Floating leaves* with the lamina 70–140 × 15–45 mm, 2.3–6 times as long as wide, opaque, coriaceous or subcoriaceous, brownish green when young, rather dark olive green when mature, elliptical to oblong-elliptical, tapering to the base, acute at the apex; lateral veins 5–10 on each side, paler than the lamina in the living plant, the secondary veins ascending near the midrib, transverse towards the margin, inconspicuous; petioles 90–180(–330) mm, without a discoloured section between the petiole and the lamina. *Stipules* 60–140 mm, open, translucent, green, colourless with a greenish tinge or pale pink, rounded to obtuse and slightly hooded at the apex but rolled so that they appear acute, persistent; veins rather prominent when dry, 2 more prominent than the others and forming ridges along the back. *Turions* absent. *Inflorescences* 22–28 × *c*. 6 mm; peduncles 45–80 mm, robust, not tapered, slightly compressed. *Flowers* numerous, contiguous, with 4 carpels. *Fruits* do not develop.

P. × *schreberi* is known from a single locality, a stretch of the R. Stour near Marnhull in Dorset (ST/7.1. and 7.2.), where it was first discovered in 1992.

A careful examination of the submerged leaves of *P.* × *schreberi* will distinguish it from both parents, as those at the base of the stem are reduced to phyllodes but the rest are linear-elliptical with a distinct lamina. All the submerged leaves of *P. natans* are reduced to phyllodes whereas *P. nodosus* never has phyllodes, and its submerged leaves (unlike those of *P.* × *schreberi*) are minutely denticulate. The floating leaves of *P.* × *schreberi* lack the discoloured section between the petiole and the lamina usually found in *P. natans*. *P.* × *schreberi* differs from *P.* × *fluitans* in having stipules with ridges which are not winged on the abaxial side and from *P.* × *sparganiifolius* in the longer petioles of the submerged leaves.

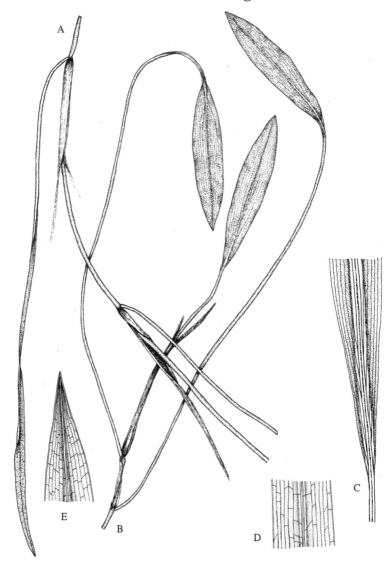

A: stem with submerged leaves; B: upper stem with floating leaves; C, D, E: submerged leaf base, middle and apex. Habit based on plant from R. Stour W. of Mounters, near Marnhull, v.c. 9, J.M. Croft, D.A. Pearman & C.D.P., 1993 (Preston 93/85, **CGE**). Drawn by L.T.E. (A, B) & K.D. (C–E).

23 Potamogeton × fluitans Roth (3 P. lucens L. × 1 P. natans L.)

Rhizomes robust to very robust. *Stems* up to 2.3 m, robust to very robust, terete, unbranched or sparingly branched; nodal glands absent. *Submerged leaves* near the base of the stem reduced or partially reduced to phyllodes, otherwise with the lamina 60–220 × 8–33 mm, 4.3–20 times as long as wide, translucent, dark green or olive green, narrowly elliptical, very gradually tapering to a petiolate base, acute, rarely acuminate, and mucronate at the apex, the midrib sometimes excurrent for up to 12 mm, entire or very obscurely denticulate at the margin; midrib not bordered by lacunae, the lateral veins 3–7 on each side, more or less equal or 1–2 more strongly developed than the others, the secondary veins ascending across the entire width of the leaf or more or less transverse near the margin; petioles 25–70(–90) mm. *Floating leaves* with the lamina 70–155 × 10–55 mm, 2–4.5(–6) times as long as wide, more or less opaque, coriaceous or subcoriaceous, green with a strong brownish tinge when young, slightly yellow green or dark green when mature, narrowly elliptical to oblong-elliptical or ovate, cuneate or rounded at the base, the lamina narrowly decurrent, acute to obtuse at the apex and often apiculate; lateral veins 5–11 on each side of the midrib, translucent in the living plant, the secondary veins ascending across the entire width of the leaf or more or less transverse near the margin, inconspicuous; petioles 25–70(–90) mm, usually shorter than the lamina, with a pale, slightly swollen junction with the stem but without a flexible section between the petiole and the lamina. *Stipules* 35–100 mm, open, rigid, enfolding the stem or projecting from it at an acute angle, translucent, dark green or brownish green when fresh, obtuse and slightly hooded at the apex, persistent; veins prominent when dry, 2 more prominent than the others and forming ridges or narrow wings along the back of the stipule in the basal part or for most of its length. *Turions* absent. *Inflorescences* 22–62 × 8–15 mm; peduncles 40–95 mm, robust to very robust, thickened and spongy towards the apex, terete. *Flowers*

B

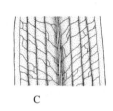

C

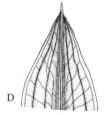

D

A: habit; B, C, D: submerged leaf base, middle and apex; E: fruit. Habit based on plant from Moors River S. of Hurn, v.c. 11, C.D.P., 1989 (Preston 89/88, **CGE**); fruit on specimen from Moors River, St Leonards Bridge, v.c. 9, P.M. Hall, 1939 (**BM**). Drawn by L.T.E. (A), K.D. (B–D) & M.T. (E).

227

numerous, contiguous or well spaced, with 4(–5) carpels. *Fruits* 3.6–4.5 × 2.5–3.3 mm, greenish brown; beak 0.3–0.4 mm, ventral, straight or recurved.

P. × *fluitans* is well established and locally abundant in the Moors River, a shallow calcareous stream in Dorset and Hampshire, where it grows with associates which include *Callitriche* sp., *Elodea nuttallii*, *Lemna minor*, *Nuphar lutea*, *Oenanthe fluviatilis*, *Potamogeton natans*, *Ranunculus penicillatus* subsp. *pseudofluitans* and *Schoenoplectus lacustris*. The other extant populations grow in ditches at Wood Walton Fen in Huntingdonshire and Limpenhoe in Norfolk. *P.* × *fluitans* was formerly recorded from ditches in the Cambridgeshire Fenland and from the Wey and Arun Canal in Surrey and Sussex.

Populations of *P.* × *fluitans* in East Anglia have well differentiated floating leaves which are almost as coriaceous as those of *P. natans*. The first leaves of the season are reduced to phyllodes; narrowly elliptical leaves soon follow and floating leaves develop later. Sometimes only floating leaves are present by the time the plant flowers. By contrast, the upper leaves of the Moors River population are intermediate between floating and submerged leaves; true floating leaves do not develop. The terrestrial rosettes of *P.* × *fluitans* which can develop when water levels drop are described from East Anglia by Fryer (1887d). Although this hybrid is normally sterile, a few well-formed fruits can sometimes be found on inflorescences in the Moors River population. Slender branches with phyllodes at the base and fascicles of narrow leaves above are produced in the leaf axils in the autumn; these produce roots from the base and act as vegetative propagules.

P. × *fluitans* differs from *P. natans* in its submerged leaves which (except in the early stages) have a distinct lamina, and in its floating leaves, which lack the flexible section between blade and petiole usually found in that parent. Because this section is absent, the floating leaves of *P.* × *fluitans* all point in the same direction whereas those of *P. natans* are variously oriented on the water surface. The narrower submerged leaves with longer petioles and the capacity to produce floating leaves distinguish *P.* × *fluitans* from *P. lucens*. *P.* × *schreberi* and *P.* × *sparganiifolius* are similar to *P.* × *fluitans* but can usually be separated by their even narrower submerged leaves and unwinged stipules; some early or late season growth forms of *P.* × *fluitans* might, however, be very difficult to separate from *P.* × *sparganiifolius*. *P. nodosus* is also similar to *P.* × *fluitans* but never has lower leaves reduced or partially reduced to phyllodes or mature leaves with an excurrent midrib, nor are its stipules ever winged. The young leaves of *P. nodosus* are minutely toothed whereas those of *P.* × *fluitans* are usually entire.

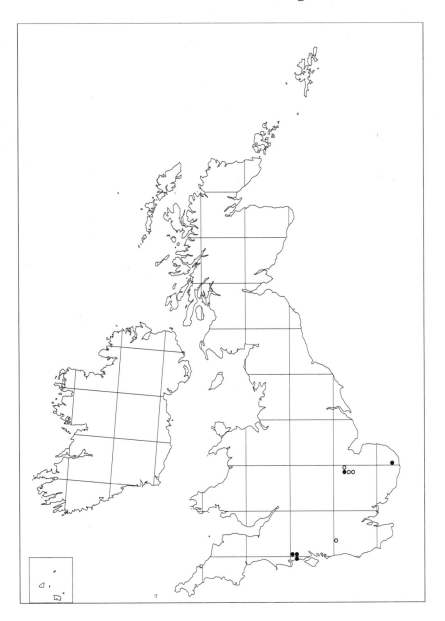

24 Potamogeton × sparganiifolius Laest. ex Fr. (4 P. gramineus L. × 1 P. natans L.)

Rhizomes slender to robust. *Stems* up to 1.4 m, slender to very robust, terete, sparingly to richly branched; nodal glands absent. *Submerged leaves* on the lowest part of the stem often reduced to linear phyllodes or with only a narrow lamina at the distal end, otherwise with the lamina 60–520 × 2–12 mm, 16–72 times as long as wide, translucent or almost opaque, pale green or dark green, linear or narrowly oblanceolate, very gradually tapering to the base, all petiolate or some sessile and some petiolate, acute or acuminate at the apex, entire or obscurely denticulate and plane at the margin; midrib bordered on each side by a broad or narrow band of small lacunae, the lateral veins 1–6 on each side, slightly stronger veins alternating with slightly weaker ones, the outermost sometimes faint, the secondary veins transverse or ascending; petioles up to 55 mm, sometimes with a slightly flexible, slightly swollen junction with the stem. *Floating leaves* with the lamina 38–115 × 9–34 mm, 2–8.3 times as long as wide, opaque, coriaceous, yellow-green or dark green, narrowly elliptical or oblong-elliptical to ovate, cuneate or rounded, rarely subcordate, at the base, the lamina often broadly or narrowly decurrent, obtuse to acute and often apiculate at the apex; lateral veins 6–12 on each side of the midrib, darker to lighter than the lamina in the living plant, the secondary veins numerous, more or less ascending towards the centre of the leaf, transverse towards the margin, inconspicuous; petioles 30–250 mm,

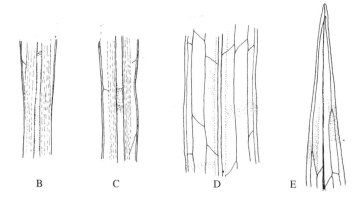

B   C   D   E

A: habit; B, C, D, E: submerged leaf base, leaf near base, middle and apex; F: section of stem and stipule. Habit based on plant from North Idle Drain, Belton, v.c. 54, C.D.P. *et al.*, 1989 (Preston 89/480, **CGE**). Drawn by L.T.E.

sometimes with a discoloured section 5–18 mm long between the petiole and the lamina. *Stipules* 17–95 mm, open, enfolding the stem throughout their length or projecting from it at an acute angle, translucent and hyaline, sometimes with a green or milky tinge when fresh, more or less opaque and green, brown or buff when dry, broadly obtuse to rounded and sometimes slightly hooded, rolled at the apex so that they can appear acute, persistent; veins prominent when dry, 2 more prominent than the others and sometimes forming ridges along the back of the stipules. *Turions* absent. *Inflorescences* 25–45 × 3.5–6.5 mm; peduncles 30–120 mm, of uniform diameter along their length or slightly broader towards the apex, terete. *Flowers* numerous, contiguous, with 4 carpels. *Fruits* do not develop.

A widespread but uncommon hybrid with a distribution which reflects that of the rarer parent, *P. gramineus*. It is most frequent in Scotland and Ireland, where it is predominantly a plant of streams and rivers, a habitat to which it seems to be well adapted morphologically, but also occurs in lakes. In England and Wales it is very rare, known from fenland drains and pools and once collected in the Basingstoke Canal.

P. × sparganiifolius is a variable plant. In still water it tends to have short, narrowly oblanceolate submerged leaves and well developed floating leaves, whereas in flowing water the submerged leaves can be long and ribbon-like and the floating leaves few or even absent. The floating leaves also vary in the extent to which they resemble those of *P. natans*, only some having the discoloured section between the lamina and the petiole characteristic of that species.

The affinities of *P. × sparganiifolius* with *P. natans* are revealed by the submerged leaves, strongly reminiscent of phyllodes, and the closely veined stipules which are opaque when dry. The fact that most submerged leaves are expanded into a narrow lamina is, however, sufficient to distinguish the hybrid. Both submerged leaves and stipules are very different to those of *P. gramineus* and confusion with this parent is unlikely.

232

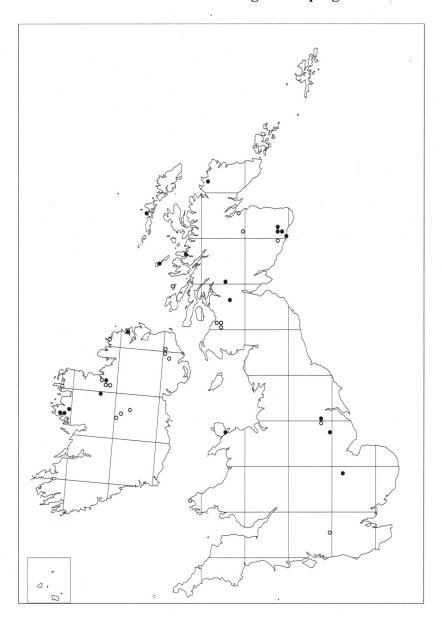

25 Potamogeton × gessnacensis G. Fisch.
(1 P. natans L. × 5 P. polygonifolius Pourr.)

Rhizomes slender. *Stems* up to 0.9 m, slender to robust, terete, unbranched; nodal glands absent. *Submerged leaves* with the lamina 15–210 × 1–4 mm, 8–175 times as long as wide, translucent or opaque, olive green, sometimes with a pinkish or reddish tinge, linear to narrowly elliptical, very gradually tapering to the petiolate base, more or less acute at the apex, entire at the margin; midrib not bordered by lacunae, the lateral veins 1–2 on each side, the secondary veins occasional, transverse or ascending, a few sometimes descending; petioles 45–175 mm. *Floating leaves* with the lamina (22–)40–90 × (7–)12–32 mm, 2.5–7 times as long as wide, opaque, coriaceous, dark olive green with a reddish or pinkish red tinge, elliptical, cuneate or rounded at the base, the lamina shortly and narrowly decurrent, acute at the apex; lateral veins (2–)4–10 on each side of the midrib, similar in colour to the lamina or appearing as very narrow translucent lines when the leaf is held up to the light, the secondary veins numerous, more or less ascending towards the midrib, more or less transverse towards the margin; petioles 80–270 mm, sometimes with a pale section 5–7 mm long between the petiole and the lamina. *Stipules* 40–85 mm, open, clasping the stems, translucent when fresh with a slightly milky tinge, pale brown, reddish brown or brownish green when dry, obtuse but rolled so that they appear acute at the apex, persistent; veins prominent when dry, 2 more prominent than the others and forming distinct ridges along the back of the stipules. *Turions* absent. *Inflorescences* 8–18 × 3.5–4 mm; peduncles 55–80 mm, slender, not tapered, terete. *Flowers* 12–22, contiguous, with 4 carpels. *Fruits* do not develop.

"British plants which appear to be this hybrid" were reported by Dandy (1975) from Llyn Anafon in Caernarvonshire and the Hill of Nigg in E. Ross. *P. × gessnacensis* was first collected in Llyn Anafon in 1884, but mistaken for *P. natans* until Dandy redetermined the material. It still occurs in this acidic upland lake, growing in water 0.5–0.8 m deep with *Callitriche hamulata* and the aquatic form of *Juncus bulbosus*. *P. polygonifolius* grows round the margin of this lake but *P. natans* is apparently absent. The record from the Hill of Nigg is based on material collected in 1970 by U. K. Duncan, who reported four plants, all similar, in a small streamlet.

The above description is based on a single specimen from the Hill of Nigg (**BM**) and from pressed specimens and living material from Llyn Anafon. The

A: habit; B: section of stem and stipule. Habit based on plant from Llyn Anafon, v.c. 49, C.D.P. & N.F. Stewart, 1988 (Preston 88/38, **CGE**). Drawn by L.T.E.

plant from the Hill of Nigg has lower leaves which resemble the phyllodes of *P. natans* but are expanded at the distal end into a narrow lamina, upper leaves which sometimes show a trace of a flexible junction between petiole and lamina and relatively long, green stipules which have fairly prominent veins but lack the pale buff colour so often found in the dried stipules of *P. natans*. It is closer than material from Llyn Anafon to the only specimen of *P.* × *gessnacensis* which I have seen from the German type locality. Plants from Llyn Anafon resemble *P. natans* very closely, but material collected in May has phyllodes which are expanded into a very narrow lamina and floating leaves in which the lateral veins are not translucent, or if translucent are much narrower than the translucent veins of *P. natans*. By August most of the submerged leaves have disappeared, leaving plants which are even closer to *P. natans*. However, the inflorescences are short and few-flowered and fruits never develop, although the plants grow in a situation where *P. natans* would normally fruit profusely. The pollen of Llyn Anafon specimens in **BM** is sterile. Small, readily detached branches bearing a few dark green phyllodes or phyllode-like leaves are present in the leaf axils of plants collected at Llyn Anafon in August, most frequently in the axils of leaves subtending the inflorescences. They resemble the fascicles of phyllodes sometimes produced by *P. natans*.

Although the Llyn Anafon plants are almost certainly a sterile hybrid of *P. natans*, further research is desirable to confirm that the other parent is *P. polygonifolius*, as Dandy rather tentatively suggested. The close resemblance of the Llyn Anafon hybrid to *P. natans* suggests that similar plants might be overlooked elsewhere. *P.* × *sparganiifolius* usually has broader submerged leaves than the Welsh *P.* × *gessnacensis* but some populations are not dissimilar from the Llyn Anafon plants and the distinction between these two hybrids requires clarification.

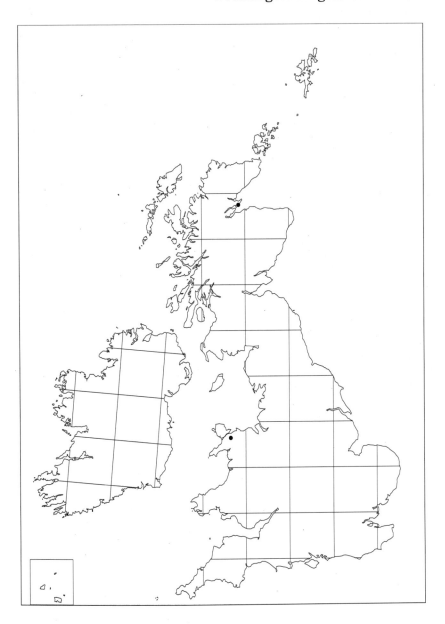

26 Potamogeton × zizii W. D. J. Koch ex Roth (4 P. gramineus L. × 3 P. lucens L.)

Rhizomes robust to very robust. *Stems* up to 1.2(–2) m, slender to robust, terete, sparingly to richly branched; nodal glands absent. *Submerged leaves* at the base of the stem reduced to phyllodes, otherwise with the lamina 50–130 × 10–25(–30) mm on the stems and main branches, as small as 30 × 8.5 mm on short branches, 3.8–7 times as long as wide, translucent, glossy yellowish green, sometimes with a pinkish tinge, green or dark olive-green, narrowly elliptical, often recurved, gradually tapering or rather abruptly narrowed to the base, all sessile or some sessile and some petiolate, acute to obtuse and usually mucronate at the apex, denticulate and undulate at the margin; midrib bordered on each side by a narrow band of lacunae, the lateral veins 4–5(–6) on each side, the inner veins more or less equally strong, the outer 1–2 veins usually fainter than the others, the secondary veins frequent, regularly or irregularly ascending across the entire width of the leaf; petioles up to 3(–7) mm. *Floating leaves* with the lamina 55–105 × 22–40 mm, 1.8–3.3 times as long as wide, opaque, coriaceous, dark green, elliptical to broadly elliptical or oblong-elliptical, tapering or abruptly narrowed to a cuneate or subcordate base, shortly and narrowly decurrent along the petiole, obtuse to subacute and apiculate at the apex; lateral veins 6–9 on each side of the midrib, lighter or darker than the lamina in the living plant, the secondary veins relatively conspicuous; petioles (10–)20–65 mm, usually shorter than the lamina. *Stipules* 20–45(–55) mm on the main stems, as short as 10 mm on short branches, open, rigid, clasping the stem or projecting from it at an acute

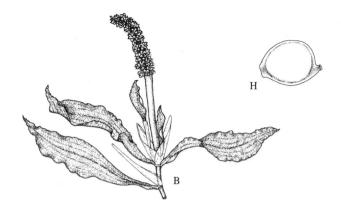

238

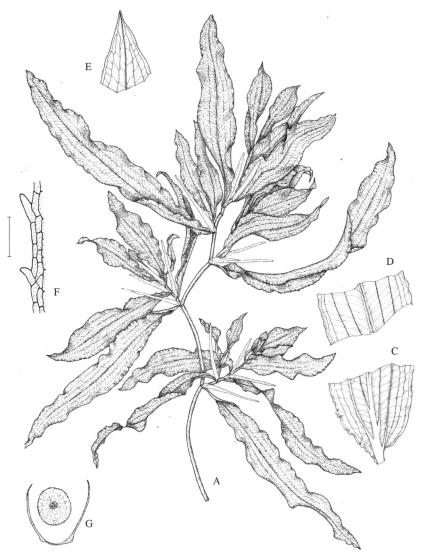

A: habit; B: inflorescence; C, D, E, F: leaf base, middle, apex and margin; G: section of stem and
stipule; H: fruit. Habit and inflorescence based on plant from Aucha Lochy, v.c. 101, C.D.P. &
N.F. Stewart, 1988 (Preston 88/103, **CGE**); fruit on specimen from Westmoor, Doddington, v.c. 29,
A. Fryer, 1886 (**BM**). Drawn by L.T.E. (A–G) & M.T. (H). Scale bar: 0.1 mm.

angle, green when fresh, olive-green or brownish green when dry, obtuse and slightly hooded at the apex, persistent; veins inconspicuous when dry, 2 much more prominent than the others, forming strong ribs in the proximal half, the ribs sometimes narrowly winged on the abaxial side towards the base. *Turions* absent. *Inflorescences* 20–50 × 8–10 mm; peduncles 30–150(–290) mm, robust to very robust, broader and spongy towards the apex, terete. *Flowers* numerous, contiguous, with (3–)4 carpels. *Fruits* 2.7–3.4 × 1.9–2.4 mm, green or pale brownish green; beak 0.2–0.5 mm, ventral, straight or recurved at the apex.

One of the commoner *Potamogeton* hybrids, frequently found in the absence of one and often of both parents. In Scotland and in parts of Ireland it is commoner than *P. lucens*, growing in mesotrophic lakes and rivers which usually have some basic influence but are apparently insufficiently calcareous to support *P. lucens*. In southern and eastern England *P. × zizii* is found in scattered reservoirs, fenland drains and ditches and in the meres of Breckland, often in the vicinity of both parents. Like *P. gramineus*, it is apparently declining at the southern edge of its range.

P. × zizii shows some morphological variation, some plants being intermediate between the parents and others closer to *P. lucens*. There is also variation in the capacity to produce floating leaves and in the extent to which fruit develops, but it is not known whether this has a genetic basis or whether it is environmentally induced. Where water has receded, land forms similar to those of *P. gramineus* can be found.

    P. × zizii is more robust than *P. gramineus* but it is a more slender and graceful plant than *P. lucens*, and unlike the latter its leaves are often slightly recurved. The main stems are usually more like those of *P. lucens* than the branches, which are often reminiscent of *P. gramineus*. It is, however, easier to recognise the difference between *P. × zizii* and its parents than it is to define it. *P. × zizii* is intermediate in the breadth of its leaves and the length of its stipules and fruits, but the variation in all three taxa results in overlap in all these measurements. The best characters for separating *P. × zizii* from *P. gramineus* are the larger leaves and stipules (which unlike those of that species are usually slightly winged), whereas it differs from *P. lucens* in usually having sessile submerged leaves with a midrib which is bordered by narrow bands of lacunae and often runs into the leaf apex but is not excurrent. Some plants of *P. × zizii*, however, have petiolate lower leaves and most will develop some petiolate leaves near the surface of the water. Plants with floating or terrestrial leaves can easily be distinguished from *P. lucens*, but only a minority of populations show these.

Potamogeton × zizii 26

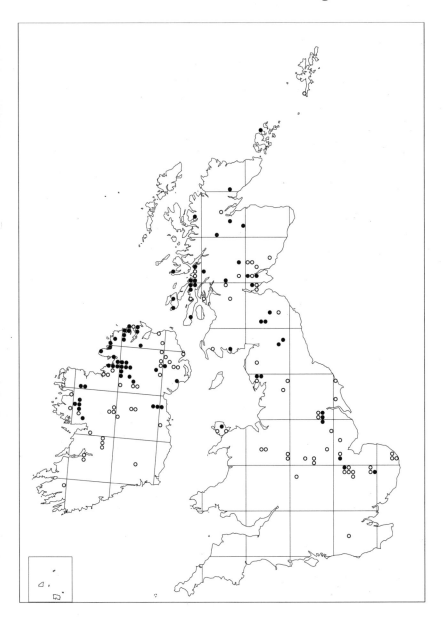

241

27 Potamogeton × lanceolatifolius (Tiselius) C.D. Preston (4 P. gramineus L. × 5 P. polygonifolius Pourr.)

Rhizomes very slender. *Stems* up to 0.55 m, very slender to slender, unbranched or sparingly branched; nodal glands absent. *Submerged leaves* towards the base of the stem sometimes reduced or partially reduced to phyllodes, otherwise with the lamina 40–110 × 3.5–13 mm, 9–16 times as long as wide, translucent, olive-green or yellowish green when dry, sometimes with a slight reddish tinge, elliptical or narrowly oblanceolate, gradually tapering to a petiolate base and to an acute apex, some sessile leaves sometimes present, obscurely and remotely denticulate at the margin; midrib bordered on each side by a narrow band of lacunae, the lateral veins 3–7 on each side, more or less equally developed or 2 stronger than the others, the secondary veins frequent, ascending; petioles up to 14 mm. *Floating leaves* with the lamina 25–75 × 7–17 mm, 3.5–5 times as long as wide, opaque, coriaceous, elliptical to ovate-elliptical, cuneate or rounded at base, with a narrowly decurrent lamina, obtuse to acute and apiculate at the apex; lateral veins 5–6 on each side of the midrib, the secondary veins numerous, transverse to ascending, obscure; petioles 52–98 mm. *Stipules* 15–40 mm, open, enfolding the stem or projecting from it at an acute angle, translucent or more or less opaque when dry, brown, obtuse at the apex, persistent; veins inconspicuous when dry, 2 more prominent than the others and forming low ridges on the abaxial side towards the proximal end. *Turions* absent. *Inflorescences* not seen in British material; in Swedish plants 12–17 × 2.5–3 mm; peduncles 43–65 mm, slender to robust. *Flowers* numerous, contiguous. *Fruits* do not develop.

A rare hybrid, known from only two localities. It was collected by G. Taylor in 1953 from the R. Bladnoch at Spittal in Wigtownshire (NX/3.5.) and from a small loch half a mile east of Nairn in E. Inverness (NJ/8.5.). I have been unable to refind this hybrid either in the R. Bladnoch or at sites east of Nairn.

P. × lanceolatifolius differs from *P. polygonifolius* in having sessile or only shortly petiolate leaves with margins which are denticulate (although the teeth are difficult to see even under the binocular microscope), and stipules which can project at an angle from the stem like those of *P. gramineus*. It can be distinguished from *P. gramineus* by the fact that at least some of the submerged leaves on each stem are petiolate (these should not be confused with the petiolate floating or transitional leaves of *P. gramineus*).

242

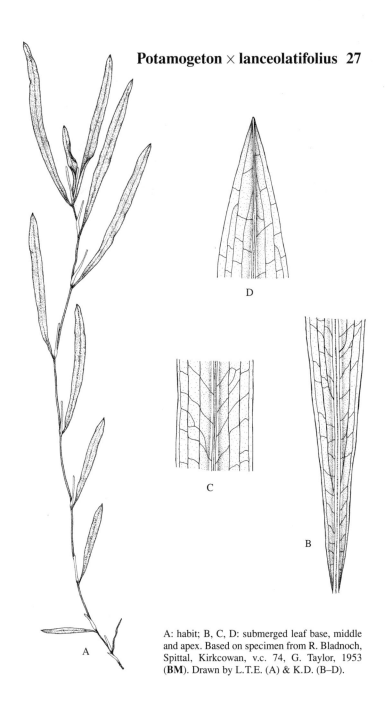

A: habit; B, C, D: submerged leaf base, middle and apex. Based on specimen from R. Bladnoch, Spittal, Kirkcowan, v.c. 74, G. Taylor, 1953 (**BM**). Drawn by L.T.E. (A) & K.D. (B–D).

28 Potamogeton × billupsii Fryer
(6 P. coloratus Hornem. × 4 P. gramineus L.)

Rhizomes slender to robust. *Stems* up to 0.35 m, slender to robust, terete, unbranched or with a few short axillary branches; nodal glands absent. *Submerged leaves* at the base of the stem sometimes reduced or partially reduced to phyllodes, otherwise with the lamina 20–75 × 4–17 mm, 3–11 times as long as wide, translucent, bright green, olive-green or yellow-green, often with a pinkish tinge along the veins or throughout, elliptical, oblong-elliptical or oblanceolate, gradually tapering to a sessile or petiolate base, obtuse and hooded or (rarely) acute and apiculate at the apex, minutely denticulate at the margin; midrib bordered by a narrow band of lacunae, the lateral veins 3–6 on each side, more or less equally developed or slightly stronger veins alternating with weaker ones, the secondary veins frequent, ascending in the centre of the leaf, ascending or more or less transverse towards the margin, conspicuous; petiole up to 27 mm. *Floating leaves* with the lamina 20–70 × 10–22 mm, 1.7–3.8 times as long as wide, translucent or more or less opaque, subcoriaceous, bright green, broadly elliptical or ovate, cuneate or rounded at the base, obtuse and often apiculate at the apex; lateral veins 6–8 on each side of the midrib, opaque, darker than the lamina in the living plant, the secondary veins numerous, transverse or ascending; petioles 10–95 mm, shorter or longer than the lamina. *Stipules* (7.5–)12–34 mm, open, clasping the stem or rolled and projecting from it at an acute angle, translucent when fresh, buff-coloured or green when dry, often strongly tinged with brown, obtuse at the apex, persistent; veins inconspicuous when dry, 2 more prominent than the others and forming ridges towards the base on the abaxial side. *Turions* absent. *Inflorescences* 10–14 × 2.5–3 mm; peduncles 20–125 mm, slender to robust, slightly broader towards the apex, terete. *Flowers* numerous, contiguous, with 4 carpels. *Fruits* do not develop.

This very rare hybrid was first discovered in 1892 by Fryer at Benwick in the Isle of Ely (TL/3.9.). Here it grew in a shallow, stagnant ditch which tended to dry out in summer. In cultivation Fryer found that it preferred similar conditions, flowering abundantly only in water less than 18 inches (0.45 m) deep. The Benwick population was exterminated soon after its discovery, when the ditch in which it grew was deepened. However, *P.* × *billupsii* was found at a second site, Loch na Liana Moire, Benbecula (NF/7.5.), by J.W. Heslop Harrison in 1940. It still grows in shallow water at the edge of this lake, which is also a site where the water level is liable to seasonal fluctuations.

A: habit; B: submerged leaf base and stipule; C: section of stem and stipule. Habit based on plant from Loch na Liana Moire, Benbecula, v.c. 110, C.D.P. *et al.*, 1987 (Preston 87/141, **CGE**). Drawn by L.T.E. For additional drawings see p. 249.

The Benwick specimens are closer to *P. gramineus* than those from Benbecula, notably in the tendency of the lowest stem leaves to be reduced to phyllodes and in the shape of the submerged leaves, which are acute and apiculate rather than obtuse and hooded at the apex. *P.* × *billupsii*, like *P. coloratus*, overwinters as submerged leafy shoots.

The toothed margin of the submerged leaves is the feature which most reliably separates *P.* × *billupsii* from *P. coloratus*. Other characters which are sometimes shown by the hybrid and which, when present, will distinguish it from *P. coloratus* are the reduction of the lowest leaves to phyllodes, the sessile base of some submerged leaves and the long petioles of some floating leaves. It is more difficult to separate *P.* × *billupsii* from the variable *P. gramineus* but the fact that the hybrid overwinters as leafy shoots, often has submerged leaves with obtuse and hooded apices, has a less clear-cut distinction between submerged and floating leaves and is sterile will help distinguish it.

29 Potamogeton × nericius Hagstr.
(7 P. alpinus Balb. × 4 P. gramineus L.)

Rhizomes very slender to slender. *Stems* up to 1.1 m, very slender to robust, terete, richly branched at the base, the longer shoots simple or with a few axillary branches; nodal glands absent. *Submerged leaves* at the base of the stem sometimes reduced or partially reduced to phyllodes, otherwise 40–80 × 6.5–13 mm, (4.5–)6.5–8.5(–10.5) times as long as wide and elliptical or oblong-elliptical on the main stems and branches, as small as 26 × 2.5 mm, 7.5–11.5 times as long as wide and narrowly elliptical on short branches, translucent, green or brown when dry, gradually tapering or abruptly narrowed to the sessile base, acute to obtuse and sometimes mucronate at the apex, entire or obscurely and remotely denticulate and undulate at the margin; midrib bordered on each side by a band of lacunae which is broad at the base of the leaf and extends almost as far as the apex, the lateral veins 3–5 on each side, more or less equally well developed or the outermost fainter than the others, the secondary veins frequent, ascending. *Floating leaves* with the lamina 38–70 × 10–20 mm, 3.2–5 times as long as wide, opaque, subcoriaceous, green or slightly reddish brown when dry, elliptical to oblong-elliptical, tapering to a cuneate base, obtuse and often apiculate at the apex; lateral veins 4–6 on each side of the midrib, the secondary veins numerous, ascending,

A: habit; B: section of stem and stipule. Habit based on plant from R. Don, Bridge of Alford, v.c. 92, C.D.P., 1988 (Preston 88/222, **CGE**). Drawn by L.T.E.

obscure; petioles 9–62 mm, usually shorter than the lamina. *Stipules* 15–25 mm on the main stems and branches, as short as 6.5 mm on short branches, open, rigid, enfolding the stem or projecting from it at an acute angle, translucent when fresh, brownish green when dry, obtuse, persistent; veins rather prominent when dry, 2 more prominent than the others and forming ribs towards the base of the stipule on the abaxial side. *Turions* absent. *Inflorescences* 13–23 × 3.5–4.5 mm; peduncles 130–210 mm, robust, not tapered. *Flowers* 13–24, contiguous, with 4 carpels. *Fruits* do not develop.

P. × *nericius* is only known from a short stretch of the R. Don at Bridge of Alford in S. Aberdeenshire (NJ/5.1.), where it was first collected (with both parents) by G. C. Druce and Mrs M. L. Wedgwood in 1918. It grows in water 0.5–1 m deep, which flows rapidly but smoothly over stones and boulders.

One collection of *P.* × *nericius* has an axillary branch with roots at the lower nodes; were such branches to become detached, they could act as a means of vegetative reproduction.

 P. × *nericius* is difficult to distinguish from *P. gramineus*, a difficulty aggravated by the great variability of this parent. The submerged leaves and sterile inflorescences provide the best characters for distinguishing them. The main stem leaves are oblong-elliptical and tend to be broader than those of *P. gramineus*, the bands of lacunae bordering the midrib are broader and the apex is more obtuse and less markedly mucronate. The young leaves are entire or much more obscurely denticulate than those of *P gramineus*, but this difference is obscured as the leaves of *P. gramineus* age and the teeth become eroded away. *P. alpinus* differs in its unbranched stems and in its longer, broader leaves and is unlikely to be confused with this hybrid.

 The morphological evidence that the Bridge of Alford plant is a hybrid rather than a variant of *P. gramineus* is rather weak, and a more detailed study is required to confirm its identity. Hagström (1916) described *P.* × *nericius* from Swedish material which had simple or weakly branched stems, and which was therefore closer in habit to *P. alpinus* than *P. gramineus*. Specimens from France and Norway at **BM** and **CGE** tentatively determined as *P.* × *nericius* by Dandy have longer, more sparingly branched stems and long, narrow leaves; they are also closer in habit to *P. alpinus* than the Bridge of Alford population.

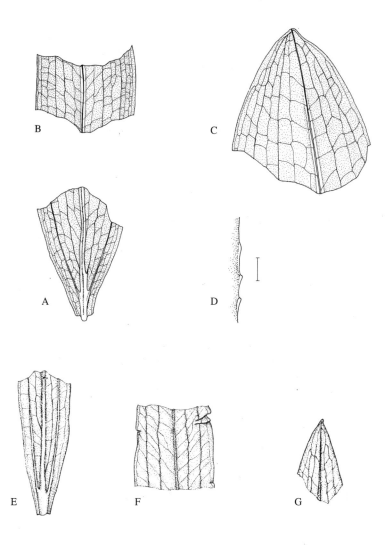

P. × billupsii A, B, C, D: submerged leaf base, middle, apex and margin. Scale bar: 0.1 mm.
P. × nericius E, F, G: submerged leaf base, middle and apex. All drawn by L.T.E.

30 Potamogeton × nitens Weber
(4 P. gramineus L. × 9 P. perfoliatus L.)

Rhizomes very slender to robust. *Stems* up to 2.5 m, very slender to robust, terete, sparingly to richly branched; nodal glands absent. *Submerged leaves* near the base of the stem sometimes reduced to phyllodes, otherwise 40–115 × 9–23 mm on the main stems and branches, as small as 23 × 5 mm on short branches, 3.5–8.5 times as long as wide, translucent, yellowish to brownish green, sometimes tinged pink along the midrib and principal lateral veins, broadly elliptical to ovate-oblong, often recurved, abruptly narrowed to a sessile, slightly amplexicaul to semi-amplexicaul base, usually acute but occasionally obtuse and hooded and sometimes apiculate or mucronate at the apex, denticulate at the margin, the teeth often lost on the older leaves; midrib bordered on each side by a narrow band of lacunae, the lateral veins 3–8 on each side, 1–2 of which are more strongly developed than the others, the secondary veins frequent, transverse or ascending, often irregular. *Floating leaves* with the lamina 35–65 × 9–23 mm, 2.4–3.7 times as long as wide, semi-opaque or opaque, subcoriaceous, pale green when young, becoming brownish green with age, elliptical to broadly elliptical, tapering to a cuneate base, acute and apiculate at the apex; lateral veins 5–7 on each side of the midrib, slightly lighter to slightly darker than the lamina in the living plant, the secondary veins inconspicuous; petioles 12–40 mm, shorter than the lamina. *Stipules* 10–30 mm, as short as 5.5 mm on short branches, open, flexible or rigid, clasping the stem or rolled and projecting from it at an acute angle, buff and translucent to dark green and opaque when dried, obtuse to rounded and slightly hooded at the apex, subpersistent, often lost on the older leaves;

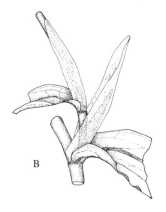

B

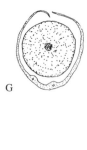

G

A: habit; B: submerged leaf base and stipule; C, D, E, F: submerged leaf base, middle, apex and margin; G: section of stem and stipule. Habit and inflorescence based on plant from Aucha Lochy, v.c. 101, C.D.P. & N. F. Stewart, 1988 (Preston 88/106, **CGE**). Drawn by L.T.E. Scale bar: 0.5 mm.

veins inconspicuous when dry, 2 often more prominent than the others but not forming ridges or wings. *Turions* absent. *Inflorescences* 5–25 × 3.5–7 mm; peduncles 20–80(–175) mm, slender to very robust, broader towards the apex but not or only slightly spongy, terete. *Flowers* usually numerous, contiguous, with 4–5(–7) carpels. *Fruits* do not develop.

P. × *nitens* is the most frequent hybrid in the genus. In the north and west it virtually behaves as an independent species, often occurring in the absence of one and sometimes both parents. It is normally found in mesotrophic, moderately base-rich waters. It is most frequently found in lakes, rivers and large streams; it often grows at the point where an outflow stream leaves a lake. It is capable of withstanding periods of emersion as terrestrial rosettes, and perhaps for this reason can be abundant in lakes which are managed as reservoirs. In lowland England it has also been recorded from canals, major fenland drains and smaller ditches and from gravel pits, although it is now extinct at many of these sites.

P. × *nitens* is a variable hybrid, ranging from plants which are intermediate between the parents to those which closely resemble *P. gramineus*. The main stems are usually closer to *P. perfoliatus* than the branches, which tend to have projecting stipules and less amplexicaul leaves reminiscent of *P. gramineus*. Land forms with rosettes of coriaceous leaves occur on mud at the edge of lakes and reservoirs. *P.* × *nitens* overwinters as buds which develop on the rhizome. Short stolons which root at the nodes are sometimes produced from leaf axils on the upper stems and at the base of peduncles. Clones often flower freely in water less than 1.5 m deep.

Although *P.* × *nitens* is often misidentified or overlooked by inexperienced observers, once it is known many plants may be identified at a glance by their combination of parental characters. Significant differences from *P. perfoliatus* include the more acute and sometimes mucronate leaf apex, more persistent stipules and the capacity of at least some clones to produce floating leaves; from *P. gramineus* the hybrid differs in its more sparingly branched habit, semi-amplexicaul leaves with a more obtuse apex, more numerous lateral veins connected by irregular secondary veins, unridged stipules and less coriaceous floating leaves. The identification of variants of *P.* × *nitens* which approach *P. gramineus* can, however, be very difficult, particularly if only fragmentary material is available. *P.* × *nitens* always has at least slightly amplexicaul stem leaves, which should not be confused with plants of *P. gramineus* with broad-based leaves which contract abruptly into the stem. Unlike its parents *P.* × *nitens* is sterile, and many clones have flowers which never open, the stigmas protruding through closed perianth segments.

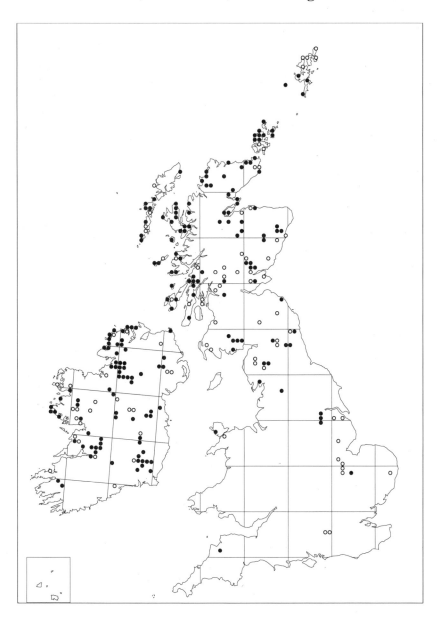

31 Potamogeton × variifolius Thore
(15 P. berchtoldii Fieber × 1 P. natans L.)

Rhizomes very slender. *Stems* up to 0.4 m, very slender, terete to slightly compressed, sparingly branched; nodal glands poorly developed to well-developed. *Submerged leaves* 20–95 × 0.5–0.8 mm, (45–)80–145 times as long as wide, more or less translucent, pale green, linear, flat on the upper side, shallowly concave on the lower side, sessile, acute at the apex, entire and plane at the margin; midrib not bordered by lacunae, the lateral veins 3–5 on each side, indistinct. *Floating leaves* with the lamina 15–40 × 3.5–9 mm, 2.5–6 times as long as wide, opaque, olive-green, often with a pinkish brown tinge, narrowly elliptical to oblong-elliptical, cuneate or rounded at the base, acute and often apiculate at the apex; lateral veins 3–5 on each side of the midrib, translucent in the living plant, the secondary veins numerous, transverse; petioles 25–155 mm, sometimes with a pale brown, discoloured section 3–6 mm long between the petiole and the lamina. *Stipules* 13–30 mm, open, more or less translucent both when fresh and dry, obtuse but rolled at the apex so that they appear acute, persistent; veins prominent when dry, 2 more prominent than the others but not forming distinct ribs. *Turions* not seen. *Inflorescences* 4.5–12 × 1.5–2.5 mm; peduncles 18–50 mm, slender slightly compressed. *Flowers* contiguous. *Fruits* do not develop.

P. × variifolius is well established and locally dominant in the Glenamoy River at Glenamoy in Co. Mayo (F/8.3. and 9.3.), where it was discovered by D.C. McClintock in 1957. It grows in the fast-flowing water of this shallow stream, and in quieter backwaters, rooted in the stony substrate. Associated species include *Callitriche hamulata*, the aquatic form of *Juncus bulbosus*, *Potamogeton natans*, *P. polygonifolius* and the moss *Fontinalis antipyretica*.

This is a remarkable hybrid, unlikely to be confused with any other pondweed. The submerged leaves are intermediate between the coriaceous phyllodes of *P. natans* and the delicate leaves of *P. berchtoldii*, and have a rather grass-like appearance. They are produced in abundance in the early summer or when water levels are high. The floating leaves, which usually predominate later in the season, are like tiny, rather narrow versions of the *P. natans* leaf. They sometimes show the discoloured section between the petiole and the lamina characteristic of this species. The prominent veins on the stipules are clearly derived from *P. natans*, although they are not as closely set as in that species. The nodal glands and small inflorescences are characters derived from *P. berchtoldii*.

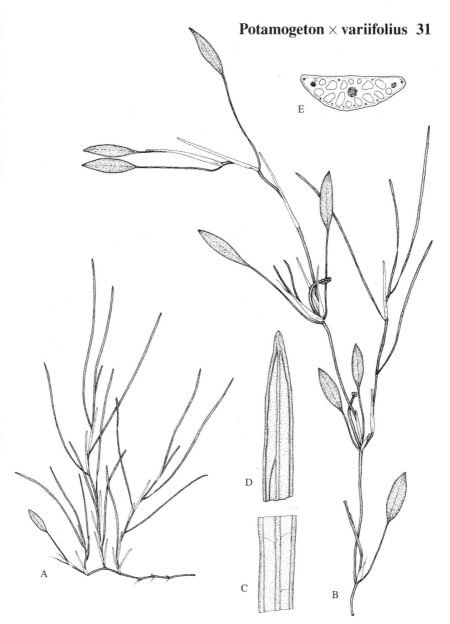

A: vegetative shoot; B: flowering shoot; C, D: submerged leaf middle and apex; E: section of submerged leaf. Habit based on plants from Glenamoy River, Glenamoy, v.c. H27, C.D.P. & N.F. Stewart, 1988 (Preston 88/341, **CGE**). Drawn by L.T.E.

32 Potamogeton × lanceolatus Sm.
(15 P. berchtoldii Fieber × 6 P. coloratus Hornem.)

Rhizomes very slender. *Stems* up to 1.2 m, very slender to slender, terete to slightly compressed, unbranched or sparingly to richly branched; nodal glands poorly developed to well-developed. *Submerged leaves* with the lamina (20–)30–75(–95) × 1.5–5.5(–7.5) mm, 10–24 times as long as wide, translucent, clear green, the upper leaves sometimes with a reddish tinge, linear or narrowly oblanceolate, often slightly twisted along their length or recurved, usually sessile but occasionally shortly petiolate, more or less acute or obtuse at the apex, entire and plane or undulate at the margin; midrib bordered on each side by a band of rather large lacunae, the lateral veins (2–)3 on each side, the outermost vein often faint, the secondary veins frequent, transverse or ascending; petioles up to 4 mm. *Floating leaves* with the lamina 15–50 × 4.5–10 mm, 2.5–7 times as long as wide, more or less opaque, green or pale pinkish green when young, dark green when mature, often with a pinkish red tinge especially along the midrib, elliptical or obovate, narrowly cuneate at the base, acute at the apex; midrib bordered on each side by a band of relatively large lacunae, the lateral veins 3–4 on each side; petioles 1–9 mm. *Stipules* 8–27 mm, open, translucent when fresh and dry, hyaline or sometimes with a slight greenish tinge, rounded to broadly obtuse at the apex, persistent; veins inconspicuous when dry, 2 more prominent than the others and forming weak ribs along the back. *Turions* 10–35 mm, axillary, with short crowded leaves and stipules which conceal the stem. *Inflorescences* 3.5–6.5 × 2–3.5 mm; peduncles 10–70 mm, very slender to slender, of uniform diameter throughout their length or slightly broader towards the apex, terete or slightly compressed. *Flowers* 6–11, contiguous, with 4–5(–6) carpels. *Fruits* do not develop.

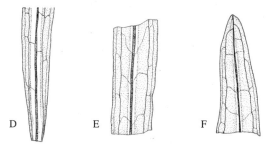

D   E   F

A: vegetative shoot; B: flowering shoot; C: submerged leaf base and stipule; D, E, F: submerged leaf base, middle and apex. Habit based on plants from Cahir River, v.c. H9, C.D.P. & N.F. Stewart, 1988 (Preston 88/332, **CGE**). Drawn by L.T.E.

P. × *lanceolatus* is a rare hybrid, usually found in more or less calcareous water less than 0.5 m deep in rapidly flowing streams. It was originally described from the Afon Lligwy in Anglesey. Discovered there in 1806, it was plentiful in the late 19th century and persisted until at least 1968; a recent attempt to refind it was unsuccessful. It still survives, however, in the Caher River in the Burren district of Co. Clare, and at several other sites in western Ireland. Associated species at the more calcareous Irish sites include *Apium nodiflorum, Oenanthe fluviatilis, Potamogeton coloratus, Schoenoplectus lacustris, Sparganium erectum* and *Zannichellia palustris*. In the less calcareous Glore River, East Mayo, the main associates are *Apium nodiflorum, Callitriche obtusangula, Elodea canadensis, Myriophyllum alterniflorum* and *Chara virgata*. There is also a record from a ditch at Burwell, Cambridgeshire, where it was collected once, in 1880.

The appearance of *P.* × *lanceolatus* varies with habitat conditions. Plants in rapidly flowing water develop only linear submerged leaves; broader floating leaves are formed where the water flow is slower. The reddish coloration develops in plants in unshaded sites.

The nodal glands, linear submerged leaves up to 5.5 mm wide and elliptical or obovate floating leaves clearly indicate that *P.* × *lanceolatus* is a hybrid between a broad-leaved species in Sect. *Potamogeton* and a narrow-leaved species in Sect. *Graminifolii*. It is unlikely to be confused with either of its parents, the leaves being broader than those of *P. berchtoldii* and narrower than those of *P. coloratus*.

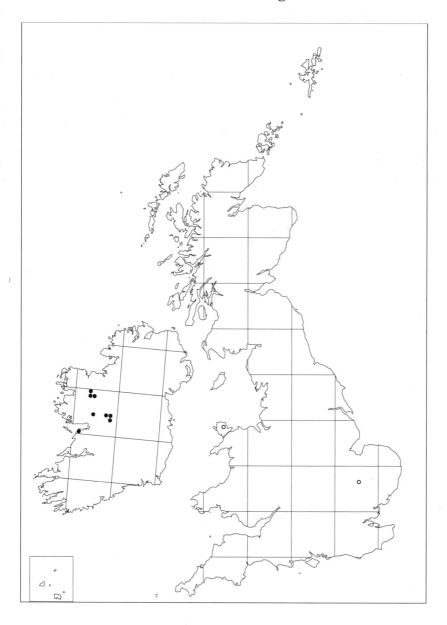

33 Potamogeton × nerviger Wolfg.
(7 P. alpinus Balb. × 3 P. lucens L.)

Rhizomes very robust. *Stems* up to 2 m, robust, terete, richly branched; nodal glands absent. *Submerged leaves* occasionally reduced to phyllodes (Dandy 1975), otherwise (80–)125–230 × (15–)20–50 mm, 4–8 times as long as wide, translucent, olive-green, with a pinkish brown tinge when fresh especially in the upper leaves and along the midrib and often with the upper leaves copper-coloured when dry, elliptical or narrowly elliptical, gradually tapering to a sessile base, acute and hooded at the apex and recurved at the extreme tip, minutely denticulate and undulate at the margin; midrib bordered by a band of lacunae which narrows above the base but extends to the apex, the lateral veins 4–6 on each side, 1 or 2 slightly more strongly developed than the others, the secondary veins frequent, ascending across the whole width of the leaf. *Floating leaves* not seen. *Stipules* 50–80 mm, open, rigid, the entire stipule or the proximal part enfolding the stem, translucent, pale green with a slightly milky tinge when fresh, olive green, often with a strong red-brown tinge when dry, obtuse at the apex, very persistent; veins inconspicuous when dry, two much stronger than the others and forming conspicuous green ribs, the ribs winged on the abaxial side for 20–40% of their length. *Turions* absent. *Inflorescences* 12–20 × 6–8 mm; peduncles 10–40 mm. *Flowers* numerous, contiguous, with 4 carpels. *Fruits* do not develop.

P. × nerviger is one of the rarer *Potamogeton* hybrids. In our area it is established in the R. Fergus in Co. Clare (R/2.9.), where it was discovered by J. G. Dony in 1947. There it grows abundantly in a short stretch of deep, sluggish river, associated with *Hippuris vulgaris*, *Potamogeton natans*, *Ranunculus peltatus* and *Sparganium emersum*. Elsewhere the only record is from Lithuania.

The sessile leaves of *P. × nerviger* with a midrib bordered by lacunae suggest *P. alpinus*, and as in that species they often develop a pinkish tinge. However, the denticulate leaf margins and the rigid stipules akin to those of *P. lucens* clearly distinguish it. The copper colour which often develops in dry leaves appears to be characteristic of this hybrid, and the leaf apex is curiously recurved at the extreme tip.

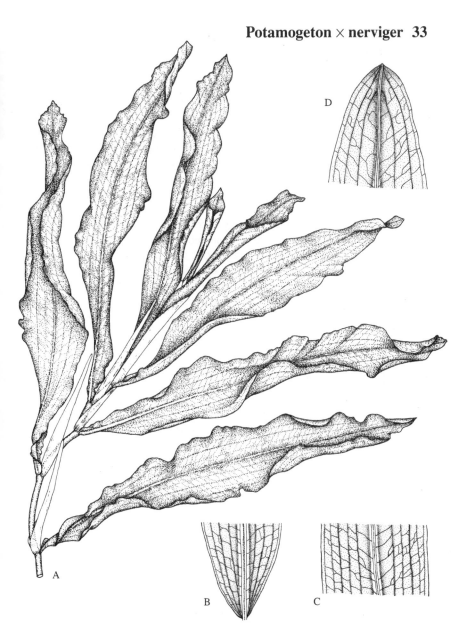

A: habit; B, C, D: leaf base, middle and apex. Habit based on plants from R. Fergus, Killinaboy, v.c. H9, C.D.P., 1988 (Preston 88/334, **CGE**). Drawn by L.T.E. (A) & K.D. (B–D).

34 Potamogeton × salicifolius Wolfg.
(3 P. lucens L. × 9 P. perfoliatus L.)

Rhizomes robust. *Stems* up to 3 m, robust to very robust, terete, sparingly to richly branched; nodal glands absent. *Submerged leaves* at the base of the stem very rarely reduced or partially reduced to phyllodes (Fryer 1890a), otherwise with the lamina 60–120(–215) × 14–40 mm on the stems and main branches, as small as 35 × 12 mm on short branches, 2.7–10 times as long as wide, translucent, yellowish green or dark green, occasionally tinged with pink especially along the veins, linear-lanceolate to elliptical or oblong, abruptly or gradually narrowed to a sessile, sometimes semi-amplexicaul, base or rarely some leaves with a very shortly petiolate base, acute or rounded and apiculate at the apex, denticulate and undulate at the margin; midrib prominent, sometimes bordered on each side at least below by a narrow band of lacunae, the lateral veins 4–8 on each side, 1–2 sometimes bordered by narrow bands of lacunae and hence more prominent than the rest, the secondary veins frequent, more or less ascending towards the centre of the leaf and transverse towards the margin; petioles up to 0.5 mm. *Floating leaves*

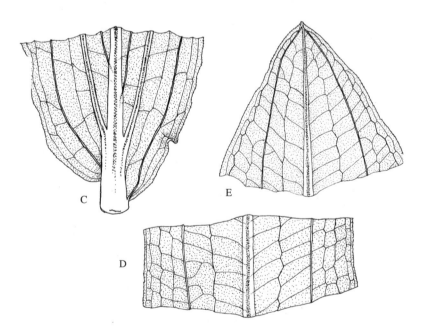

A: habit; B: leaf base and stipule; C, D, E, F: leaf base, middle, apex and margin; G: section of stem and stipule. Habit based on plants from Grand Canal, Belan, v.c. H14, D. Doogue & C.D.P., 1987 (Preston 87/101, **CGE**). Drawn by L.T.E. Scale bar: 1 mm.

absent. *Stipules* 20–55(–70) mm, open, flexible or rigid, translucent, hyaline, sometimes with a pinkish tinge, rounded at the apex, fairly persistent; veins inconspicuous when dry, 2 slightly more prominent than the others and forming very weak ribs, or much stronger than the others and forming distinct green ribs, the ribs sometimes narrowly winged on the abaxial side for up to 75% of their length. *Turions* absent. *Inflorescences* 12–40 × 6.5–9.5 mm; peduncles 30–100 mm, robust to very robust, broader and spongy towards the apex, slightly compressed especially towards the base. *Flowers* numerous, contiguous, with (3–)4 carpels. *Fruits* do not develop.

The distribution of *P.* × *salicifolius* reflects that of the rarer parent, *P. lucens*. Most records are from rivers, canals or (in East Anglia) major fenland drains. In some of these water bodies, such as the lower reaches of the R. Tweed, it has been recorded for well over a century and it is clearly well-established and persistent. There are a few records from lakes in Scotland and Ireland. It is often overlooked because of its similarity to *P. lucens*.

The leaf shape of *P.* × *salicifolius* is very variable: in flowing water the leaves may be very long and narrow with an acute apex whilst in shallow ditches they may be very short, almost as broad as long and have a rounded, mucronate apex. The stipules also vary greatly in size and in the extent to which they are winged. *P.* × *salicifolius* overwinters as buds which develop on the rhizome. Although specialised turions are not produced, short slender stolons with both leafy shoots and roots at the nodes are sometimes produced in the leaf axils of mature plants towards the end of the summer.

This hybrid resembles *P. lucens* in habit and leaf characters, and can sometimes be difficult to distinguish from it. The best character is the leaf base of *P.* × *salicifolius*, which is almost always sessile and sometimes slightly amplexicaul. The leaves of *P. lucens* are distinctly petiolate. The leaf tip of the hybrid is more rounded than that of many forms of *P. lucens*, and the midrib is never excurrent. The leaves themselves are sometimes involute in the water and often become so as they dry. The lateral veins can be more numerous than those of *P. lucens*, 1–2 are often more prominent than the others, and the secondary veins tend to be less regularly ascending. The stipules are usually shorter and much more flexible than those of *P. lucens*, and only winged towards the base, but forms of *P.* × *salicifolius* occur in which the stipules are winged for up to 75% of their length. *P.* × *salicifolius* in flowing water has been confused with *P. alpinus*, but can be distinguished by the ridged stipules and the absence of a broad band of lacunae along the midrib. *P. praelongus* differs in having an entire leaf margin, a hooded leaf apex and more fibrous stipules.

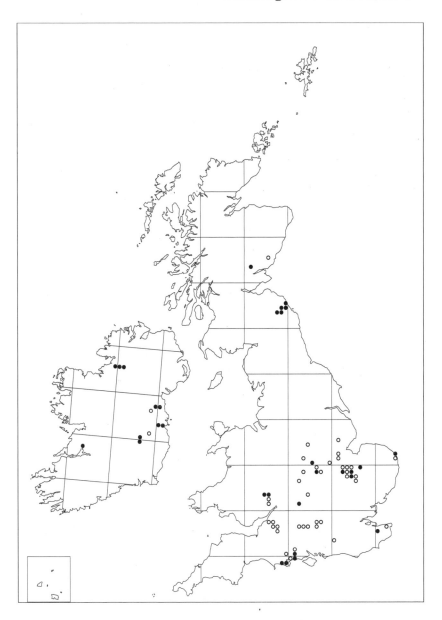

35 Potamogeton × griffithii A. Benn.
(7 P. alpinus Balb. × 8 P. praelongus Wulfen)

Rhizomes slender. *Stems* up to 1.7 m, robust, terete, branched towards the apex; nodal glands absent. *Submerged leaves* with the lamina (70–)120–240 (–330) × 10–25 mm, 7.5–15.5 times as long as wide, translucent, mid green to dark green with an oily sheen, sometimes with a pinkish tinge especially along the midrib when fresh and a reddish tinge when dry, narrowly oblong, oblong-elliptical or oblong-lanceolate, slightly recurved, at least some leaves gradually tapering or more abruptly contracted to a sessile, sometimes slightly amplexicaul, base, some shortly petiolate leaves sometimes present, obtuse or rounded and hooded at the apex and sometimes splitting when pressed, entire at the margin and sometimes minutely undulate for up to 20 mm above the base, otherwise plane or shallowly undulate; midrib bordered on each side by a broad band of lacunae especially towards the base, the lateral veins 4–9 on each side, more or less similar or 1–2 more strongly developed than the

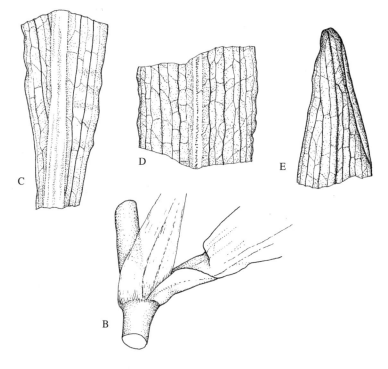

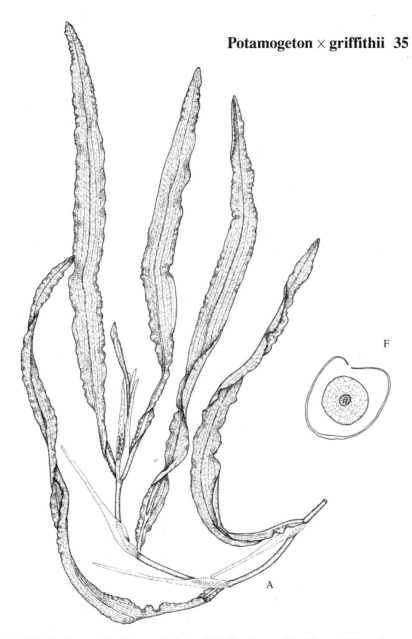

A: habit; B: submerged leaf base and stipule; C, D, E: submerged leaf base, middle and apex; F: section of stem and stipule. Habit based on plant from Llyn Anafon, v.c. 49, C.D.P. & N.F. Stewart, 1988 (Preston 88/34, **CGE**). Drawn by L.T.E.

others, the secondary veins frequent, rather conspicuous, ascending or more or less transverse; petioles up to 3.5 mm. *Floating leaves* with the lamina 85–105 × 13–20 mm, 6–7 times as long as wide, opaque, coriaceous, dark green, elliptical, gradually tapering to the petiole, obtuse at the apex; lateral veins 8–9 on each side of the midrib, opaque in the living plant, the secondary veins numerous, conspicuous, ascending in the centre of the leaf, more or less transverse towards the margin; petioles 50–90 mm, shorter than the lamina. *Stipules* 15–105 mm, open, colourless with a slight milky tinge when fresh, sometimes also with a pinkish tinge, more or less opaque when dry, broadly obtuse to rounded at the apex, persistent, becoming eroded or detached on the oldest stems but not splitting into fibrous remnants; veins prominent when dry, two slightly more prominent than the others but not forming distinct ribs. *Turions* absent. *Inflorescences* 10–20 × 3.5–7.5 mm; peduncles 45–190 mm, robust, not tapered, terete. *Flowers* numerous, contiguous. *Fruits* do not develop.

A rare and possibly relict hybrid, only known from four lakes in Wales, Scotland and Ireland. It still survives in its type locality, Llyn Anafon, Caernarvonshire, where it was discovered by J. E. Griffith in 1882. The Scottish sites, in Westerness, were discovered by S. M. Macvicar in the 1890s: Loch na Creige Dubh, Ardnamurchan, where it was refound by G. Taylor in 1932, and Loch Don, Moidart. In Ireland it was recently collected from a small lake on the Fanad peninsula, Donegal (Preston & Stewart 1992). In its Welsh and Irish sites *P.* × *griffithii* grows in oligotrophic water over 1 m deep; its associates include the aquatic form of *Juncus bulbosus*, *Myriophyllum alterniflorum*, *Potamogeton* × *nitens* and *Utricularia vulgaris sensu lato*. *P. praelongus* has not been found at any of the *P.* × *griffithii* sites, and is not even known from Caernarvonshire.

Potamogeton × *griffithii*, like *P. praelongus*, persists as leafy stems through the winter months (Fryer & Bennett 1915).

The branched habit of *P.* × *griffithii* resembles that of *P. praelongus* and distinguishes it from *P. alpinus*. The submerged leaves resemble those of *P. alpinus* but differ from most states of that species in their broader, distinctly hooded apex. The leaf base is never as amplexicaul as that of *P. praelongus* and, unlike either parent, it is sometimes shortly petiolate. The stipules are intermediate between those of the parents, being rather more opaque than those of *P. alpinus* but less fibrous than those of *P. praelongus*. The capacity to produce floating leaves is inherited from *P. alpinus* but the few such leaves I have seen lack the reddish tinge so often found in that species.

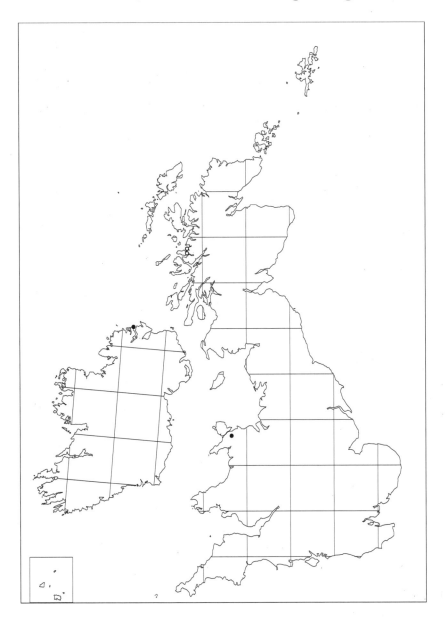

36 Potamogeton × prussicus Hagstr.
(7 P. alpinus Balb. × 9 P. perfoliatus L.)

Rhizomes not seen. *Stems* up to 0.5 m, slender, unbranched; nodal glands absent. *Submerged leaves* 45–80 × 8–14 mm, 5–8 times as long as wide, olive-green when dry, the upper leaves sometimes with a strong orange-brown tinge, oblong-lanceolate to oblong-elliptical, sessile and semi-amplexicaul or amplexicaul at the base, obtuse or subacute and sometimes slightly hooded at the apex, minutely and rather obscurely denticulate at the margin; midrib bordered on each side by a narrow band of lacunae, the lateral veins 4–7 on each side, one of which is usually more strongly developed than the others, the secondary veins frequent, more or less ascending in the centre of the leaf, more or less transverse towards the margin. *Floating leaves* not seen. *Stipules* 13–17 mm, open, translucent, obtuse at the apex, subpersistent, becoming eroded to a basal portion on the older leaves; veins inconspicuous when dry, 2 slightly stronger than the others but not forming distinct ribs. *Turions* absent. *Inflorescences* not seen.

P. × prussicus was collected in 1940 by J. Heslop Harrison from at least three lochs on Colonsay in S. Ebudes (NR/3.9.) and by J. W. Heslop Harrison from a loch on Benbecula in the Outer Hebrides (NF/8.5.). Material from all these localities was confirmed by J. E. Dandy and G. Taylor, but I have traced only a single rather scrappy specimen, at Kew. Taylor visited Colonsay in 1953 without rediscovering *P. × prussicus*. The relevant area of Benbecula has also been searched more than once in recent years, but neither the hybrid nor either of its parents have been found there. However, a specimen collected in the Grand Canal at Wilson's Bridge, S.W. of Rathangan in Co. Kildare (N/6.1.), by D. A. Webb in May 1962 was tentatively identified as this hybrid by J. E. Dandy, an identification with which I agree. The material Webb collected consists of young shoots; a recent attempt to find more mature material was unsuccessful. The above description is based on both the Scottish and the Irish plants.

The leaves of *P. × prussicus* resemble those of *P. alpinus* in shape, but differ in being minutely denticulate and amplexicaul. The stipules are more persistent than those of *P. perfoliatus*, and the Irish specimen also differs from that species in the orange-brown tinge to the upper leaves.

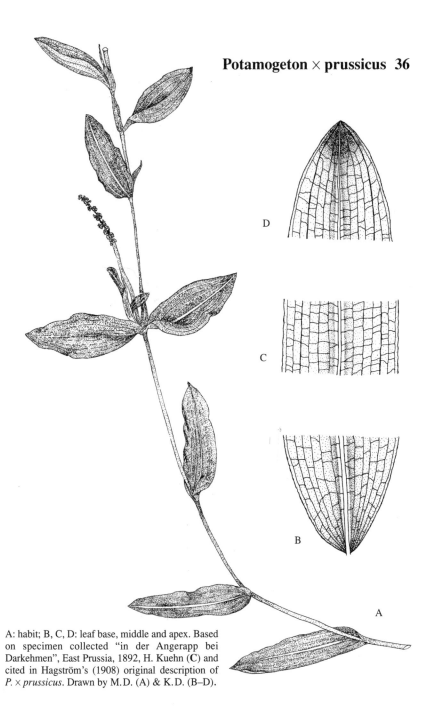

A: habit; B, C, D: leaf base, middle and apex. Based on specimen collected "in der Angerapp bei Darkehmen", East Prussia, 1892, H. Kuehn (**C**) and cited in Hagström's (1908) original description of *P. × prussicus*. Drawn by M.D. (A) & K.D. (B–D).

37 Potamogeton × cognatus Asch. & Graebn.
(9 P. perfoliatus L. × 8 P. praelongus Wulfen)

Rhizomes robust. *Stems* up to 1.3 m, robust, terete, unbranched or sparingly branched below, sometimes richly branched above; nodal glands absent. *Submerged leaves* (20–)45–110 × (11–)14–40 mm, 2–4 times as long as wide, translucent, deep green, often with a brownish tinge, ovate-lanceolate to ovate-oblong, sessile, with an amplexicaul base with auricles which do not overlap on the far side of the stem, obtuse and hooded at the apex and often splitting when pressed, sparsely denticulate and plane or shallowly undulate at the margin; midrib bordered on each side by a narrow band of lacunae, the lateral veins 6–12 on each side, 1–3 of which are more strongly developed than the others, the secondary veins numerous, transverse or ascending in the centre of the leaf, more or less transverse elsewhere. *Floating leaves* absent. *Stipules* 15–65 mm, open, flexible, translucent with a milky or pinkish tinge when fresh, buff-coloured and somewhat opaque when dried, rounded at the apex, persisting for a while on the younger stems; veins inconspicuous when dry and not persisting as fibrous remnants when the stipule decays, 2 slightly more prominent than the others but not forming distinct ribs. *Turions* absent. *Inflorescences* 8–24 × 3–6.5 mm; peduncles 33–200(–255) mm, robust, not tapered, terete. *Flowers* numerous, contiguous, with 4 carpels. *Fruits* do not develop.

P. × cognatus is known from only two vice-counties. In N. Lincolnshire, where J. M. Taylor discovered it in 1943, two colonies grew in major fenland drains at Belton and Crowle. It has not been seen there since 1944, and I could

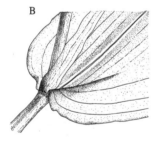

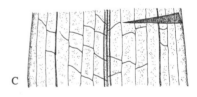

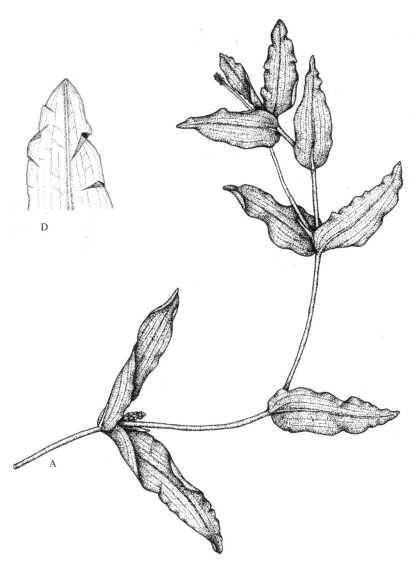

A: habit; B, C, D: leaf base, middle and apex. Habit based on plants from Loch Borralie, v.c. 108, C.D.P. *et al.*, 1993 (Preston 93/53, **CGE**). Drawn by L.T.E. (A) & G.L. (B–D).

not find either *P. × cognatus* or *P. praelongus* on a visit to the area in 1989. However, the hybrid still persists in Loch Borralie, a limestone loch in W. Sutherland, where it was first collected in 1948. Here it grows with both parents in clear, highly calcareous water at least 1.5 m deep.

P. praelongus is winter-green whereas the shoots of *P. perfoliatus* decay in late summer or autumn, the plant perennating by buds on the rhizome. The hybrid is intermediate in duration, the shoots remaining green until December and then dying down (Taylor & Sledge 1944). Although *P. × cognatus* lacks specialised turions, stolons up to 60 mm long and terminated by buds arise in the axils of some mature stems. These send out roots even before they are detached from the parent plant, and no doubt provide a means of vegetative dispersal.

P. × cognatus is morphologically intermediate between its parents. The hooded leaf apex is reminiscent of *P. praelongus*, but the margin is denticulate, not entire, and the stipules are less opaque, with less prominent veins. Variants of *P. × cognatus* with entire leaves have, however, been reported from Denmark by Hagström (1916). From *P. perfoliatus* the hybrid can be distinguished by its more sparsely denticulate leaves with auricles which never overlap on the far side of the stem, by its more persistent stipules and by a more broadly hooded leaf apex than is usual in that species. *P. perfoliatus* is, however, variable with respect to all these characters and care must therefore be taken to distinguish the hybrid from the many forms of this parent.

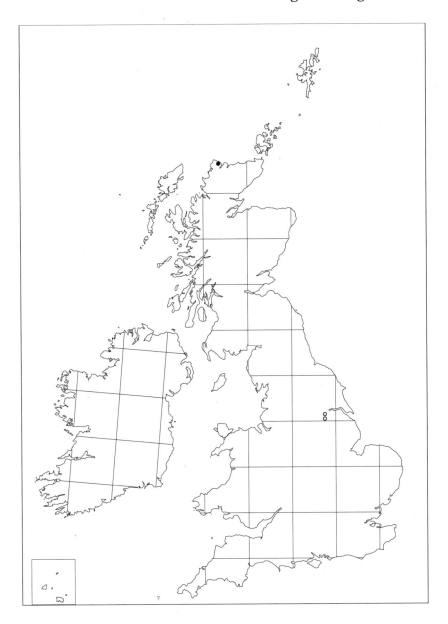

38 Potamogeton × cadburyae Dandy & G. Taylor (19 P. crispus L. × 3 P. lucens L.)

Rhizomes slender. *Stems* up to 0.12 m, slender, unbranched; nodal glands absent. *Submerged leaves* with the lamina 50–95 × 7–15 mm, 4.3–8 times as long as wide, translucent, yellowish green, sometimes with a reddish tinge especially along the midrib, oblong-elliptical, gradually or rather abruptly tapering to a sessile or very shortly petiolate base, usually obtuse and some-times mucronate, rarely acute, at the apex, the margin denticulate or serrulate towards the base, serrulate towards the apex, minutely undulate; midrib bordered on each side by a band of lacunae, the lateral veins 2–3 on each side, the outermost usually the faintest, the secondary veins frequent, ascending across the entire width of the leaf or more or less transverse towards the margin; petioles up to 1.5 mm. *Floating leaves* absent. *Stipules* 12–22 mm, open, clasping the stem or projecting at an angle to it, apparently rigid, translucent, truncate at the apex, persistent; veins inconspicuous when dry, 2 stronger than the others and towards the base forming raised ridges on the abaxial side. *Turions* unknown. *Inflorescences* unknown.

P. × cadburyae is the rarest conceivable *Potamogeton* hybrid. A single plant was collected in 1948 by Miss D.A. Cadbury at Seeswood Pool in Warwickshire (SP/3.9.), where it grew with both parents. The hybrid has never been refound at Seeswood Pool, not has it been discovered elsewhere despite the considerable overlap in the distribution and ecological require-ments of the parent species.

P. × cadburyae is clearly intermediate between *P. crispus* and *P. lucens*. Its leaves resemble those of *P. crispus*, particularly in the shape of the apex (usually obtuse) and in the small number of lateral veins. The leaves are, how-ever, tapered towards the base. Their serrulate margin is clearly derived from *P. crispus*, but towards the base some leaves are merely denticulate like those of *P. lucens*. The stipules of *P. × cadburyae* are much smaller than those of *P. lucens* but resemble them in their rigid appearance and in having two raised ridges towards the base.

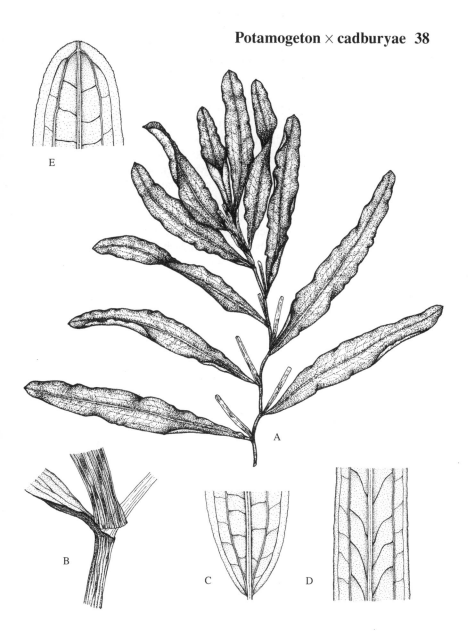

A: habit; B: leaf base and stipule; C, D, E: leaf base, middle and apex. Based on holotype from Seeswood Pool, v.c. 38, D.A. Cadbury, 1948 (**BM**). Drawn by L.T.E. (A) & K.D. (B–E).

39 Potamogeton × olivaceus Baagöe ex G. Fisch.
(7 P. alpinus Balb. × 19 P. crispus L.)

Rhizomes slender. *Stems* up to 0.9 m, slender to robust, slightly compressed to compressed, with a shallow groove running down one or both of the broader sides, usually unbranched, occasionally with short axillary branches; nodal glands absent. *Submerged leaves* 45–120 × 6–15 mm, (5–)8–15(–20) times as long as wide, translucent, bright green, olive-green or dark green, with a pink tinge along the midrib and sometimes along the lateral veins when fresh, often with a reddish brown tinge when dry, linear to narrowly oblong, tapered to a sessile, slightly auriculate base, obtuse or subacute at the apex, undulate and more or less entire, denticulate or bluntly serrulate at the margin especially towards the apex; midrib bordered on each side by a band of lacunae

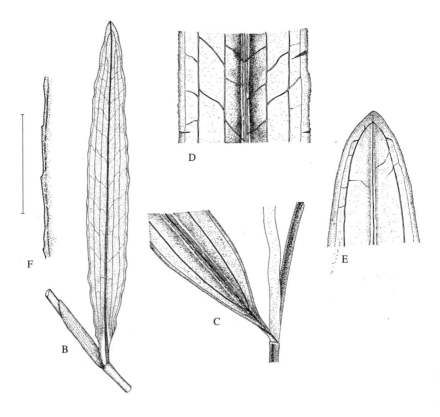

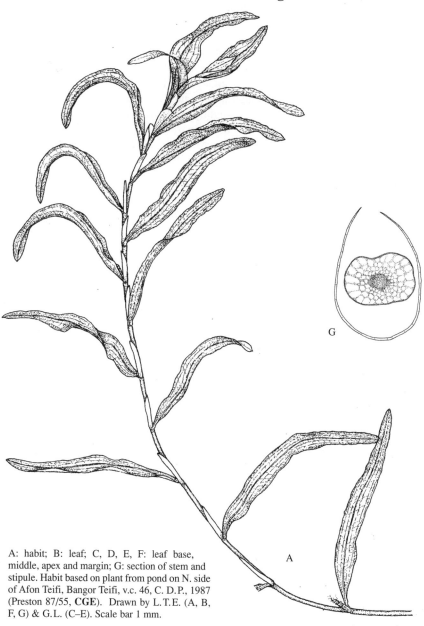

A: habit; B: leaf; C, D, E, F: leaf base, middle, apex and margin; G: section of stem and stipule. Habit based on plant from pond on N. side of Afon Teifi, Bangor Teifi, v.c. 46, C. D.P., 1987 (Preston 87/55, **CGE**). Drawn by L.T.E. (A, B, F, G) & G.L. (C–E). Scale bar 1 mm.

which is broad at the base of the leaf but narrows rapidly above, extending almost to the leaf apex, the lateral veins 2–3 on each side, the outermost vein often faint, the secondary veins frequent, ascending in the centre of the leaf, ascending, transverse or wavy towards the margin. *Floating leaves* not seen, described by Dandy (1975) as occasionally present, tapering to a short petiole. *Stipules* 8–23 mm, open, delicate, translucent, hyaline, sometimes with a pinkish tinge, truncate or slightly emarginate at the apex, frequently persisting on the lower leaves although often with the distal portion eroded away; veins inconspicuous when dry, 2 slightly more prominent than the others but not forming distinct ribs. *Turions* not seen. *Inflorescences* 5–9.5 × 2–6.5 mm; peduncles 7–60(–105) mm, slender to robust, of uniform diameter throughout their length or slightly broader at the base, slightly compressed to compressed at the base, more or less terete or slightly compressed towards the apex. *Flowers* (7–)10–12, contiguous, with (3–)4 carpels. *Fruits* do not develop.

P. × *olivaceus* is established in several rivers in Wales, northern England and Scotland, notably the Afon Teifi, the R. Tweed and its tributaries and the R. Ythan. It was first collected in the Tweed system in 1831. Although not discovered in the Teifi until 1972, it is now known to be widespread in the absence of both parents so it seems that here too it may have been established for many years. It is presumably a relic of a time when both parents grew in the river system, rather than a result of long distance dispersal of vegetative propagules or, even less likely, of seed of hybrid origin. The only record of plants not growing in rivers is of a population found in a pond on the flood plain of the Afon Teifi.

This is not an especially variable hybrid. There is some variation in the leaf-shape, from narrowly oblong to linear, and in the serration of the leaf margin. I have not seen floating leaves on British material of this hybrid, even on plants from the Teifi flood plain cultivated in a shallow pond. The dispersal mechanism of *P.* × *olivaceus* is not known: turions are produced in the leaf axils of many *P. crispus* hybrids but have not yet been observed on this plant. The leafy shoots of *P.* × *olivaceus* persist through the winter.

    P. × *olivaceus* can be distinguished from *P. alpinus* by its compressed stem and by the narrower leaves with fewer lateral veins, only 2–3 on each side of the midrib in *P.* × *olivaceus* compared with 4–7 in *P. alpinus*. From *P. crispus* it differs in the frequent occurrence of leaves with 3 pairs of lateral veins and in the serration of the leaf margin: the leaves are often more or less entire or at most rather obscurely serrulate with teeth which are not visible to the naked eye. For the distinction from *P.* × *undulatus* see under that hybrid.

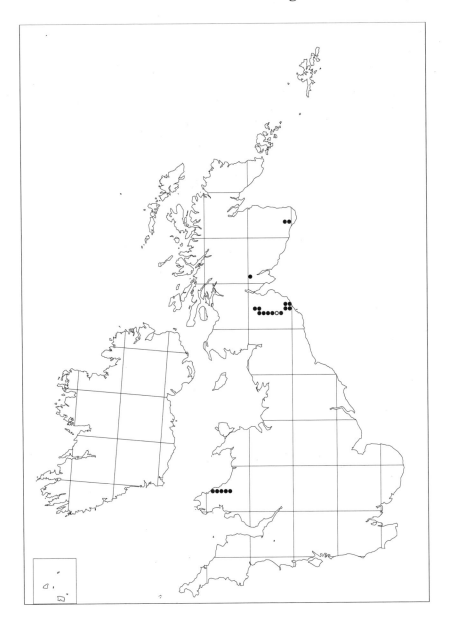

40 Potamogeton × undulatus Wolfg.
(19 P. crispus L. × 8 P. praelongus Wulfen)

Rhizomes robust. *Stems* up to 1.4 m, robust, slightly compressed, with a shallow groove running down one or both of the broader sides, contracted at the nodes, unbranched below, sparingly or richly branched above; nodal glands absent. *Submerged leaves* 45–150 × 8–22 mm, (4.8–)6–12 times as long as wide, translucent, glossy bright green, olive-green or dark green when fresh, sometimes with a pink tinge along the midrib, linear-oblong to oblong-lanceolate, sessile, auriculate or semi-amplexicaul at the base, obtuse or sub-acute at the apex, not hooded or hooded but not splitting when pressed, the margin undulate and entire or very obscurely toothed towards the apex; midrib bordered on each side by a band of lacunae which is broad at the base

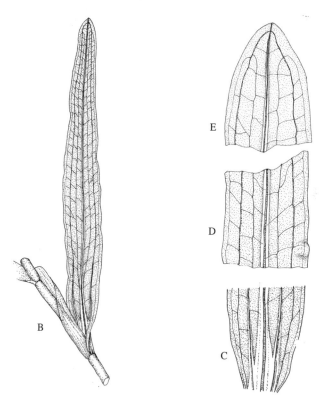

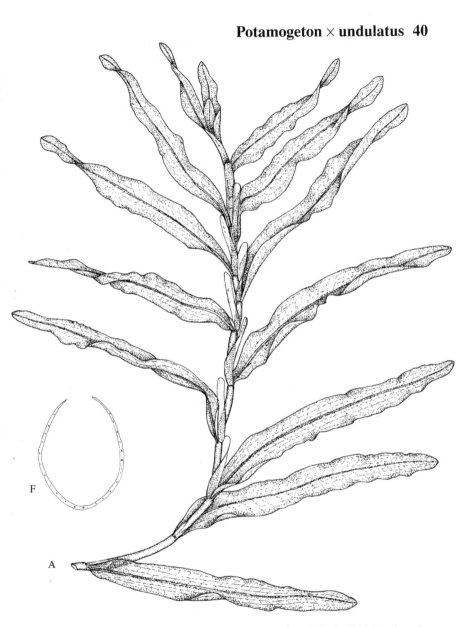

A: habit; B: leaf; C, D, E: leaf base, middle and apex; F: section of stipule. Habit based on plant from R. Lagan, Shaw's Bridge, Belfast, v.c. H38, C.D.P. *et al.*, 1987 (Preston 87/84, **CGE**). Drawn by L.T.E.

of the leaf but narrows rapidly above, the lateral veins 2–4 on each side, the central vein sometimes more strongly developed than the others, the outermost vein often faint, the inner secondary veins ascending, those toward the margin more or less ascending, transverse or wavy. *Floating leaves* absent. *Stipules* 6–25 mm, open, translucent and hyaline when fresh, translucent or opaque and buff-coloured when dry, truncate or slightly emarginate at the apex, persisting as entire stipules or as fibrous remnants; veins distinct when dry, 2 slightly more prominent than the others but not forming distinct ridges. *Turions* 15–70 mm, axillary, slender, with 2–5 free leaves, resembling the slender turions produced by *P. crispus*. *Inflorescences* not seen in British or Irish material; in European plants 7.5–20 × 3.5–4.5 mm; peduncles 18–115 mm, slender or robust. *Flowers* 10–15, contiguous or well-spaced, with 4 carpels. *Fruits* do not develop.

P. × *undulatus* is a rare hybrid, recorded from Llynheilyn, Radnorshire, where it was collected in 1938 and 1945, and from the R. Lagan, Six Mile Water and Lough Neagh in Co. Antrim and Co. Down. In Ireland it was first collected in the R. Lagan in 1908; in 1973–1977 Hackney (1981) found it in many places along a 7.5 km stretch of this river. It grew both in the river itself and in the associated canals, drainage ditches and sluices, often in great abundance and even occurring in water polluted by the outfall from a sewage works. Both the parents of *P.* × *undulatus* are recorded from Llynheilyn and from the Lagan.

Plants from Llynheilyn have short internodes and hooded leaves, and thus closely resemble some forms of *P. praelongus*. Irish plants tend to have longer internodes, presumably reflecting the fact that they grow in flowing water, and the leaves are not hooded. The stipules of *P.* × *undulatus* are also variable, sometimes opaque and becoming reduced to fibrous remnants like those of *P. praelongus* and sometimes translucent.

   P. × *undulatus* might be confused with *P. praelongus*, especially as it can resemble this parent closely in habit. The stems are, however, compressed and although the leaves are similar to those of *P. praelongus* they are narrower and only have 2–4 lateral veins on each side of the midrib. The latter distinction is crucial, and also separates *P.* × *undulatus* from the superficially similar *P. alpinus*. *P.* × *undulatus* is more difficult to separate from the hybrid *P. alpinus* × *crispus* (*P.* × *olivaceus*): *P.* × *olivaceus* can have a pronounced reddish tinge never found in *P.* × *undulatus*, its stems are usually unbranched or only have short axillary branches and its leaves taper more gradually to a less amplexicaul base. It is remarkable that *P.* × *undulatus* shows so little evidence of the serrate leaf margin of *P. crispus*, and confusion with this parent is therefore unlikely.

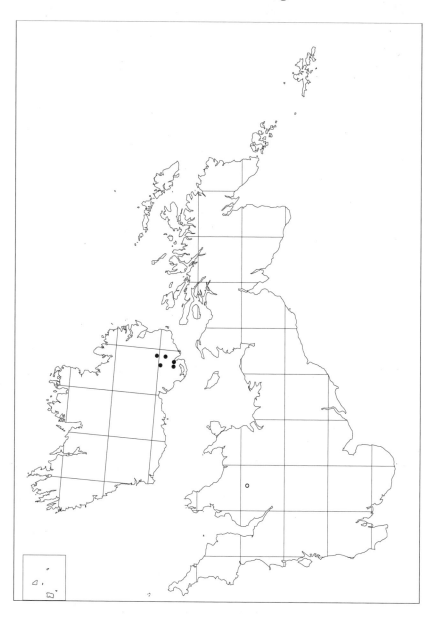

41 Potamogeton × cooperi (Fryer) Fryer (19 P. crispus L. × 9 P. perfoliatus L.)

Rhizomes slender to robust. *Stems* up to 1.5 m, rarely up to 4 m (Fryer 1891), robust, slightly compressed to compressed, with a shallow groove running down the broader sides of the mature stems, unbranched or with numerous axillary branches; nodal glands absent. *Submerged leaves* 25–85 × 8–25 mm, 2.3–6 times as long as wide, translucent, bright green, dark green or brownish green, sometimes tinged red along the midrib and principal lateral veins, linear-oblong to ovate, sessile, semi-amplexicaul or more or less amplexicaul at the base, obtuse or subacute and sometimes slightly but distinctly hooded at the apex, denticulate or serrulate at the margin, especially towards the apex of the leaf, and undulate; midrib bordered on each side by a band of lacunae which is broad at the base of the leaf but rapidly narrows above, the lateral veins 3–5(–6) on each side, the secondary veins transverse or ascending between the midrib and the innermost lateral veins, otherwise more or less transverse. *Floating leaves* absent. *Stipules* 5–20 mm, open, clasping the stem along their entire length, delicate, translucent, hyaline, truncate or shallowly emarginate at the apex, fugacious, the bases sometimes persisting as fibrous remnants; veins inconspicuous when dry, 2 sometimes very slightly stronger

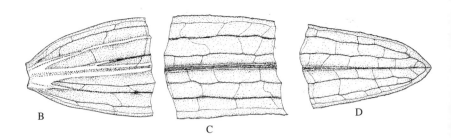

B   C   D

A: habit; B, C, D: leaf base, middle and apex. Habit based on plant from Union Canal, Ashley Terrace, Edinburgh, v.c. 83, N.F. Stewart, 1988 (Preston 88/378, **CGE**). Drawn by L.T.E.

than the others. *Turions* 7–55 mm, axillary, slender, with 5–10 short, distant, erecto-patent to slightly recurved leaves, resembling the slender turions produced by *P. crispus*. *Inflorescences* 4–13 × 2–6 mm; peduncles (8–) 40–100 mm, slender to robust, not tapered, slightly compressed to compressed at the base, terete to slightly compressed towards the apex. *Flowers* 8–15, contiguous, with (3–)4 carpels. *Fruits* do not develop.

One of the more frequent *Potamogeton* hybrids, widespread at scattered localities north to Edinburgh. It is a plant of relatively eutrophic, lowland waters, usually occurring with both parents. Most records are from canals, particularly in the English Midlands, but it is established in several rivers, including the R. Solva (Pembrokeshire), R. Wharfe (Yorkshire), Whiteadder Water (Northumberland and Berwickshire) and R. Slaney (Carlow and Wexford). It has also been found, albeit rarely, in lakes, reservoirs, brick pits and major fenland drains. There are few recent records of *P.* × *cooperi*, but it may be overlooked because of its similarity to *P. perfoliatus*.

P. × *cooperi* is a variable plant. Young shoots can have linear-oblong leaves with a subacute apex, resembling those of *P. crispus*. Mature plants usually have broader, more obtuse leaves which can bear a close resemblance to those of *P. perfoliatus*. Variation in the leaf-shape of mature plants is almost certainly environmentally induced, as Fryer grew dissimilar clones from several localities and found that their differences were not maintained in cultivation (Fryer & Bennett 1915). Unlike *P. perfoliatus*, the leafy shoots of *P.* × *cooperi* persist throughout the year.

The two characters which most reliably separate *P.* × *cooperi* from *P. perfoliatus* are the compressed stem of the hybrid and the fewer lateral veins, 3–5 compared with 5–12 on each side of the midrib. Most forms of *P.* × *cooperi* are readily distinguished from *P. crispus* by their broader leaves with more numerous lateral veins. Whereas *P. crispus* usually has conspicuously toothed leaves, the teeth of *P.* × *cooperi* are scarcely visible to the naked eye. *P.* × *nitens* differs from *P.* × *cooperi* in having terete stems, acute submerged leaves and more persistent stipules which usually stick out from the stem at an acute angle.

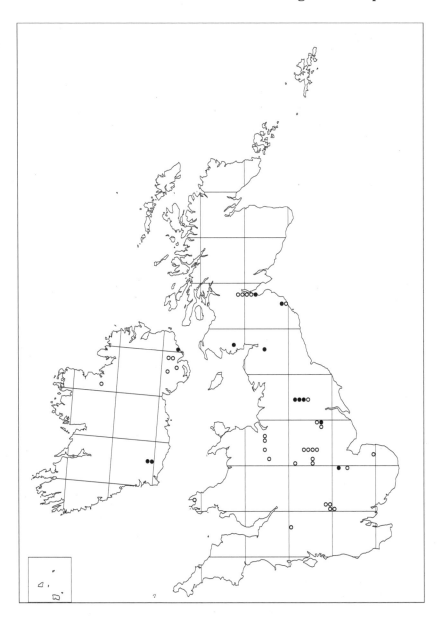

42 Potamogeton × lintonii Fryer
(19 P. crispus L. × 11 P. friesii Rupr.)

Rhizomes very slender to slender. *Stems* up to 0.9 m, slender, rarely very slender, compressed, the most robust stems with a shallow groove running down one or both of the broader sides, contracted at the nodes, simple or much-branched; nodal glands absent. *Submerged leaves* 25–60 × 1.7–5 mm, 7–17 times as long as wide, dark green or brownish green, tinged pinkish red along the midrib, linear to linear-oblong, often slightly twisted, sessile, rounded, obtuse or acute at the apex, the margin entire in proximal part, usually denticulate towards the apex, rarely serrulate or more or less entire, plane or slightly undulate; midrib bordered on each side by a band of lacunae which is broad at the base but rapidly contracts to a narrow band which extends or almost extends to the apex, the lateral veins 1–2 on each side, the secondary veins few, ascending in the centre of the leaf, ascending or transverse towards the margin. *Floating leaves* absent. *Stipules* 6–12 mm, tubular at the base for 0.5–2.2 mm, translucent and pale buff when fresh and dry, truncate or shallowly concave in outline at the apex, persistent although soon eroding to

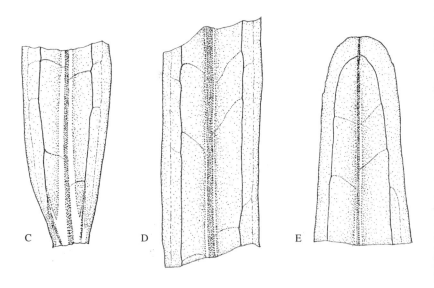

C   D   E

A: habit; B: leaf; C, D, E: leaf base, middle and apex; F: turions. Habit based on plant from Chesterfield Canal, East Retford, v.c. 56, C.D.P., 1988, (Preston 88/375, **CGE**). Drawn by L.T.E. (A–E) & M.T. (F).

291

fibrous strands at the apex, with a rather weak green rib along each side; veins rather prominent when dry, 2 slightly stronger than the others but not forming raised ribs. *Turions* 12–75 mm, usually axillary, rarely terminal, very slender, with 3–12 well-spaced short, narrow, erect, erecto-patent or slightly recurved leaves which do not conceal the axis. *Inflorescences* 3–11 × 2–5 mm; peduncles 8–43 mm, very slender to slender, slightly compressed. *Flowers* 2–4, dense, with (3–)4 carpels. *Fruits* do not develop.

A plant of shallow water, most frequently found in canals but also recorded from lakes, rivers, streams, flooded marl pits and even from a water storage tank. It is most frequent in the English Midlands, but also occurs at scattered sites elsewhere in England, in southern Scotland and in Ireland. At some of its sites populations have probably originated by *in situ* hybridisation. However, plants often produce turions in abundance and have undoubtedly spread vegetatively in the canal system, and perhaps to other water bodies from which *P. friesii* is absent.

P. × *lintonii* is not particularly variable. Young shoots usually have narrower, less undulate leaves than older stems and mature plants show some variation in leaf width and serration. The turions are very variable in size, even on a single plant.

Careful examination is needed to distinguish *P.* × *lintonii* from several similar taxa. Plants with inconspicuously toothed leaves are sometimes mistaken for *P. friesii* or (more frequently) *P. obtusifolius*, but at least some leaves on all hybrid plants are obscurely toothed towards the apex. The grooved stems, absence of nodal glands and the truncate stipules also distinguish *P.* × *lintonii* from the larger linear-leaves species. Conspicuously toothed variants of *P.* × *lintonii* closely resemble *P. crispus* but differ in the stipules, which are tubular at the extreme base. *P.* × *bennettii* is a very similar hybrid but it has open stipules and a reduced number of carpels in the flowers.

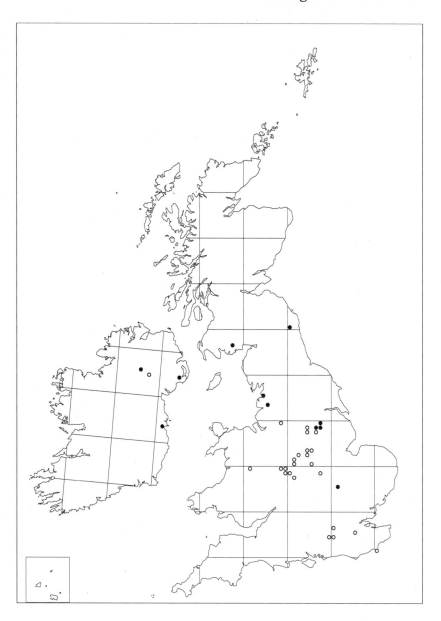

43 Potamogeton × bennettii Fryer
(19 P. crispus L. × 16 P. trichoides Cham. & Schltdl.)

Rhizomes slender. *Stems* up to 1.5 m, slender, compressed, with a shallow groove running down one or both of the broader sides, sparingly to much-branched; nodal glands absent or rudimentary. *Submerged leaves* 20–80 × 2–5 mm, 10–20 times as long as wide, olive-green, with a reddish tinge along the midrib of the older leaves, linear-oblong, often slightly twisted, sessile, sometimes slightly auriculate at the base, subacute or acute at the apex, the margin entire in the proximal part, usually denticulate towards the apex, rarely more or less entire throughout; midrib bordered by a band of lacunae

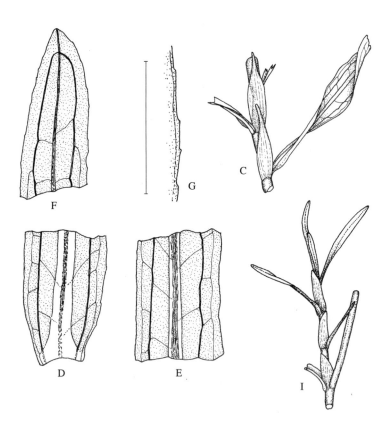

A: habit; B: leaf; C: bases of leaves and stipules; D, E, F, G: leaf base, middle, apex and margin; H: section of stem and stipule; I: turion. Habit based on plant from Forth & Clyde Canal between Drumchapel and Yoker, v.c. 99, C.D.P., 1987, (Preston 87/113, **CGE**). Drawn by L.T.E. Scale bar: 1 mm.

which almost extends to the apex, the lateral veins 1–2 on each side, the secondary veins few, more or less transverse or ascending. *Floating leaves* absent. *Stipules* 4–14 mm, open, translucent, hyaline, truncate or shallowly concave in outline at the apex, soon becoming eroded at the apex but the basal part persistent; veins prominent when dry, 2 more prominent than the others but not forming distinct ribs. *Turions* 12–33 mm, axillary, slender, with 3–7 well-spaced, short, narrow, erecto-patent or slightly recurved leaves which do not conceal the axis, resembling the slender turions produced by *P. crispus*. *Inflorescences* 3–7 × 2.5–3.5 mm; peduncles 8–43 mm, slender, slightly compressed. *Flowers* 3–5, dense, with 2–3(–4) carpels. *Fruits* do not develop.

This rare hybrid was discovered near the east end of the Forth and Clyde Canal at Grangemouth in 1890, growing in ponds used to store wood. It persisted there until at least 1937, but these ponds have now been drained. However, the hybrid was collected in the Forth and Clyde Canal itself in 1960, and it is now known to be widespread and locally abundant in the western part of the Canal. Both parents grew in the wood ponds and still occur in the Canal.

P. × *bennettii* is not a variable plant. It resembles a small form of *P. crispus*, but differs in the narrower, less serrulate leaves. The teeth of *P. crispus* are usually easily visible to the naked eye, whereas those of *P.* × *bennettii* can at best only just be discerned. *P.* × *bennettii* can also resemble *P. obtusifolius*, especially when young. At least some leaves of the hybrid, however, are toothed, at least towards the apex, and its nodal glands are much less conspicuous. *P.* × *bennettii* is very similar to *P.* × *lintonii*, but its stipules are open throughout their length whereas those of *P.* × *lintonii* are tubular towards the base. *P.* × *bennettii* differs from all these taxa in the reduced numbers of carpels in the flowers, a character derived from *P. trichoides*.

Potamogeton × bennettii 43

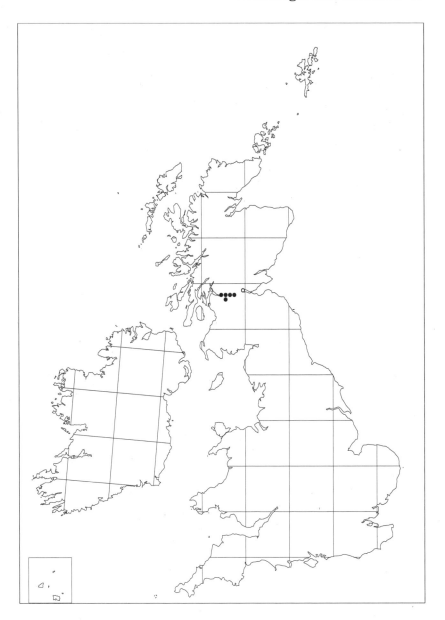

44 **Potamogeton** × **grovesii** Dandy & G. Taylor (**13 P. pusillus** L. × **16 P. trichoides** Cham. & Schltdl.)

Rhizomes not seen, probably absent. *Stems* up to 0.35 m, very slender, much branched especially towards the apex; nodal glands absent or poorly developed. *Submerged leaves* 14–30 × 0.35–0.7 mm, 30–50(–60) times as long as wide, linear, sessile, gradually tapering to an acuminate apex, entire and plane at the margin; midrib prominent, occupying 20–40% of the leaf width near the base, not bordered by lacunae, the lateral veins 1 on each side, indistinct, secondary veins absent. *Floating leaves* absent. *Stipules* 5.5–9 mm, tubular for 0.5–2.5 mm at the base when young but splitting with age, hyaline with a greenish tinge, rather abruptly tapering to an obtuse apex, persistent, with a green rib along each side; veins inconspicuous when dry. *Turions* 8–11 × 0.5–0.8 mm, terminal on axillary branches, cylindrical, with (1–)2 erecto-patent free leaves. *Inflorescences* 4–5.5 × 1.5–2.5 mm; peduncles 12–55 mm, very slender. *Flowers* 3–4, contiguous, with 1–3 carpels. *Fruits* do not develop.

Apparently a very rare hybrid, known from only two collections. It was gathered by J. Groves in a ditch between Ingham and Palling in E. Norfolk (TG/4.2.) on 11 August 1897. Groves named his material *P. trichoides* but it includes both *P. pusillus* and *P. trichoides* as well as their hybrid. The second collection was made on 1 August 1900 by A. Bennett, J. Bennett and C. E. Salmon from the New Cut between Stalham and Palling, perhaps the same locality. The hybrid was not recognised until J. E. Dandy and G. Taylor detected it amongst the material collected by Groves and named it after him (Sell 1967). The area where *P. × grovesii* was collected is much more intensively farmed now than in former years, drainage is deeper, and some fields have been converted from fen or pasture to arable. Recent attempts to refind the hybrid have been unsuccessful.

Superficially *P. × grovesii* resembles *P. trichoides* as its leaves have an acuminate apex, a nerve which is prominent in section and rather indistinct lateral veins. However, the stipules of *P. × grovesii* are distinctly tubular at the base. The flowers of the hybrid have fewer carpels than those of *P. pusillus*.

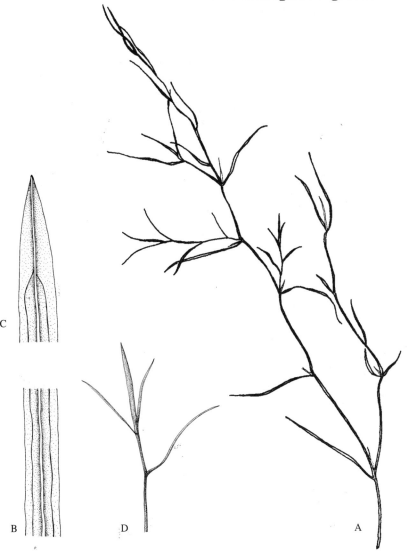

A: habit; B, C: leaf middle and apex; D: turion. Habit based on specimen from dyke between Ingham and Palling, v.c. 27, J. Groves, 1897 (**BM**). Drawn by L.T.E. (A) & K.D. (B–D).

45 Potamogeton × pseudofriesii Dandy & G. Taylor (18 P. acutifolius Link × 11 P. friesii Rupr.)

Rhizomes absent. *Stems* up to 0.5 m, slender, probably strongly compressed, with long axillary branches; nodal glands well-developed. *Submerged leaves* 42–50 × 1.3–2.1 mm, 20–32 times as long as wide, linear, sessile, bordered by a strong marginal vein, abruptly contracted to a distinctly mucronate apex, entire and plane at the margin; midrib bordered on each side by a narrow band of lacunae towards the base of the leaf, the lateral veins 2 on each side of the midrib, the secondary veins infrequent, transverse or ascending; sclerenchymatous strands scattered along the length of the lamina, rather inconspicuous. *Floating leaves* absent. *Stipules* 10–20 mm, tubular at the base, opaque and buff-coloured when dry, obtuse at the apex, persistent but soon becoming eroded into fibrous strands at the apex and splitting longitudinally into two with age, with a strong green rib along each side; veins prominent when dry. *Turions* unknown. *Inflorescences* unknown.

P. × pseudofriesii is known only from the type material, collected in 1952 by Miss D. A. Cadbury from a ditch near Buckenham Ferry in E. Norfolk (TG/3.0.). She also collected both parents in the vicinity. Further attempts to refind this hybrid have been unsuccessful. The area of grazing marshes where it grew is probably more intensively cultivated now than it was forty years ago, and even *P. acutifolius* has not been seen there in recent years.

As its name implies, *P. × pseudofriesii* resembles *P. friesii*. It differs in having sclerenchymatous strands in the leaf lamina, although these are less numerous than in the leaves of *P. acutifolius*. It also differs from *P. acutifolius* in having well developed nodal glands, more slender leaves with two lateral veins on each side of the midrib and stipules which are tubular towards the base.

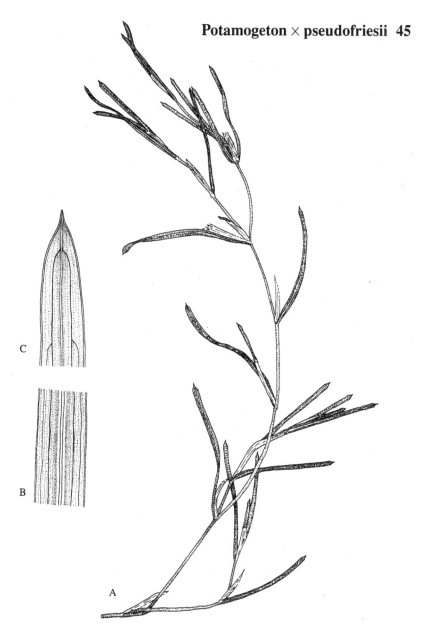

A: habit; B, C: leaf middle and apex. Habit based on holotype from ditch near Buckenham Ferry, Strumpshaw, v.c. 27, D.A. Cadbury, 1952 (**BM**). Drawn by M.D. (A) & K.D. (B, C).

46 Potamogeton × sudermanicus Hagstr.
(18 P. acutifolius Link × 15 P. berchtoldii Fieber)

Rhizomes absent. *Stems* up to 1 m, very slender to robust, compressed, unbranched or sparingly branched with long axillary branches below, richly branched above; nodal glands poorly developed to well-developed. *Submerged leaves* 25–105 × 1.1–3(–3.5) mm, 16–40 times as long as wide, green or dark green, sometimes with a strong brown or reddish brown tinge, linear, sessile, bordered by a strong marginal vein, gradually tapering or more frequently abruptly contracted to a distinctly mucronate apex, entire and plane at the margin; midrib occupying 5–15% of the leaf width near the base, bordered on each side by a band of lacunae which is very broad towards the base of the leaf but narrows gradually until reaching the apex, the lateral veins 1–2 on each side, the outer vein, if present, faint, the secondary veins very few, ascending; sclerenchymatous strands scattered along the length of the lamina, inconspicuous in the living plant. *Floating leaves* absent. *Stipules* 12–25 mm, open, translucent, hyaline, rounded to obtuse at the apex, persistent but the apex eroding to fibrous strands, with a green or colourless rib along each side; veins fairly prominent when dry. *Turions* 18–40 × 1.8–4.5 mm, terminal on the main stems and the axillary branches, composed of tightly appressed, short, dark green leaves surrounded by conspicuous or inconspicuous stipules, with 2–4 erecto-patent leaves at the base. *Inflorescences* 3.5–8 × 2–3 mm; peduncles 10–44 mm, very slender to slender, slightly compressed to compressed. *Flowers* 2–4(–5), contiguous, with 1–3(–4) carpels. *Fruits* 2.0–3.1 × 1.7–2.7 mm, green, the dorsal edge very slightly muriculate; beak 0.6–0.9 mm, ventral, straight.

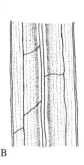

B

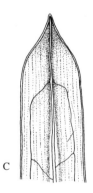

C

D

A: habit; B, C: leaf middle and apex; D: turion; E: fruit. Habit and fruit based on plant from ditch, Stoborough, v.c. 9, R. FitzGerald, D.A. Pearman & C.D.P., 1989 (Preston 89/252, **CGE**). Drawn by L.T.E. (A), K.D. (B–D) & M.T. (E).

P. × *sudermanicus* is known from only a single locality, at Stoborough in Dorset (SY/9.8.). It grows in water of pH 7–8 in drainage ditches in grazing marshes, where it is more frequent than the only one of its parents which accompanies it, *P. acutifolius*. It was first collected here by J. H. Salter in 1921, but not recognised until J. E. Dandy and G. Taylor identified it from herbarium material. Effective reproduction is by turions, which develop from July onwards. Fruits usually fail to develop but occasionally an inflorescence bears a single fruit. These fruits appear to be only partially developed and may not be viable.

P. × *sudermanicus* looks superficially like a narrow-leaved *P. acutifolius*, but differs in the presence of well developed, semi-globose or more or less globose nodal glands, the less frequent sclerenchymatous strands in the lamina of the leaf and the flowers which often possess more than one carpel. The sclerenchymatous strands immediately rule out *P. berchtoldii*. In fresh material the ratio of the longer to the shorter axis of the stem in section provides a very good means of identifying the hybrid: it is 2.9–4.7:1 in *P. acutifolius*, 1.6–2.4:1 in *P.* × *sudermanicus* and 1.0–1.5:1 in *P. berchtoldii*.

47 Potamogeton × suecicus K. Richt.
(20 P. filiformis Pers. × 21 P. pectinatus L.)

Rhizomes very slender to very robust. *Stems* up to 1.3 m, very slender to robust, terete, branched near the base, otherwise simple, sparingly or richly branched; nodal glands absent. *Submerged leaves* (24–)50–160 × 0.3–2.3 mm, (20–)50–170 times as long as wide, mid green or dark green, linear to filiform, semicircular or canaliculate in cross-section, sessile, broad leaves on pioneer shoots obtuse at the apex, the other leaves subacute to acuminate, entire and plane at the margin; midrib bordered on each side by one large or 0–4 large and several smaller air channels, the lateral veins 1 on each side, inconspicuous. *Floating leaves* absent. *Leaf sheaths* 10–40 mm, closed and tubular at the base when young for up to 5(–12) mm but splitting with age, or some open and convolute throughout their length, others on the same plant closed and tubular at the base, the side from which the leaf arises green, the opposite side hyaline; ligule 7–24 mm, hyaline, rounded, asymmetrically obtuse, emarginate or irregularly truncate at the apex. *Turions* absent. *Inflorescences* 14–26 × 3.5–4.5 mm; peduncles 30–225 mm, very slender, terete, flexous. *Flowers* (4–)8–13, in 3–7 groups of 1–3, all groups usually

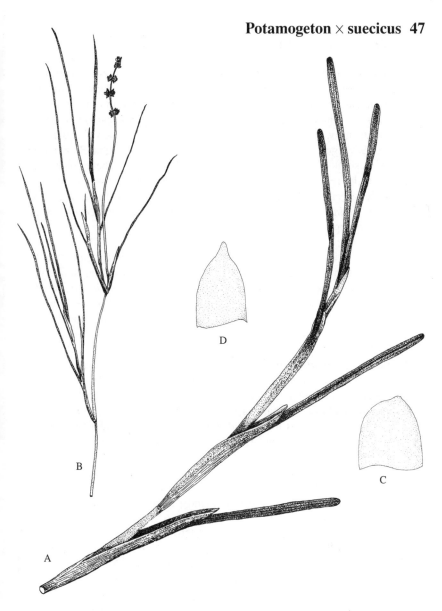

A: vegetative shoot; B: flowering shoot (at same scale as A); C, D: apex of leaves on vegetative and flowering shoots. Vegetative shoot based on specimen from tributary of R. Ure, Westwick, v.c. 64, G. Taylor, 1943 (**BM**); flowering shoot based on specimen from R. Ure, Langthorpe, v.c. 65, G. Taylor, 1944 (**BM**). Drawn by M.D.

distant; carpels 4; stigmas sessile or borne on a distinct style 0.15–0.3 mm long. *Fruits* do not develop.

P. × *suecicus* is found in fairly shallow water in lakes, pools, streams and rivers near the sea in those parts of Scotland and Ireland where the distribution of its parents overlap. The hybrid is well established in at least some of the localities, where it has been recorded for many years and is still present in some quantity. It is easily overlooked and is probably more frequent than the records suggest. In addition it is known from the R. Ure and R. Wharfe in Yorkshire, south of the current distribution of *P. filiformis*. These colonies are thought to be relics of an earlier period when *P. filiformis* was more widespread. It is locally abundant in the R. Wharfe, growing with *Elodea nuttallii*, *Lemna minor*, *Myriophyllum spicatum*, *Potamogeton perfoliatus* and *Ranunculus* spp.

Populations of *P.* × *suecicus* differ in the combination of parental characters which they exhibit. They are always sterile, but reproduce vegetatively by ovoid tubers on the rhizome which resemble those of *P. pectinatus*. In addition tubers are formed on the leafy shoots towards the end of the flowering season and in rivers the hybrid can be uprooted and carried downstream, where pieces root and become established (Dandy & Taylor 1946).

The habit of *P.* × *suecicus* in Scotland and Ireland is not dissimilar to that of typical *P. pectinatus*, and it is easily overlooked as that species. It rarely, however, produces the mass of branches at the surface of the water which is often found in *P. pectinatus*. At least some leaf sheaths on each shoot are closed and tubular at the base, a feature never found in *P. pectinatus*. The colonies of *P.* × *suecicus* in the Yorkshire rivers are more robust plants very reminiscent of the '*flabellatus*' variant of *P. pectinatus*, with a short rhizome, broad, obtuse leaves on pioneer shoots and relatively broad, more or less acute mature leaves. Careful examination of these plants is needed to demonstrate that some of the sheaths are tubular towards the base (the sheaths of the pioneer shoots are perhaps more frequently tubular than those of mature shoots). These plants, like *P. filiformis*, have sessile stigmas. The Yorkshire plants are discussed in detail by Bance (1946) and Dandy & Taylor (1946). The populations in the R. Tweed and its tributary the R. Till which were identified as *P.* × *suecicus* by Dandy & Taylor (1946) and Dandy (1975) have recently been reinvestigated. Unlike the Yorkshire plants, they do not have all the morphological features of *P.* × *suecicus* and isozyme studies provide no support for the suggestion that they are this hybrid. Their correct identity is currently being investigated.

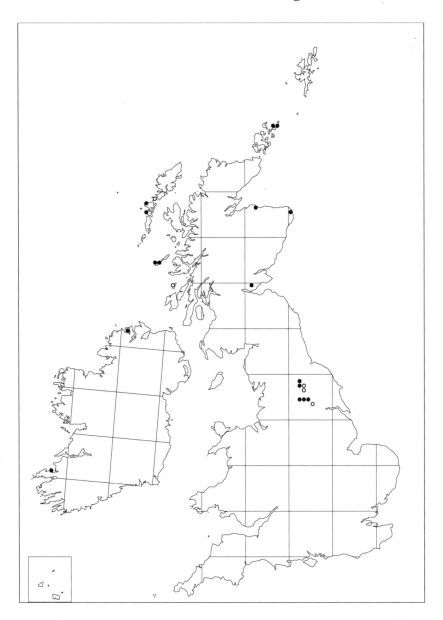

48 Groenlandia densa (L.) Fourr.

Opposite-leaved Pondweed

Rhizomes slender to robust. *Stems* up to 0.65 m, slender to robust, terete, unbranched or sparingly to richly branched, often rooting at the lower nodes; nodal glands absent. *Submerged leaves* opposite, 6–42 × 1.5–13 mm, 1.8–9 times as long as wide, translucent, bright green, the upper leaves sometimes tinged reddish brown, lanceolate to ovate, often recurved, sessile, amplexicaul and more or less hyaline at the base, usually narrowly obtuse, sometimes broadly obtuse, at the apex, denticulate at the margin; midrib bordered on each side by a band of lacunae which is broad towards the base of the leaf, narrows rapidly above and ceases just below or in the apex, the lateral veins 1–3 on each side, the secondary veins few, transverse or ascending. *Floating leaves* absent. *Stipules* only present on leaves which subtend branches or peduncles, 2–4.5 × 1–1.5 mm, oblong to ovate-oblong or triangular-oblong, delicate, hyaline, obtuse at the apex, forming lateral auricles on each side of the leaf base with the lower part adnate to the leaf; veins very faint. *Turions*

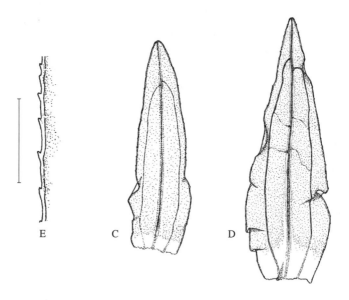

E   C   D

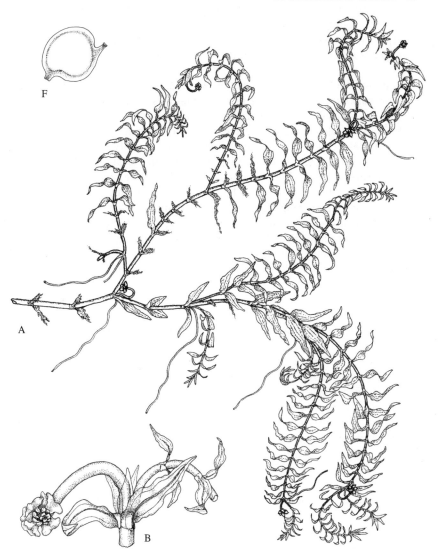

A: habit; B: inflorescence; C, D: leaves; E: leaf margin; F: fruit. Habit based on plant from Coldham's Brook, Cambridge, v.c. 29, Q.C.B. Cronk & C.D.P., 1987 (Preston 87/29, **CGE**); fruit on specimen from Uxbridge, v.c. 21, J. Benbow, 1885 (**BM**). Drawn by L.T.E. (A–E) & M.T. (F). Scale bar: 0.5 mm.

absent. *Inflorescences* 2–4.5 × 2.5–4 mm; peduncles 4–14 mm, erect in flower, becoming strongly recurved in fruit, very slender to slender, not tapered, slightly compressed to compressed. *Flowers* 2, opposite, with 4 carpels. *Fruits* 3.0–4.0 × 2.0–2.8 mm, brown; beak 0.5–0.9 mm, more or less apical, broad at the base, often recurved at the tip.

A plant of shallow, usually calcareous, water in ponds, ditches, streams, rivers and canals, but rarely in lakes or reservoirs. It is a characteristic species of chalk rivers, a habitat in which *Potamogeton* species are rarely found (Holmes 1983). It can also occur in calcareous water over an acidic substrate of peat or sand, associated with calcifuge species such as *Myriophyllum alterniflorum*. *Groenlandia* is widespread, although rather local, in England. It has disappeared from the London area as its habitats have become engulfed by urban sprawl. It also appears to be sensitive to eutrophication, and for this reason may be becoming increasingly restricted to streams and ditches fed by pure water flowing from chalk and limestone aquifers. In Scotland it is extinct as a native species; the only confirmed records since 1930 have been from ponds in the grounds of two hotels and a castle, where it was presumably introduced. In Ireland it has also declined, and in the Republic it is now a protected species.

The rhizome of *Groenlandia* often lies on or just beneath the surface of the substrate. It is less well differentiated from the stem than in many broadleaved *Potamogeton* species, and unlike these *Groenlandia* regularly sends out roots from the nodes of the stem. It overwinters as leafy shoots, and the over-wintering leaves are relatively long in relation to their width, distant and not recurved. Flowering shoots vary considerably in leaf size, shape, density and recurvature. The statement in most descriptions that the leaves can be grouped in whorls of three must either be erroneous or refer to aberrant individuals: I have never seen plants like this, either in the field or in the herbarium. Short branchlets with crowded leaves are sometimes formed in the leaf axils; they are readily detached, and may act as a means of vegetative propagation.

G. densa is the only species in the genus *Groenlandia*. It is easily recognised by its opposite, amplexicaul leaves and two-flowered inflorescences. Of the species with which it might conceivably be confused, *Potamogeton crispus* and *P. perfoliatus* have alternate leaves and *Elodea* species have leaves which lack lateral veins and, except at the base of the stem, are arranged in whorls of three.

No hybrids between *Groenlandia* and other genera are known.

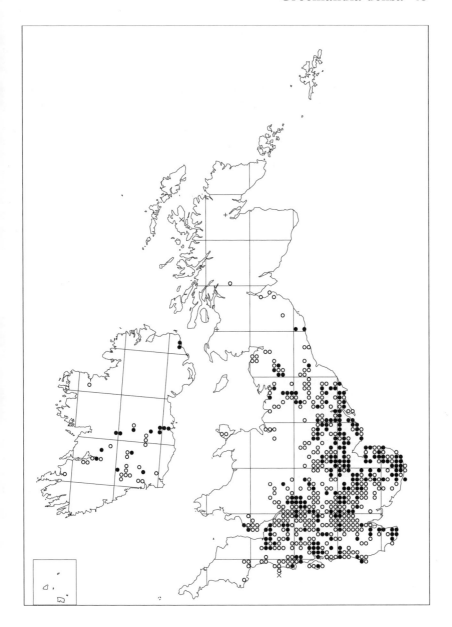

49 Ruppia maritima L.

Beaked Tasselweed, Widgeongrass

Rhizomes very slender to slender. *Stems* up to 0.4 m, very slender, terete, sparingly to richly branched; nodal glands absent. *Submerged leaves* (20–)35–115 × 0.35–0.9 mm, 50–210 times as long as wide, bright green, filiform, elliptical in cross-selection, sessile, acute at the apex, the margin denticulate at the apex, otherwise entire and plane; midrib bordered on each side by an air channel, lateral veins absent. *Floating leaves* absent. *Leaf sheaths* 5–22 mm, open and convolute, the side from which the leaf arises green, the opposite side hyaline; ligule absent; sheaths of involucral leaves slightly dilated, hyaline when young, becoming brown with age. *Turions* absent. *Inflorescences* with 2 flowers *c.* 1.5 mm apart; peduncles (8–)12–26 mm, 0.5–1.8 times as long as the longest carpel stalk when the fruit is mature, rarely as much as 3.3 times as long in dwarf forms, very slender, terete, straight, slightly recurved, arcuate-recurved or coiled with a single turn. *Flowers* with 3–5 carpels, the carpels initially with a very short stalk so that they appear sessile at anthesis, the stalk elongating after fertilisation, the stalks of mature fruits 3–35 mm (the longest on each peduncle being (3–)10–35 mm), very slender, terete, straight. *Fruits* 2.0–2.8 × 1.3–1.8 mm, pyriform, asymmetrical about the longitudinal axis, dark brown, with slightly raised more or less elongated wine-red tubercles on the surface; beak 0.4–0.65 mm, apical, straight.

Ruppia maritima grows in a wide variety of shallow coastal waters, including lakes and ditches, rocky cliff-top pools, creeks and pools in saltmarshes, slowly-flowing streams and tidal estuaries. It is found all round the coasts of Britain and Ireland, and also occurs in brackish water by inland salt deposits near Nantwich and Sandbach in Cheshire (Lee 1977). It is tolerant of a wide range of salinity, growing both in coastal streams which at times are virtually fresh and in ponds which are "brackish, muddy, often slimy and stagnant" (Scott & Palmer 1987). Associated species are usually few, but may include *Potamogeton pectinatus* and *Zannichellia palustris*. *R. maritima* also grows on the muddy flats of saltmarshes, often with *Zostera noltii*. Stratigraphic evidence suggests that in Poole Harbour such mudflat communities disappeared after *Spartina* invasion (Hubbard & Stebbings 1968).

The main variation shown by *Ruppia maritima* is in habit. In the typical plant branched flowering stems without roots at the nodes arise from the weakly

A: habit; B: leaf apex; C: fruit. Habit based on specimen from Hayling Island, v.c. 11, P. M. Hall, 1933 (Hall 987, **BM**); fruit on specimen from Holme next the Sea, v.c. 28, J. Boswell Syme, 1867 (**BM**). Drawn by M.D. (A), K.D. (B) & M.T. (C).

differentiated rhizome. However, dwarf forms with all their axes buried are found on mudflats, especially in Scotland; at first glance their appearance resembles that of *Eleocharis acicularis*. Such plants, in which the fruit stalks are usually less than 10 mm long, were described by Boswell (1881) as *R. rostellata* var. *nana*. Similar plants with even shorter fruit stalks (less than 5 mm long) are found on the coasts of mainland Europe; they are treated by Reese (1962) as var. *brevirostris* Agardh (*Ruppia brachypus* J. Gay). Few British or Irish plants match this extreme. Plants with very short fruit stalks can have the peduncles over three times as long as the longest fruit stalk even though the peduncles themselves are very short. Such a ratio is normally characteristic of the long-peduncled *R. cirrhosa*.

The genus *Ruppia* resembles *Potamogeton* Subgenus *Coleogeton* in vegetative structure, differing in the less clearly differentiated, monopodial, rhizome, the absence of a ligule at the apex of the leaf sheath and the denticulate leaf apex. The toothed leaf apex (which is more easily seen on fresh or rehydrated than on dried material) will also distinguish *Ruppia* from the other aquatic monocots of similar vegetative structure. The flowers of *Ruppia* lack tepals and the stalked fruits are very distinctive. For the differences between our two *Ruppia* species, see under *R. cirrhosa*. The plants illustrated by Ross-Craig (1973) as *R. maritima* and *R. cirrhosa* (under its synonym *R. spiralis*) are both *R. cirrhosa*.

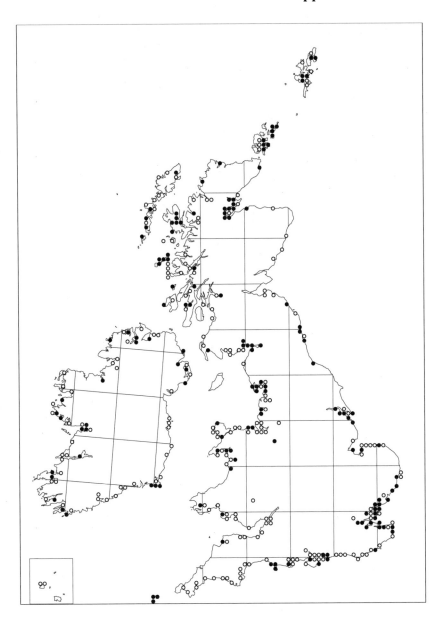

50 **Ruppia cirrhosa** (Petagna) Grande

Spiral Tasselweed

Rhizomes very slender to slender. *Stems* up to 0.6 m, very slender, terete, richly branched; nodal glands absent. *Submerged leaves* 45–120(–175) × (0.2–)0.4–1.4 mm, 70–250(–500) times as long as wide, bright green or dark green, filiform to linear, elliptical in cross-section, sessile, obtuse to acute at the apex, the margin denticulate at the leaf apex, otherwise entire and plane; midrib bordered on each side by one large or several smaller air channels, the air channels sometimes absent from the younger leaves, lateral veins absent. *Floating leaves* absent. *Leaf sheaths* 10–25 mm, open and convolute, the side from which the leaf arises green, the opposite side hyaline; ligule absent; sheaths of involucral leaves dilated, hyaline when young, becoming brown with age. *Turions* absent. *Inflorescences* with 2 flowers *c.* 1.5 mm apart; peduncles 40–300(–770) mm, (1.6–)2–10(–30) times as long as the longest carpel stalk when the fruit is mature, very slender, terete, sinuous or spirally coiled. *Flowers* with 2–8 carpels, the carpels initially with a very short stalk so that they appear sessile at anthesis, the stalks then elongating after fertilisation, the stalk of mature fruits 4–32 mm (the longest on each peduncle being 14–32 mm), very slender, terete, straight. *Fruits* 2.7–3.4 × (1.2–)1.4–1.9 mm, pyriform, symmetrical or slightly asymmetrical about the longitudinal axis, brown or grey-brown with raised, more or less elongated, wine-red tubercles on the surface; beak 0.5–0.95 mm, usually subapical or apical, occasionally ventral, straight.

Ruppia cirrhosa grows on soft sediments in the brackish water of ditches, ponds, coastal lagoons, tidal inlets and in lakes near the sea. Unlike *R. maritima*, it is rarely found in very shallow water. It favours more brackish conditions than *R. maritima* and is, for example, dominant in Loch an-t-Saile, Outer Hebrides, where the conductivity measured by Spence, Allen & Fraser (1979) was 31,800 µs cm^{-1} (compared to 43,900 µs cm^{-1} for seawater). It is a rarer plant than *R. maritima*, being most frequent in south-east England but also occurring at scattered localities elsewhere in Britain and Ireland. It extends north to the Outer Hebrides, Orkney and Shetland.

R. cirrhosa is much less variable in habit than *R. maritima*. Variation in the length of the peduncle reflects water depth, and degree of coiling varies considerably.

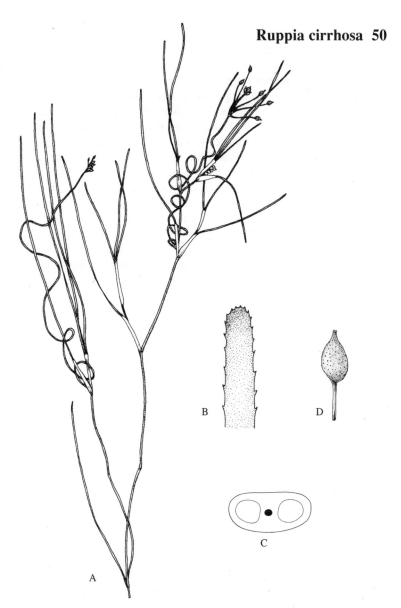

A: habit; B: leaf apex; C: section of leaf; D: fruit. Habit based on specimen from Loch an Duin, N. Uist, v.c. 110, A.J. Wilmott, 1937 (**BM**); fruit on specimen from Port Victoria, v.c. 16, A. Wolley Dod, 1893 (**BM**). Drawn by L.T.E. (A), K.D. (B) & M.T. (C, D).

Ruppia is a taxonomically difficult genus, as the differences between the species are rather slight and the species show considerable environmental variation. Identification should be based on material with mature fruits. *R. maritima* has shorter peduncles, with the longest carpel stalk usually less than 1.8 times as long as the peduncle, and smaller more asymmetrical fruits. Some botanists (e.g. Crackles 1983, Scott & Palmer 1987) have noted that *R. maritima* can be distinguished from *R. cirrhosa* by its narrower leaves which are bright green (not dark green) and acute (not rounded) at the apex. Identification using such characters might be possible in some areas, but although *R. cirrhosa* tends to have more obtuse apices than *R. maritima* the range of variation in leaf apex is considerable. This is shown by Luther's (1947) illustrations of 22 apices. Furthermore, I have seen fresh material from two sites where both species grew and where they were apparently indistinguishable vegetatively. The more dilated leaf sheaths of *R. cirrhosa* are often cited as a distinguishing character but this only applies to involucral leaves and the difference is not sufficiently marked to be relied upon for identification.

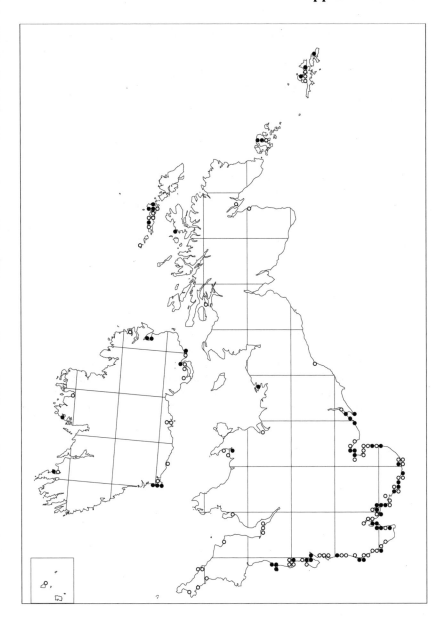

GUIDE TO THE LITERATURE

The main sources of information on the topics covered in the introductory chapters are cited in those chapters. This chapter covers the literature relevant to particular taxa.

Potamogetonaceae

There is no recent monograph of the Potamogetonaceae, although Wiegleb (1988b) has published a useful overview of *Potamogeton*. The world monographs of Ascherson & Graebner (1907) and Hagström (1916) are very outdated but are nevertheless useful sources of information. The European species are covered by Dandy's (1980) contribution to *Flora europaea*. Many of our species are also found in North America and are dealt with in the accounts of the broad-leaved species (Ogden 1943) and the narrow-leaved species (Fernald 1932, Haynes 1974) of that continent. There are also treatments of the species in tropical Africa (Dandy 1937b; see also Denny & Lye 1973 and Symoens, van de Velden & Büscher 1979), Argentina (Tur 1982) and Australia (Aston 1973). The accounts in regional and national floras are too numerous to be cited here; Frodin (1984) provides an excellent guide to these works.

Previous accounts of the British species include those published by Fryer & Bennett (1915) and Pearsall (1930, 1931). These are discussed in the chapter on the history of pondweed studies in Britain and Ireland; those accounts in Fryer & Bennett (1915) which were written by Alfred Fryer contain a wealth of original observation and are all cited below. Dandy (1975) is an essential source of information on the British and Irish hybrids. There are also a number of publications which deal with the pondweeds of other western European countries, including Denmark (Pedersen 1976), the Netherlands (Ploeg 1990, van Wijk & Verbeek 1986) and Luxembourg (Diederich 1983). Ploeg's book deals with broad-leaved species and hybrids in a similar style to a B.S.B.I. Handbook, but it is illustrated by photographs as well as line drawings. Fischer's (1907) classic account of the Bavarian species contains detailed descriptions of several rare hybrids; these hybrids are not covered in Markgraf's (1981) account in Hegi's *Illustrierte Flora von Mitteleuropa*.

The major references which deal with the taxonomy and ecology of particular species and hybrids are listed below. There are many papers about a few species, particularly *P. crispus* and *P. pectinatus*, and the references for these species cited below are only intended to give a lead into this literature. However, it is difficult to find information on many species and hybrids. I have, for example, found very few studies of *P. natans*, although this is such a frequent species in western Europe. In the list below I have not cited the standard references listed in the last two paragraphs, unless they provide a major source of information on a little-studied taxon.

Groenlandia densa: Curtis & McGough (1988), Downey (1991), Fryer & Bennett (1915), Guo & Cook (1990), Kohler & Meyer (1986), Posluszny & Sattler (1973), Preston (1986), Wyse Jackson (1988).

P. acutifolius: Driscoll & Waterford (1994), Hagström (1916), Pearsall (1930, 1934), van Wijk & Verbeek (1986), Sauvageau (1893–94).

P. alpinus: Brux, Todeskino & Wiegleb (1987), Brux *et al.* (1988), Fryer & Bennett (1915), Luther (1951), Wiegleb (1983, 1984), Wiegleb & Todeskino (1983a, b).

P. × *bennettii* (*P. crispus* × *trichoides*): Dandy & Taylor (1939f), Fryer (1895), Fryer & Bennett (1915), Raymond & Silverside (1978).

P. berchtoldii: Clason (1958), Dandy & Taylor (1938a, 1940b, 1944a), Hagström (1916), Heslop Harrison (1949), Luther (1951), Pearsall (1930), Pearsall & Pearsall (1921), Philbrick (1983).

P. × *billupsii* (*P. coloratus* × *gramineus*): Dandy & Taylor (1941), Fryer (1893), Fryer & Bennett (1915), Heslop Harrison (1949), Heslop Harrison & Clark (1941a), Preston (1988b).

P. × *cadburyae* (*P. crispus* × *lucens*): Dandy (1975), Dandy & Tayor (1957).

P. coloratus: Eelman & Ploeg (1979), Fryer (1887d), Fryer & Bennett (1915), Heslop Harrison (1949), Roweck, Weiss & Kohler (1986), Stewart, Pearman & Preston (1994), Wiegleb (1989).

P. × *cognatus* (*P. perfoliatus* × *praelongus*): Preston (in press), Taylor & Sledge (1944).

P. compressus: Pearsall (1930, 1934), Stewart, Pearman & Preston (1994), van Wijk & Verbeek (1986).

P. × *cooperi* (*P. crispus* × *perfoliatus*): Fryer (1890b, 1891, 1892c), Fryer & Bennett (1915), Hackney (1981), Preston (1988b), Wolfe-Murphy, Smith & Preston (1991).

P. crispus: Allen & Spence (1981), Catling & Dobson (1985), Chambers, Spence & Weeks (1985), Cragg *et al.* (1980), Fryer (1890d), Fryer & Bennett (1915), Grime, Hodgson & Hunt (1988), Heslop Harrison (1949), Kadono (1982b), Kunii (1989), Moore (1913), Pieterse & Murphy (1990),

Rodgers & Breen (1980), Sastroutomo (1980, 1981), Sastroutomo *et al.* (1979), Sauvageau (1893–94), Spence, Campbell & Chrystal (1973), Stuckey (1979).

P. epihydrus: Bennett (1908a, b, c), Fernald (1908, 1932), Heslop Harrison (1949, 1950, 1951, 1952), Perring & Farrell (1983), Philbrick (1983), Preston (1991).

P. filiformis: Bance (1946), Heslop Harrison (1949), Jupp & Spence (1977a, b), Luther (1951), Preston (1990), Spence (1964), Spence & Chrystal (1970a), Stewart, Pearman & Preston (1994).

P. × fluitans (*P. lucens × natans*): Beeby (1890), Dandy & Taylor (1939g), Fryer (1886a, 1887d, 1888b, 1890e, f, 1897), Fryer & Bennett (1915), Ploeg (1977), Preston (1988b, 1995a).

P. friesii: Fernald (1932), Haynes (1974), Pearsall (1930), Stewart, Pearman & Preston (1994).

P. × gessnacensis (*P. natans × polygonifolius*): Dandy (1975), Fischer (1907).

P. gramineus: Fryer (1887c, d, 1889b, c, 1890c, 1892a), Heslop Harrison (1949), Luther (1951), Moore (1913), Preston (1988b), Spencer & Ksander (1990a, b, 1991, 1992).

P. × griffithii (*P. alpinus × praelongus*): Bennett (1883, 1907b), Dandy & Taylor (1939e), Fryer & Bennett (1915), Preston & Stewart (1992).

P. × grovesii (*P. pusillus × trichoides*): Dandy (1975), Sell (1967).

P. × lanceolatifolius (*P. gramineus × polygonifolius*): Dandy (1975), Preston (1987).

P. × lanceolatus (*P. berchtoldii × coloratus*): Babington (1881), Bennett (1881, 1882), Fryer (1894b), Preston (1989a, 1993).

P. × lintonii (*P. crispus × friesii*): Dandy & Taylor (1939f), Fryer (1900), Meijer & Ploeg (1994), Neveceral & Krahulec (1994), Preston & Wolfe-Murphy (1992), Stewart & Preston (1990), Vannerom & Andiressen (1987).

P. lucens: Daumann (1963), Fryer (1886c, 1887a, d), Sauvageau (1893–94).

P. natans: Daumann (1963), Fryer (1886b, 1887d, 1889d), Fryer & Bennett (1915), Grime, Hodgson & Hunt (1988), Heslop Harrison (1949), Luther (1951), Sauvageau (1893–94), Spence (1964), Spence & Chrystal (1970a).

P. × nericius (*P. alpinus × gramineus*): Dandy (1975), Hagström (1916).

P. × nerviger (*P. alpinus × lucens*): Dandy (1975), Sell (1967), Preston, Stewart & Webster (1991).

P. × nitens (*P. gramineus × perfoliatus*): Fryer (1896), Heslop Harrison (1949), Luther (1951), Moore (1864), Preston (1988b).

P. nodosus: Archer (1989), Coops, Zant & Doef (1993), Dandy & Taylor (1939a), Daumann (1963), Druce (1920), Fryer (1899), Fryer & Bennett (1915), Perring & Farrell (1983), Preston (1988b), Spencer & Anderson (1987), Spencer & Ksander (1992), Symoens, van de Velden & Büscher (1979).

P. obtusifolius: Luther (1951), Seddon (1972), Spence, Campbell & Chrystal (1973), Spence & Chrystal (1970a, b).

P. × olivaceus (*P. alpinus × crispus*): Dandy & Taylor (1942b).

P. pectinatus: Anderson (1978), Anderson & Low (1976), Bance (1946), Bijl, Sand-Jensen & Hjermind (1989), Cragg *et al.* (1980), Fryer (1888c), Guo & Cook (1989), Heslop Harrison (1949), Hodgson (1966), Jupp & Spence (1977b), Kalkman & Van Wijk (1984), Kautsky (1987), Luther (1951), Madsen & Adams (1989), Moore (1913), Pieterse & Murphy (1990), Sauvageau (1893–94), Spence (1964), Spencer (1986, 1987), Spencer & Anderson (1987), Spencer & Ksander (1992), van Dijk, Breukelaar & Gijlstra (1992), van Wijk (1983, 1988, 1989a, b, c), van Wijk, van Goor & Verkley (1988), Vöge (1991), Yeo (1965).

P. perfoliatus: Fryer & Bennett (1915), Haynes (1985), Heslop Harrison (1949), Jacobsen & Sand-Jensen (1994), Luther (1951), Pearsall (1931), Pearsall & Hanby (1925), Pearsall & Pearsall (1923), Roberts & Haynes (1986), Sauvageau (1893–94), Spence, Campbell & Chrystal (1973).

P. polygonifolius: Allen & Spence (1981), D'Hose (1978), Fryer (1894a), Fryer & Bennett (1915), Heslop Harrison (1949), McVean & Ratcliffe (1962), Preston (1988b), Rodwell (1991), Roweck, Weiss & Kohler (1986), Spence & Chrystal (1970a, b).

P. praelongus: Bennett (1903), Dandy & Taylor (1944b), Fryer & Bennett (1915), Haynes (1985), Luther (1951), Roberts & Haynes (1986), Spence (1964), Spence, Campbell & Chrystal (1973), Spence & Chrystal (1970a), Stewart, Pearman & Preston (1994), Vöge (1992), Weeda (1976).

P. × prussicus (*P. alpinus × perfoliatus*): Dandy (1975), Dandy & Taylor (1941), Hagström (1908), Heslop Harrison (1941), Heslop Harrison (1949), Heslop Harrison & Clark (1941a).

P. × pseudofriesii (*P. acutifolius × friesii*): Dandy (1975), Dandy & Taylor (1957).

P. pusillus: Brummitt (1986), Clason (1958), Dandy & Taylor (1938a, 1940a), Hagström (1916), Heslop Harrison (1949), Luther (1951).

P. rutilus: Clark (1943), Dandy & Taylor (1938c), Perring & Farrell (1983).

P. × *salicifolius* (*P. lucens* × *perfoliatus*): Dandy & Taylor (1939b, h), Fryer (1890a), Ploeg (1977).

P. × *schreberi* (*P. natans* × *nodosus*): Fischer (1907), Preston (1995a).

P. × *sparganiifolius* (*P. natans* × *gramineus*): Fryer & Bennett (1915), Heslop Harrison (1949), Ploeg (1974), Preston (1989b, 1995a).

P. × *sudermanicus* (*P. acutifolius* × *berchtoldii*): Dandy (1975), Hagström (1916), Ploeg (1987).

P. × *suecicus* (*P. filiformis* × *pectinatus*): Bance (1946), Dandy & Taylor (1940c, 1946), Heslop Harrison (1949), Heslop Harrison & Clark (1942b), Preston & Stewart (1994).

P. trichoides: Dandy & Taylor (1938b), Preston (1990), Raymond & Silverside (1978), Sauvageau (1893–94), Stewart, Pearman & Preston (1994), van Wijk & Trompenaars (1985).

P. × *undulatus* (*P. crispus* × *praelongus*): Sell (1967), Hackney (1981).

P. × *variifolius* (*P. berchtoldii* × *natans*): Hagström (1916), Preston (1993), Sell (1967), Wolff (1989, 1992).

P. × *zizii* (*P. gramineus* × *lucens*): Dandy & Taylor (1939c), Fryer (1887b, d, 1889a, 1890b, 1892b), Ploeg (1977), Spence, Campbell & Chrystal (1973), Spence & Chrystal (1970a).

Ruppiaceae

There is no recent world monograph of the Ruppiaceae. Fortunately, the western European plants have been studied in detail by Luther (1951), Reese (1962, 1963), van Vierssen, van Kessel & van der Zee (1984), van Vierssen, van Wijk & van der Zee (1981), Verhoeven (1975, 1979, 1980a, b) and Verhoeven & van Vierssen (1978). Although the studies of Jacobs & Brock (1982) in Australia, Mason (1967) in New Zealand and Setchell (1924) in North America are not directly relevant to the western European plants, they are of interest in illustrating the problems which taxonomists encounter in dealing with this genus.

A few references relevant to our species are listed below.

R. cirrhosa: Crackles (1983), Gamerro (1968), Menendez & Peñuelas (1993), Preston (1985), Scannell (1975).

R. maritima: Boswell (1881), Lee (1977).

BIBLIOGRAPHY

AALTO, M. 1970. Potamogetonaceae fruits. I. Recent and subfossil endocarps of the Fennoscandian species. *Acta botanica fennica*, **88**: 1–85.

AL-BERMANI, A.-K.K.A., AL-SHAMMARY, K.I.A., BAILEY, J.P. & GORNALL, R.J. 1993. Contributions to a cytological catalogue of the British and Irish flora, 3. *Watsonia*, **19**: 269–271.

ALLEN, D.E. 1976. *The Naturalist in Britain*. London: Allen Lane.

ALLEN, E.D. & SPENCE, D.H.N. 1981. The differential ability of aquatic plants to utilize the inorganic carbon supply in fresh waters. *New Phytologist*, **87**: 269–283.

ANDERSON, M.G. 1978. Distribution and production of Sago Pondweed (*Potamogeton pectinatus* L.) on a northern prairie marsh. *Ecology*, **59**: 154–160.

ANDERSON, M.G. & LOW, J.B. 1976. Use of Sago Pondweed by waterfowl on the Delta Marsh, Manitoba. *Journal of Wildlife Management*, **40**: 233–242.

ARBER, A. 1920. *Water Plants*. Cambridge: Cambridge University Press.

ARCHER, D.F. 1989. *Potamogeton nodosus* Poir – Loddon Pondweed. *Reading Naturalist*, **41**: 10–14.

AROHONKA, T. 1982. Chromosome counts of vascular plants of the island Seili in Nauvo, SW Finland. *Turun Yliopiston Biologian-Laitoksen Julkaisuja*, **3**: 1–12.

ASCHERSON, P. & GRAEBNER, P. 1907. *Das Pflanzenreich*, **IV.11** (**Heft 31**). *Potamogetonaceae*. Berlin: Wilhelm Engelmann.

ASTON, H.I. 1973. *Aquatic Plants of Australia*. Carlton: Melbourne University Press.

BABINGTON, C.C. 1839. *Primitiae Florae sarnicae*. London: Longman & Co.

BABINGTON, C.C. 1843. *Manual of British Botany*. London: John van Voorst.

BABINGTON, C.C. 1850. A notice of *Potamogeton trichoides* of Chamisso as a native of Britain. *Botanical Gazette (edited by A. Henfrey)*, **2**: 285–288.

BABINGTON, C.C. 1856. *Manual of British Botany*. Ed. 4. London: John van Voorst.

BABINGTON, C.C. 1874. *Manual of British Botany*. Ed. 7. London: John van Voorst.

BABINGTON, C.C. 1881. On *Potamogeton lanceolatus* of Smith. *Journal of Botany*, **19**: 9–11.

BAKER, J.G. (ed.) 1879. Report of the plants gathered in 1878. *Report of the botanical Exchange Club*, **1877–78**: 13–20.

BAKER, J.G. & TRIMEN, H. 1867. Report of the London Botanical Exchange Club for the year 1866. *Journal of Botany*, **5**: 65–73.

BALDWIN, M. & BURTON, A. (eds) 1984. *Canals: a new Look*. Chichester: Phillimore & Co.

BANCE, H.M. 1946. A comparative account of the structure of *Potamogeton filiformis* Pers. and *P. pectinatus* L. in relation to the identity of a supposed hybrid of these species. *Transactions and Proceedings of the botanical Society of Edinburgh*, **34**: 361–367.

BEEBY, W.H. 1890. On *Potamogeton fluitans* Roth. *Journal of Botany*, **28**: 203–204.

BENNETT, A. 1881. On *Potamogeton lanceolatus* of Smith. *Journal of Botany*, **19**: 65–67.

BENNETT, A. 1882. *Potamogeton lanceolatus* in Ireland. *Journal of Botany*, **20**: 20.

BENNETT, A. 1883. Two new Potamogetons. *Journal of Botany*, **21**: 65–67.

BENNETT, A. 1900. *Potamogeton rutilus* Wolfg. in Britain. *Journal of Botany*, **38**: 65–67.

BENNETT, A. 1903. *Potamogeton praelongus* Wulf. in Britain. *Journal of Botany*, **41**: 165–166.

BENNETT, A. 1907a. Forms of *Potamogeton* new to Britain. *Journal of Botany*, **45**: 172–176.

BENNETT, A. 1907b. *Potamogeton Macvicarii*, mihi, *P. praelongus* × *P. polygonifolius*, a new hybrid. *Annals of Scottish natural History*, **1907**: 106–108.

BENNETT, A. 1907c. *Potamogeton undulatus*, Wolfgang, in Scotland. *Annals of Scottish natural History*, **1907**: 104–106.

BENNETT, A. 1908a. *Potamogeton pensylvanicus* in England. *Naturalist*, **1908**: 10–11.

BENNETT, A. 1908b. *Potamogeton pensylvanicus*, Cham. et Schlecht., introduced to England. *Transactions and Proceedings of the botanical Society of Edinburgh*, **23**: 311–312.

BENNETT, A. 1908c. The Halifax *Potamogeton*. *Naturalist*, **1908**: 373–375.

BENNETT, A. 1922. *Potamogeton* × *sudermanicus* in England. *Journal of Botany*, **60**: 55.

BENNETT, A. 1924. Notes on *Potamogeton*. *Transactions and Proceedings of the botanical Society of Edinburgh*, **29**: 45–53.

BENNETT, A. 1926. Notes on the genus *Potamogeton* of the 'London Catalogue'. *Journal of Botany*, **64**: 329–331.

BENTHAM, G. 1858. *Handbook of the British flora*. London: Lovell Reeve.

BENTHAM, G. 1878. *Handbook of the British flora*. Ed. 4. London: Lovell Reeve & Co.

BHATTACHARYA, G.N. & GHOSH, D.K. 1978. Cytotypes in *Potamogeton crispus* L. *Proceedings of the 65th Indian Science Congress, Armedabad, 1978, Part III, Section X*: 84.

BIJL, L. VAN DER, SAND-JENSEN, K. & HJERMIND, A.L. 1989. Photosynthesis and canopy structure of a submerged plant, *Potamogeton pectinatus*, in a Danish lowland stream. *Journal of Ecology*, **77**: 947–962.

BOSWELL, J.T. 1881. *Ruppia rostellata*, Koch, var. *nana* mihi. *Report of the botanical Exchange Club of the British Isles*, **1**: 36.

BRIAN, A.D., PRICE, P.S., REDWOOD, B.C. & WHEELER, E. 1987. The flora of the marl-pits (ponds) in one Cheshire parish. *Watsonia*, **16**: 417–426.

BRICHAN, J.B. 1842. *Potamogeton praelongus*. *Phytologist*, **1**: 236–237.

BRITISH ECOLOGICAL SOCIETY. 1946. Check list of British vascular plants. *Journal of Ecology*, **33**: 308–347.

BRUMMITT, R.K. 1986. Report of the committee for Spermatophyta: 30. *Taxon*, **35**: 556–563.

BRUMMITT, R.K. & POWELL, C.E. 1992. *Authors of Plant Names*. Kew: Royal Botanic Gardens.

BRUX, H., HERR, W., TODESKINO, D. & WIEGLEB, G. 1988. A study on floristic structure and dynamics of communities with *Potamogeton alpinus* Balbis in water bodies in the northern part of the Federal Republic of Germany. *Aquatic Botany*, **32**: 23–44.

BRUX, H., TODESKINO, D. & WIEGLEB, G. 1987. Growth and reproduction of *Potamogeton alpinus* Balbis growing in disturbed habitats. *Archiv für Hydrobiologie Beihefte*, **27**: 115–127.

BUHR, H. 1965. *Bestimmungstabellen der Gallen (Zoo- und Phytocecidien) an Pflanzen Mittel- und Nordeuropas*. 2 vols. Jena: Gustav Fischer.

BYFIELD, A. 1990. The Basingstoke Canal – Britain's richest waterway under threat. *British Wildlife*, **2**: 13–21.

CAMPBELL, J.W. 1946. The food of the Wigeon and Brent Goose. *British Birds*, **39**: 194–200, 226–232.

CATLING, P.M. & DOBSON, I. 1985. The biology of Canadian weeds. 69. *Potamogeton crispus* L. *Canadian Journal of Plant Science*, **65**: 655–668.

CHAMBERS, P.A., SPENCE, D.H.N. & WEEKS, D.C. 1985. Photocontrol of turion formation by *Potamogeton crispus* L. in the laboratory and natural water. *New Phytologist*, **99**: 183–194.

CHAMISSO, A. de & SCHLECHTENDAL, D. de 1827. De plantis in expeditione speculatoria Romanzoffiana observatis. Alismaceae. *Linnaea*, **2**: 149–233.

CHARLTON, W.A. & POSLUSZNY, U. 1991. Meristic variation in *Potamogeton* flowers. *Botanical Journal of the Linnean Society*, **106**: 265–293.

CHASE, M.W. *et al.* 1993. Phylogenetics of seed plants: an analysis of nucleotide sequences from the plastid gene *rbc*L. *Annals of the Missouri Botanical Garden*, **80**: 528–580.

CLAPHAM, A.R. 1971. William Harold Pearsall 1891–1964. *Biographical Memoirs of Fellows of the Royal Society*, **17**: 511–540.

CLAPHAM, A.R., TUTIN, T.G. & WARBURG, E.F. 1952. *Flora of the British Isles*. Cambridge: Cambridge University Press.

CLAPHAM, A.R., TUTIN, T.G. & WARBURG, E.F. 1981. *Excursion Flora of the British Isles.* Ed. 3. Cambridge: Cambridge University Press.

CLARK, W.A. 1943. Pondweeds from North Uist (V.-C. 110), with a special consideration of *Potamogeton rutilus* Wolfg. and a new hybrid. *Proceedings of the University of Durham philosophical Society*, **10**: 368–373.

CLASON, E.W. 1958. *Potamogeton pusillus* L. en *P. berchtoldi* Fbr. in Nederland. *Acta botanica neerlandica*, **7**: 250–264.

COOK, C.D.K. 1988. Wind pollination in aquatic angiosperms. *Annals of the Missouri Botanical Garden*, **75**: 768–777.

COOK, C.D.K. 1990. *Aquatic plant book.* The Hague: SPB Academic Publishing.

COOPS, H., ZANT, F.M. & DOEF, R.W. 1993. Het voorkomen van Rivierfonteinkruid (*Potamogeton nodosus* Poir.) in Nederland. *Gorteria*, **19**: 44–52.

COX, P.A. & KNOX, R.B. 1988. Pollination postulates and two-dimensional pollination in hydrophilous monocotyledons. *Annals of the Missouri Botanical Garden*, **75**: 811–818.

CRACKLES, F.E. 1983. *Ruppia spiralis* L. ex Dumort. and *R. maritima* L. in S.E. Yorkshire. *Watsonia*, **14**: 274–275.

CRAGG, B.A., FRY, J.C., BACCHUS, Z. & THURLEY, S.S. 1980. The aquatic vegetation of Llangorse Lake, Wales. *Aquatic Botany*, **8**: 187–196.

CRAMP, S. (ed.) 1977. *Handbook of the Birds of Europe, the Middle East and North Africa: the Birds of the western Palearctic*, **1**. *Ostrich to Ducks.* Oxford: Oxford University Press.

CRAMP, S. (ed.) 1980. *Handbook of the Birds of Europe, the Middle East and North Africa: the Birds of the western Palearctic*, **2**. *Hawks to Bustards.* Oxford: Oxford University Press.

CRAWFORD, R.M.M. (ed.) 1987. *Plant Life in aquatic and amphibious Habitats.* Oxford: Blackwell Scientific Publications.

CROCKER, W. 1907. Germination of seeds of water plants. *Botanical Gazette*, **44**: 375–380.

CRONQUIST, A. 1981. *An integrated System of Classification of flowering Plants.* New York: Columbia University Press.

CURTIS, T.G.F. & McGOUGH, H.N. 1988. *The Irish Red Data Book. 1 Vascular Plants.* Dublin: Stationery Office.

D'HOSE, R. 1978. Variabiliteit van *Potamogeton polygonifolius* Pourr. in Belgie. *Dumortiera*, **9**: 11–13.

DAHLGREN, R.M.T., CLIFFORD, H.T. & YEO, P.F. 1985. *The Families of the Monocotyledons.* Berlin: Springer-Verlag.

DANDY, J.E. 1937a. *Alisma coreana* and *Ruppia taquetii. Journal of Botany*, **75**: 142.

DANDY, J.E. 1937b. The genus *Potamogeton* L. in tropical Africa. *Journal of the Linnean Society of London, Botany*, **50**: 507–540.

DANDY, J.E. 1958. *List of British vascular Plants.* London: British Museum (Natural History) & Botanical Society of the British Isles.

DANDY, J.E. 1969. Nomenclatural changes in the *List of British vascular Plants. Watsonia*, **7**: 157–178.

DANDY, J.E. 1970. *Potamogeton* and *Ruppia* in the Azores. *Boletim da Sociedade broteriana*, **2nd ser., 44**: 5–11.

DANDY, J.E. 1975. *Potamogeton* L., in C. A. Stace (ed.), *Hybridization and the flora of the British Isles*, pp. 444–459. London: Academic Press.

DANDY, J.E. 1980. *Potamogeton* L., in T. G. Tutin, V. H. Heywood, N. A. Burges, D. M. Moore, D. H. Valentine, S. M. Walters & D. A. Webb (eds), *Flora europaea*, **5**, *Alismataceae to Orchidaceae (Monocotyledones)* pp. 7–11. Cambridge: Cambridge University Press.

DANDY, J.E. & TAYLOR, G. 1938a. Studies of British Potamogetons.– I. *Journal of Botany*, **76**: 89–92.

DANDY, J.E. & TAYLOR, G. 1938b. Studies of British Potamogetons.– II. Some British records of *Potamogeton trichoides. Journal of Botany*, **76**: 166–171.

DANDY, J.E. & TAYLOR, G. 1938c. Studies of British Potamogetons.– III. *Potamogeton rutilus* in Britain. *Journal of Botany*, **76**: 239–241.

DANDY, J.E. & TAYLOR, G. 1939a. Studies of British Potamogetons.– IV. The identity of *Potamogeton Drucei*. *Journal of Botany*, **77**: 56–62.

DANDY, J.E. & TAYLOR, G. 1939b. Studies of British Potamogetons.– V. The identity of *Potamogeton salignus*. *Journal of Botany*, **77**: 97–101.

DANDY, J.E. & TAYLOR, G. 1939c. Studies of British Potamogetons.– VI. The identity of *Potamogeton Babingtonii*. *Journal of Botany*, **77**: 161–164.

DANDY, J.E. & TAYLOR, G. 1939d. Studies of British Potamogetons.– VII. Some new county records. *Journal of Botany*, **77**: 253–259.

DANDY, J.E. & TAYLOR, G. 1939e. Studies of British Potamogetons.– VIII. *Potamogeton Griffithii* and *P. Macvicarii*. *Journal of Botany*, **77**: 277–282.

DANDY, J.E. & TAYLOR, G. 1939f. Studies of British Potamogetons.– IX. × *Potamogeton Bennettii* and × *P. Lintonii*. *Journal of Botany*, **77**: 304–311.

DANDY, J.E. & TAYLOR, G. 1939g. Studies of British Potamogetons.– X. Another record of × *Potamogeton fluitans* from South Hants. *Journal of Botany*, **77**: 342.

DANDY, J.E. & TAYLOR, G. 1939h. Studies of British Potamogetons.– XI. × *Potamogeton decipiens* in South Wilts. *Journal of Botany*, **77**: 342–343.

DANDY, J.E. & TAYLOR, G. 1940a. Studies of British Potamogetons.– XII. *Potamogeton pusillus* in Great Britain. *Journal of Botany*, **78**: 1–11.

DANDY, J.E. & TAYLOR, G. 1940b. Studies of British Potamogetons.– XIII. *Potamogeton Berchtoldii* in Great Britain. *Journal of Botany*, **78**: 49–66.

DANDY, J.E. & TAYLOR, G. 1940c. Studies of British Potamogetons.– XIV. *Potamogeton* in the Hebrides (Vice-county 110). *Journal of Botany*, **78**: 139–147.

DANDY, J.E. & TAYLOR, G. 1941. Studies of British Potamogetons.– XV. Further records of *Potamogeton* from the Hebrides. *Journal of Botany*, **79**: 97–101.

DANDY, J.E. & TAYLOR, G. 1942a. The identification of some Hebridean Potamogetons. *Journal of Botany*, **80**: 21–24.

DANDY, J.E. & TAYLOR, G. 1942b. Studies of British Potamogetons.– XVI. × *Potamogeton olivaceus* (*P. alpinus* × *crispus*). *Journal of Botany*, **80**: 117–120.

DANDY, J.E. & TAYLOR, G. 1944a. Studies of British Potamogetons.– XVII. Further remarks on *Potamogeton Berchtoldii*. *Journal of Botany*, **80**: 121–124.

DANDY, J.E. & TAYLOR, G. 1944b. Studies of British Potamogetons.– XVIII. *Potamogeton praelongus* in Crag Lough. *Journal of Botany*, **80**: 124.

DANDY, J.E. & TAYLOR, G. 1946. An account of × *Potamogeton suecicus* Richt. in Yorkshire and the Tweed. *Transactions and Proceedings of the botanical Society of Edinburgh*, **34**: 348–360.

DANDY, J.E. & TAYLOR, G. 1957. Two new British hybrid pondweeds. *Kew Bulletin*, **1957**: 332.

DAUMANN, E. 1963. Zur Frage nach dem Ursprung der Hydrogamie. Zugleich ein Beitrag zur Blütenökologie von *Potamogeton*. *Preslia*, **35**: 23–30.

DAWSON, F.H. 1988. Water flow and the vegetation of running waters, in J. J. Symoens (ed.), *Vegetation of inland Waters*, pp. 283–309. Dordrecht: Kluwer Academic Publishers.

DELANY, V.T.H. & DELANY, D.R. 1966. *The Canals of the South of Ireland*. Newton Abbot: David & Charles.

DENNY, P. 1980. Solute movement in submerged angiosperms. *Biological Reviews of the Cambridge philosophical Society*, **55**: 65–92.

DENNY, P. & LYE, K.A. 1973. The *Potamogeton schweinfurthii* complex in Uganda. *Kew Bulletin*, **28**: 117–120.

DIEDERICH, P. 1983. Le genre *Potamogeton* L. *s.l.* au Grand-Duché de Luxembourg et dans les régions voisines. *Dumortiera*, **27**: 26–36.

DONY, J.G. & DONY, C.M. 1986. Further notes on the flora of Bedfordshire. *Watsonia*, **16**: 163–172.

DOWNEY, M. 1991. *Groenlandia densa* (L.) Fourr in the Royal Canal, Dublin. *Irish Naturalists' Journal*, **23**: 383–384.

DRISCOLL, R.J. & WATERFORD, Z.L. 1994. *Potamogeton acutifolius* and epiphytic diatoms at Buckenham. *Transactions of the Norfolk and Norwich Naturalists' Society*, **30**: 80–88.

DRUCE, G.C. 1913. Alfred Fryer. *Report of the botanical Exchange Club and Society of the British Isles*, **3**: 195–201.

DRUCE, G.C. 1920. *Potamogeton Drucei* Fryer in Fryer's correspondence. *Report of the botanical Society and Exchange Club of the British Isles*, **5**: 713–718.

DRUCE, G.C. 1929a. Arthur Bennett (1843–1929). *Journal of Botany*, **67**: 217–221.

DRUCE, G.C. 1929b. *Potamogeton Drucei* Fryer. *Report of the botanical Society and Exchange Club of the British Isles*, **8**: 928.

DRUCE, G.C. 1930. Arthur Bennett. *Report of the botanical Society and Exchange Club of the British Isles*, **9**: 81–89.

EELMAN, W. & PLOEG, D.T.E. VAN DER 1979. *Potamogeton coloratus* Hornem. opnieuw in Nederland gevonden. *Gorteria*, **9**: 325–330.

EVANS, A.H. & BRITTEN, J. 1912. Alfred Fryer. (1826–1912.). *Journal of Botany*, **50**: 105–110.

FERNALD, M.L. 1908. Notes on *Potamogeton pensylvanicus* Cham. *Naturalist*, **1908**: 375–376.

FERNALD, M.L. 1932. The linear-leaved North American species of *Potamogeton*, Section *Axillares. Memoirs of the American Academy of Arts and Sciences*, **17**: 1–183.

FICINI, G., GARBARI, F., GIORDANI, A. & TOMEL, P.E. 1980. Numeri cromosomici per la flora Italiana. *Informatore botanico italiano*, **12**: 113–116.

FISCHER, G. 1907. Die Bayerischen Potamogetonen und Zannichellien. *Bericht der Bayerischen botanischen Gesellschaft zur Erforschung der heimischen Flora*, **11**: 20–162.

FOCKE, W.O. 1881. *Die Pflanzen-mischlinge*. Berlin: Gebrüder Borntraeger.

FOWLER, M.C. & ROBSON, T.O. 1978. The effects of the food preferences and stocking rates of grass carp (*Ctenopharyngodon idella* Val.) on mixed plant communities. *Aquatic Botany*, **5**: 261–276.

FRODIN, D.G. 1984. *Guide to the standard Floras of the World*. Cambridge: Cambridge University Press.

FRYER, A. 1886a. *Potamogeton fluitans* Roth. in Cambridgeshire. *Journal of Botany*, **24**: 306–307.

FRYER, A. 1886b. Notes on pondweeds. 1. *Potamogeton natans* L. *Journal of Botany*, **24**: 337–338.

FRYER, A. 1886c. Notes on pondweeds. 2. *Potamogeton lucens* L. *Journal of Botany*, **24**: 378–380.

FRYER, A. 1887a. Notes on pondweeds. 3. *Potamogeton lucens* L. *Journal of Botany*, **25**: 50–52.

FRYER, A. 1887b. Notes on pondweeds. 4. *Potamogeton Zizii* Roth. *Journal of Botany*, **25**: 113–115.

FRYER, A. 1887c. Notes on pondweeds. 5. *Potamogeton heterophyllus* Schreb. *Journal of Botany*, **25**: 163–165.

FRYER, A. 1887d. Notes on pondweeds. 6. On land-forms of *Potamogeton*. *Journal of Botany*, **25**: 306–310.

FRYER, A. 1888a. On leaf-bearing stipules in *Potamogeton*. *Journal of Botany*, **26**: 57–58.

FRYER, A. 1888b. Notes on pondweeds. *Potamogeton fluitans* Roth. *Journal of Botany*, **26**: 273–278.

FRYER, A. 1888c. Notes on pondweeds. *Potamogeton flabellatus* Bab. *Journal of Botany*, **26**: 297–299.

FRYER, A. 1889a. Notes on pondweeds. *Potamogeton coriaceus* mihi (*P. lucens* var. *coriaceus* Nolte). *Journal of Botany*, **27**: 8–10.

FRYER, A. 1889b. Notes on pondweeds. *Potamogeton varians* Morong in Herb. ined. *Journal of Botany*, **27**: 33–36.

FRYER, A. 1889c. Notes on pondweeds. *Potamogeton falcatus* mihi. *Journal of Botany*, **27**: 65–67.

FRYER, A. 1889d. Irish potamogetons. *Journal of Botany*, **27**: 183–184.

FRYER, A. 1890a. Notes on pondweeds. *Potamogeton decipiens* Nolte. *Journal of Botany*, **28**: 137–139.

FRYER, A. 1890b. Supposed hybridity in *Potamogeton*. *Journal of Botany*, **28**: 173–179.

FRYER, A. 1890c. *Potamogeton falcatus*. *Journal of Botany*, **28**: 219–220.

FRYER, A. 1890d. Notes on pondweeds. *Potamogeton crispus* L. *Journal of Botany*, **28**: 225–227.

FRYER, A. 1890e. *Potamogeton fluitans* Roth. *Journal of Botany*, **28**: 249.

FRYER, A. 1890f. On a new hybrid *Potamogeton* of the *fluitans* group. *Journal of Botany*, **28**: 321–326.

FRYER, A. 1891. On a new British *Potamogeton* of the *nitens* group. *Journal of Botany*, **29**: 289–292.

FRYER, A. 1892a. Notes on pondweeds. *Potamogeton gramineus* L. v. *graminifolius* Fries = *P. heterophyllus* var. *Journal of Botany*, **30**: 33–37.

FRYER, A. 1892b. On the specific rank of *Potamogeton Zizii*. *Journal of Botany*, **30**: 114–118.

FRYER, A. 1892c. *Potamogeton undulatus*, Wolfgang, in Stirlingshire. *Annals of Scottish natural History*, **1892**: 115–119.

FRYER, A. 1893. Notes on pondweeds. A new hybrid *Potamogeton*. *Journal of Botany*, **31**: 353–355.

FRYER, A. 1894a. *Potamogeton polygonifolius* v. *pseudo-fluitans*. *Journal of Botany*, **32**: 97–100.

FRYER, A. 1894b. *Potamogeton rivularis* Gillot. *Journal of Botany*, **32**: 337–340.

FRYER, A. 1895. *Potamogeton Bennettii*. *Journal of Botany*, **33**: 1–3.

FRYER, A. 1896. *Potamogeton nitens* Weber, f. *involuta*. *Journal of Botany*, **34**: 1–3.

FRYER, A. 1897. × *Potamogeton fluitans* in Huntingdonshire. *Journal of Botany*, **35**: 355–356.

FRYER, A. 1899. *Potamogeton Drucei* Fryer. *Journal of Botany*, **37**: 524.

FRYER, A. 1900. *P. crispus*, Linn. var. *serratus*, Huds. *Annual Report of the Watson botanical Exchange Club*, **1899–1900**: 21.

FRYER, A. & BENNETT, A. 1915. *The Potamogetons (Pond Weeds) of the British Isles*. London: L. Reeve & Co.

GAMERRO, J.C. 1968. Observaciones sobre la biologia floral y morfologia de la Potamogetonácea *Ruppia cirrhosa* (Petag.) Grande (=*R. spiralis* L. ex Dum.). *Darwiniana*, **14**: 575–608.

GARDINER, W. 1848. *The Flora of Forfarshire*. London: Longman, Brown, Green & Longmans.

GEORGE, M. 1992. *The Land Use, Ecology and Conservation of Broadland*. Chichester: Packard Publishing.

GERARDE, J. 1597. *The Herball or generall Historie of Plantes*. London.

GERARDE, J. 1633. *The Herball or generall Historie of Plantes*. Ed. 2, revised by T. Johnson. London.

GHOSH, D.K. & BHATTACHARYA, G.N. 1980. Chromosomes in some species of *Potamogeton* and *Aponogeton*. *Bulletin of the botanical Society of Bengal*, **34**: 83–88.

GOATER, B. 1986. *British pyralid Moths*. Colchester: Harley Books.

GODWIN, H. 1975. *The History of the British Flora*. Ed 2. Cambridge: Cambridge University Press.

GOSLING, L.M. & BAKER, S.J. 1980. Acidity fluctuations at a Broadland site in Norfolk. *Journal of applied Ecology*, **17**: 479–490.

GRIGSON, G. 1958. *The Englishman's Flora*. London: Phoenix House.

GRIME, J.P., HODGSON, J.G. & HUNT, R. 1988. *Comparative Plant Ecology*. London: Unwin Hyman.

GUO, Y.-H. & COOK, C.D.K. 1989. Pollination efficiency of *Potamogeton pectinatus* L. *Aquatic Botany*, **34**: 381–384.

GUO, Y.-H. & COOK, C.D.K. 1990. The floral biology of *Groenlandia densa* (L.) Fourreau (Potamogetonaceae). *Aquatic Botany*, **38**: 283–288.

GUPPY, H.B. 1894. Water-plants and their ways. *Science-Gossip*, **n.s., 1**: 145–147.

GUPPY, H.B. 1897. On the postponement of the germination of the seeds of aquatic plants. *Proceedings of the royal physical Society*, **13**: 344–359.

GUPPY, H.B. 1906. *Observations of a Naturalist in the Pacific between 1896 and 1899*, **2**. *Plant-dispersal*. London: Macmillan & Co.

HAAG, R.W. 1983. Emergence of seedlings of aquatic macrophytes from lake sediments. *Canadian Journal of Botany*, **61**: 148–156.

HACKNEY, P. 1981. *Potamogeton* × *cooperi* (Fryer) and *P.* × *undulatus* Wolfg. in N E Ireland. *Irish Naturalists' Journal*, **20**: 250–251.

HADFIELD, C. 1984. *British Canals. An illustrated History*. Ed. 7. Newton Abbot: David & Charles.

HAGSTRÖM, [J.]O. 1908. New potamogetons. *Botaniska Notiser*, **1908**: 97–108.

HAGSTRÖM, J.O. 1916. Critical researches on the Potamogetons. *Kungliga svenska Vetenskapsakademiens Handlingar*, **55 (5)**: 1–281.

HARADA, I. 1956. Cytological studies in Helobiae, 1. Chromosome idiograms and a list of chromosome numbers in seven families. *Cytologia*, **21**: 306–328.

HAYNES, R.R. 1974. A revision of North American *Potamogeton* Subsection *Pusilli* (Potamogetonaceae). *Rhodora*, **76**: 564–649.

HAYNES, R.R. & WILLIAMS, D.C. 1975. Evidence for the hybrid origin of *Potamogeton longiligulatus* (Potamogetonaceae). *Michigan Botanist*, **14**: 94–100.

HAYNES, R.R. 1985. A revision of the clasping-leaved *Potamogeton* (Potamogetonaceae). *Sida*, **11**: 173–188.

HAYNES, R.R. 1986. Typification of Linnaean species of *Potamogeton* (Potamogetonaceae). *Taxon*, **35**: 563–573.

HELLQUIST, C.B. 1980. Correlation of alkalinity and the distribution of *Potamogeton* in New England. *Rhodora*, **82**: 331–344.

HELLQUIST, C.B. & HILTON, R.L. 1983. A new species of *Potamogeton* (Potamogetonaceae) from Northeastern United States. *Systematic Botany*, **8**: 86–92.

HERR, W. & WIEGLEB, G. 1985. Die Potamogetonaceae Niedersächsischer Fliessgewässer, Teil 2. *Göttinger floristische Rundbriefe*, **19**: 2–16.

HESLOP HARRISON, J. 1941. Notes on the pondweeds of the Isle of Colonsay. *Occasional Notes from the Department of Botany, King's College, Newcastle upon Tyne*, 2, **3**: 3.

HESLOP HARRISON, J.W. 1944. Hebridean Potamogetons once more. *Occasional Notes from the Department of Botany, King's College, Newcastle upon Tyne*, 2, **5**: 1–6.

HESLOP HARRISON, J.W. 1949. Potamogetons in the Scottish Western Isles, with some remarks on the general natural history of the species. *Transactions and Proceedings of the botanical Society of Edinburgh*, **35**: 1–25.

HESLOP HARRISON, J.W. 1950. A pondweed, new to the European flora, from the Scottish Western Isles, with some remarks on the phytogeography of the island group. *Phyton, Horn*, **2**: 104–109.

HESLOP HARRISON, J.W. 1951. Vascular plants in the Outer Hebrides in 1950. *Proceedings of the University of Durham philosophical Society*, **11**: 1–11.

HESLOP HARRISON, J.W. 1952. Occurrence of the American Pondweed, *Potamogeton epihydrus* Raf., in the Hebrides. *Nature*, **169**: 548–549.

HESLOP HARRISON, J.W. & CLARK, W.A. 1941a. Hybrid Potamogetons on the Isle of Benbecula. *Occasional Notes from the Department of Botany, King's College, Newcastle upon Tyne*, 2, **2**: 1–4.

HESLOP HARRISON, J.W. & CLARK, W.A. 1941b. Pondweeds in the Outer Hebrides. *Occasional Notes from the Department of Botany, King's College, Newcastle upon Tyne*, 2, **3**: 1–3.

HESLOP HARRISON, J.W. & CLARK, W.A. 1942a. Hebridean Potamogetons and their identification. *Occasional Notes from the Department of Botany, King's College, Newcastle upon Tyne,* 2, **4**: 1–4.

HESLOP HARRISON, J.W. & CLARK, W.A. 1942b. A note on × *Potamogeton suecicus* Richt. *Occasional Notes from the Department of Botany, King's College, Newcastle upon Tyne,* 2, **4**: 4.

HESLOP HARRISON, J.W. & CLARK, W.A. 1942c. More notes on local pondweeds. *Vasculum,* **27**: 29.

HESLOP HARRISON, J.W., HESLOP HARRISON, H., CLARK, W.A. & COOKE, R.B. 1942. Further observations on the vascular plants of the Outer Hebrides (V.-C. 110). *Proceedings of the University of Durham philosophical Society,* **10**: 358–367.

HETTIARACHCHI, P. & TRIEST, L. 1991. Isozyme polymorphism in the genus *Potamogeton* (Potamogetonaceae). *Opera botanica belgica,* **4**: 87–114.

HEYWOOD, V.H. (ed.) 1978. *Flowering Plants of the World.* Oxford: Oxford University Press.

HISINGER, E. 1887. Recherches sur les tubercules du *Ruppia rostellata* et du *Zanichellia polycarpa* provoqués par le *Tetramyxa parasitica. Meddelanden af Societas pro Fauna et Flora fennica,* **14**: 53–62.

HODGSON, R.H. 1966. Growth and carbohydrate status of Sago Pondweed. *Weeds,* **14**: 263–268.

HOLMES, N.T.H. 1983. *Typing British Rivers according to their Flora.* Focus on Nature Conservation no. 4. Shrewsbury: Nature Conservancy Council.

HOLMES, N.[T.H.] & NEWBOLD, C. 1984. *River Plant Communities – Reflectors of Water and Substrate Chemistry.* Focus on Nature Conservation, no. 9. Shrewsbury: Nature Conservancy Council.

HOOKER, J.D. 1878. *The Student's Flora of the British Islands,* 2nd ed. London: Macmillan & Co.

HOOKER, W.J. 1830. *The British Flora.* London: Longman, Rees, Orme, Brown & Green.

HOOKER, W.J. 1831. *Supplement to the English Botany of the late Sir J.E. Smith and Mr. Sowerby,* **1**. London.

HOOKER, W.J. 1835. *The British Flora.* Ed. 3. London: Longman, Rees, Orme, Brown, Green & Longman.

HOOKER, W.J. 1843. *Supplement to the English Botany of the late Sir J.E. Smith and Mr. Sowerby,* **3**. London.

HUBBARD, J.C.E. & STEBBINGS, R.E. 1968. *Spartina* marshes in southern England. VII. Stratigraphy of the Keysworth Marsh, Poole Harbour. *Journal of Ecology,* **56**: 707–722.

HULTÉN, E. 1958. The amphi-atlantic plants and their phytogeographical connections. *Kungliga svenska Vetenskapsakademiens Handlingar, Fjärde Serien,* **7**: 1–340.

HULTÉN, E. & FRIES, M. 1986. *Atlas of north European vascular Plants north of the Tropic of Cancer.* 3 vols. Königstein: Koeltz Scientific Books.

HUTCHINSON, G.E. 1975. *A Treatise on Limnology,* **3**. *Limnological Botany.* New York: John Wiley & Sons.

IVIMEY COOK, W.R. 1933. A monograph of the Plasmodiophorales. *Archiv für Protistenkunde,* **80**: 179–254.

JACKSON, M.J. 1978. The changing status of aquatic macrophytes in the Norfolk Broads. *Transactions of the Norfolk and Norwich Naturalists' Society,* **24**: 137–152.

JACOBS, S.W.L. & BROCK, M.A. 1982. A revision of the genus *Ruppia* (Potamogetonaceae) in Australia. *Aquatic Botany,* **14**: 325–337.

JACOBSEN, D. & SAND-JENSEN, K. 1994. Invertebrate herbivory on the submerged macrophyte *Potamogeton perfoliatus* in a Danish stream. *Freshwater Biology,* **31**: 43–52.

JESSEN, K. 1955. Key to subfossil *Potamogeton. Botanisk Tidsskrift,* **52**: 1–7.

JUPP, B.P. & SPENCE, D.H.N. 1977a. Limitations on macrophytes in a eutrophic lake, Loch Leven I. Effects of phytoplankton. *Journal of Ecology,* **65**: 175–186.

JUPP, B.P. & SPENCE, D.H.N. 1977b. Limitations of macrophytes in a eutrophic lake, Loch Leven II. Wave action, sediments and waterfowl grazing. *Journal of Ecology,* **65**: 431–446.

KADONO, Y. 1982a. Distribution and habitat of Japanese *Potamogeton*. *Botanical Magazine (Tokyo)*, **95**: 63–76.

KADONO, Y. 1982b. Germination of the turion of *Potamogeton crispus* L. *Physiology and Ecology Japan*, **19**: 1–5.

KALKMAN, L. & VAN WIJK, R.J. 1984. On the variation in chromosome number in *Potamogeton pectinatus* L. *Aquatic Botany*, **20**: 343–349.

KARLING, J.S. 1968. *The Plasmodiophorales*. Ed. 2. New York: Hafner Publishing Company.

KAUTSKY, L. 1987. Life-cycles of three populations of *Potamogeton pectinatus* L. at different degrees of wave exposure in the Askö area, northern Baltic proper. *Aquatic Botany*, **27**: 177–186.

KEELEY, J.E. & MORTON, B.A. 1982. Distribution of diurnal acid metabolism in submerged aquatic plants outside the genus *Isoetes*. *Photosynthetica*, **16**: 546–553.

KENT, D.H. 1992. *List of vascular Plants of the British Isles*. London: Botanical Society of the British Isles.

KENT, D.H. & ALLEN, D.E. 1984. *British and Irish Herbaria*. London: Botanical Society of the British Isles.

KOHLER, A. & MEYER, U. 1986. Experimentelle Untersuchungen zur Autökologie von *Groenlandia densa*. *Archiv für Hydrobiologie*, **106**: 525–540.

KUNII, H. 1989. Continuous growth and clump maintenance of *Potamogeton crispus* L. in Narutoh River, Japan. *Aquatic Botany*, **33**: 13–26.

LAIRD, M. 1986. *English Misericords*. London: John Murray.

LEE, J.A. 1977. The vegetation of British inland salt marshes. *Journal of Ecology*, **65**: 673–698.

LES, D.H. 1983. Taxonomic implications of aneuploidy and polyploidy in *Potamogeton* (Potamogetonaceae). *Rhodora*, **85**: 301–323.

LES, D.H. 1988. Breeding systems, population structure, and evolution in hydrophilous angiosperms. *Annals of the Missouri Botanical Garden*, **75**: 819–835.

LES, D.H. & PHILBRICK, C.T. 1993. Studies of hybridization and chromosome number variation in aquatic angiosperms: evolutionary implications. *Aquatic Botany*, **44**: 181–228.

LES, D.H. & SHERIDAN, D.J. 1990a. Hagström's concept of phylogenetic relationships in *Potamogeton* L. (Potamogetonaceae). *Taxon*, **39**: 41–58.

LES, D.H. & SHERIDAN, D.J. 1990b. Biochemical heterophylly and flavonoid evolution in North American *Potamogeton* (Potamogetonaceae). *American Journal of Botany*, **77**: 453–465.

LIGHTFOOT, J. 1777. *Flora scotica*. 2 vols. London.

LINNAEUS, C. 1753. *Species Plantarum*. 2 vols. Stockholm.

LLOYD, C. 1970. *The well-tempered Garden*. London: Collins.

LODGE, D.M. 1991. Herbivory on freshwater macrophytes. *Aquatic Botany*, **41**: 195–224.

LOHAMMAR, G. 1954. The effect of digestion on the germination of *Potamogeton* seeds [In Swedish with English summary]. *Fauna och Flora*, **1954**: 17–32.

LÖVE, A. & KJELLQVIST, E. 1973. Cytotaxonomy of Spanish plants. II. Monocotyledons. *Lagascalia*, **3**: 147–182.

LÖVE, A. & LÖVE, D. 1942. Chromosome numbers of Scandinavian plant species. *Botaniska Notiser*, **1942**: 19–59.

LUTHER, H. 1947. Morphologische und systematische Beobachtungen an Wasserphanerogamen. *Acta botanica fennica*, **40**: 1–28.

LUTHER, H. 1950. Beobachtungen über *Tetramyxa parasitica* Goebel. *Memoranda Societatis pro Fauna et Flora fennica*, **25**: 88–96.

LUTHER, H. 1951. Verbreitung und Ökologie der höheren Wasserpflanzen im Brackwasser der Ekenäs-gegend in Südfinnland. *Acta botanica fennica*, **50**: 1–370.

MABERLY, S.C. & SPENCE, D.H.N. 1983. Photosynthetic inorganic carbon use by freshwater plants. *Journal of Ecology*, **71**: 705–724.

MACKERETH, F.J.H., HERON, J. & TALLING, J.F. 1978. *Water Analysis: some revised Methods for Limnologists*. Ambleside: Freshwater Biological Association.

MADSEN, J.D. & ADAMS, M.S. 1989. The light and temperature dependence of photosynthesis and respiration in *Potamogeton pectinatus* L. *Aquatic Botany*, **36**: 23–31.

MAITLAND, P.S., BOON, P.J. & McLUSKY, D.S. (eds) 1994. *The fresh Waters of Scotland*. Chichester: John Wiley & Sons.

MARKGRAF, F. 1981. Potamogetonaceae, in *Illustrierte Flora von Mitteleuropa*, **1** (2), 3rd ed., pp. 214–246. Berlin & Hamburg: Verlag Paul Parey.

MARTIN, A.C., ZIM, H.S. & NELSON, A.L. 1951. *American Wildlife & Plants*. New York: McGraw-Hill Book Company.

MASON, R. 1967. The species of *Ruppia* in New Zealand. *New Zealand Journal of Botany*, **5**: 519–531.

MATTHEWS, J.R. 1955. *Origin and Distribution of the British Flora*. London: Hutchinson & Co.

McCUTCHEON, W.A. 1965. *The Canals of the North of Ireland*. Dawlish: David & Charles.

McVEAN, D.N. & RATCLIFFE, D.A. 1962. *Plant Communities of the Scottish Highlands*. Monographs of the Nature Conservancy, no. 1. London: Her Majesty's Stationery Office.

MEIJER, K. & PLOEG, D. VAN DER 1994. *Potamogeton* × *lintonii* Fryer in een tuinvijvertje. *Gorteria*, **20**: 70–72.

MELACK, J.M. 1988. Aquatic plants in extreme environments, in J. J. Symoens (ed.), *Vegetation of inland Waters*, pp. 341–378. Dordrecht: Kluwer Academic Publishers.

MENENDEZ, M. & PEÑUELAS, J. 1993. Seasonal photosynthetic and respiratory responses of *Ruppia cirrhosa* (Petagna) Grande to changes to light and temperature. *Archiv für Hydrobiologie*, **129**: 221–230.

MEUSEL, H., JÄGER, E. & WEINERT, E. 1965. *Vergleichende Chorologie der zentraleuropäischen Flora*, **1**. 2 vols. Jena: Gustav Fischer.

MISRA, M.P. 1972. Cytological studies in some Indian *Potamogeton* and *Aponogeton* species. *Bulletin of the botanical Society of Bengal*, **26**: 47–51.

MOORE, D. 1864. On *Potamogeton nitens*, Weber, as an Irish plant. *Journal of Botany*, **2**: 325–326.

MOORE, E. 1913. The Potamogetons in relation to pond culture. *Bulletin of the Bureau of Fisheries*, **33**: 255–291.

MOORE, J.A. 1986. *Charophytes of Great Britain and Ireland*. B.S.B.I. Handbook no. 5. London: Botanical Society of the British Isles.

MOUNTFORD, J.O. 1994. Floristic change in English grazing marshes: the impact of 150 years of drainage and land-use change. *Watsonia*, **20**: 3–24.

MOUNTFORD, J.O. & SHEAIL, J. 1989. *The effects of agricultural land use change on the flora of three grazing marsh areas*. Focus on Nature Conservation, no. 20. Peterborough: Nature Conservancy Council.

MUENSCHER, W.C. 1936. The germination of seeds of *Potamogeton*. *Annals of Botany*, **50**: 805–821.

MURPHY, K.J. & EATON, J.W. 1983. Effects of pleasure-boat traffic on macrophyte growth in canals. *Journal of applied Ecology*, **20**: 713–729.

NEVECERAL, P. & KRAHULEC, F. 1994. Two *Potamogeton* species new to the flora of the Czech Republic: *P. polygonifolius* and *P.* × *lintonii* (*P. crispus* × *P. friesii*). *Preslia*, **66**: 151–158.

OGDEN, E.C. 1943. The broad-leaved species of *Potamogeton* of North America north of Mexico. *Rhodora*, **45**: 57–214.

OLNEY, P.J.S. 1968. The food and feeding-habits of the Pochard, *Aythya ferina*. *Biological Conservation*, **1**: 71–76.

OLNEY, P.J.S. & MILLS, D.H. 1963. The food and feeding habits of Goldeneye *Bucephala clangula* in Great Britain. *Ibis*, **105**: 293–300.

PALMER, M.[A.] 1986. The impact of a change from permanent pasture to cereal farming on the flora and invertebrate fauna of watercourses in the Pevensey Levels, Sussex. *Proceedings of the EWRS/AAB 7th Symposium on aquatic Weeds, 1986, Loughborough*, 233–238.

PALMER, M.A., BELL, S.L. & BUTTERFIELD, I. 1992. A botanical classification of standing waters in Britain: applications for conservation and monitoring. *Aquatic Conservation: Marine and freshwater Ecosystems*, **2**: 125–143.

PALMER, M.[A.] & NEWBOLD, C. 1983. *Wetland and riparian Plants in Great Britain*. Focus on Nature Conservation, no. 1. Nature Conservancy Council.

PALMGREN, O. 1939. Cytological studies in *Potamogeton*. Preliminary note. *Botaniska Notiser*, **1939**: 246–248.

PASSARGE, H. 1992. Mitteleuropäische Potamogetonetea I. *Phytocoenologia*, **20**: 489–527.

PASSARGE, H. 1994. Mitteleuropäische Potamogetonetea II. *Phytocoenologia*, **24**: 337–367.

PEARSALL, W.H. 1920. Hagstrom's Critical Researches on the Potamogetons. *Report of the botanical Society and Exchange Club of the British Isles*, **5**: 701–713.

PEARSALL, W.H. 1930. Notes on *Potamogeton*. I. The British grass-leaved species. *Report of the botanical Society and Exchange Club of the British Isles*, **9**: 148–156.

PEARSALL, W.H. 1931. Notes on *Potamogeton*. II. The larger British species. *Report of the botanical Society and Exchange Club of the British Isles*, **9**: 380–415.

PEARSALL, W.H. 1933. *Potamogeton Macvicarii* Ar. Benn. *Journal of Botany*, **71**: 45–47.

PEARSALL, W.H. 1934. *P. zosterifolius* Schum. *Report of the botanical Society and Exchange Club of the British Isles*, **10**: 484–485.

PEARSALL, W.H. & PEARSALL fil., W.H. 1921. *Potamogeton* in the English Lakes. *Journal of Botany*, **59**: 160–164.

PEARSALL, W.H. & PEARSALL fil., W.H. 1923. *Potamogeton* in the English Lakes. *Journal of Botany*, **61**: 1–7.

PEARSALL fil., W.H. 1920. The aquatic vegetation of the English lakes. *Journal of Ecology*, **8**: 163–201.

PEARSALL fil., W.H. 1921. The development of vegetation in the English Lakes, considered in relation to the general evolution of glacial lakes and rock basins. *Proceedings of the Royal Society of London*, **92B**: 259–284.

PEARSALL fil., W.H. & HANBY, A.M. 1925. The variation of leaf form in *Potamogeton perfoliatus*. *New Phytologist*, **24**: 112–120.

PEDERSEN, A. 1976. Najadaceernes, Potamogetonaceernes, Ruppiaceernes, Zannichelliaceernes og Zosteraceernes udbredelse i Danmark. *Botanisk Tidsskrift*, **70**: 205–262.

PERRING, F.H. & FARRELL, L. 1983. *British Red Data Books: 1. Vascular Plants*. Ed. 2. Lincoln: Royal Society for Nature Conservation.

PERRING, F.H. & SELL, P.D. (eds) 1968. *Critical Supplement to the Atlas of the British Flora*. London: Thomas Nelson & Sons.

PERRING, F.H., SELL, P.D. & WALTERS, S.M. 1964. *A Flora of Cambridgeshire*. Cambridge: Cambridge University Press.

PERRING, F.H. & WALTERS, S.M. (eds) 1962. *Atlas of the British Flora*. London: Thomas Nelson & Sons.

PHILBRICK, C.T. 1983. Aspects of floral biology in three species of *Potamogeton* (pondweeds). *Michigan Botanist*, **23**: 35–38.

PHILBRICK, C.T. 1988. Evolution of underwater outcrossing from aerial pollination systems: a hypothesis. *Annals of the Missouri Botanical Garden*, **75**: 836–841.

PHILBRICK, C.T. & ANDERSON, G.J. 1987. Implications of pollen/ovule ratios and pollen size for the reproductive biology of *Potamogeton* and autogamy in aquatic angiosperms. *Systematic Botany*, **12**: 98–105.

PHILIP, C. 1994. *The Plant Finder*. Ed. 8. London: BCA.

PIETERSE, A.H. & MURPHY, K.J. (eds) 1990. *Aquatic Weeds*. Oxford: Oxford University Press.

PLOEG, D.T.E. VAN DER 1974. Een drietal *Potamogeton*-hybriden in Friesland, waaronder *Potamogeton × sparganifolius* Laest. ex Fries nieuw voor Nederland. *Gorteria*, **7**: 1–6.

PLOEG, D.T.E. VAN DER 1977. Nieuwe vondsten van enige *Potamogeton*-hybriden in Friesland. *Gorteria*, **8**: 129–133.

PLOEG, D.T.E. VAN DER 1987. *Potamogeton* × *sudermanicus* Hagström, de vermoedelijke bastaard van *P. acutifolius* Link en *P. berchtoldii* Fieber, in Nederland gevonden. *Gorteria*, **13**: 173–176.

PLOEG, D.T.E. VAN DER 1990. De nederlandse breedbladige Fonteinkruiden. *Wetenschappelijke Mededelingen van der Koninklijke nederlandse natuurhistorische Vereniging*, **195**: 1–98.

POSLUSZNY, U. & SATTLER, R. 1973. Floral development of *Potamogeton densus*. *Canadian Journal of Botany*, **51**: 647–656.

PRAEGER, R.L. 1913. On the buoyancy of the seeds of some Britannic plants. *Scientific Proceedings of the Royal Dublin Society*, **n.s.**, **14**: 13–62.

PRESTON, C.D. 1985. *Ruppia spiralis* L. ex Dumort. in Yorkshire. *Watsonia*, **15**: 274–275.

PRESTON, C.D. 1986. Is *Groenlandia densa* extinct in Scotland? *BSBI Scottish Newsletter*, **8**: 13–14.

PRESTON, C.D. 1987. A binomial for the hybrid *Potamogeton gramineus* L. × *P. polygonifolius* Pourret. *Watsonia*, **16**: 436–437.

PRESTON, C.D. 1988a. Alfred Fryer and the study of the genus *Potamogeton* in the British Isles. *Archives of natural History*, **15**: 15–33.

PRESTON, C.D. 1988b. The *Potamogeton* L. taxa described by Alfred Fryer. *Watsonia*, **17**: 23–35.

PRESTON, C.D. 1989a. *Potamogeton* × *lanceolatus* Sm. in the British Isles. *Watsonia*, **17**: 309–317.

PRESTON, C.D. 1989b. Typification of *Potamogeton sparganifolius* Laest. ex Fr. and *P. natans* subsp. *kirkii* Hooker fil. *Watsonia*, **17**: 361–363.

PRESTON, C.D. 1990. *Potamogeton filiformis* Pers. in Anglesey. *Watsonia*, **18**: 90–91.

PRESTON, C.D. 1991. *Potamogeton* L., in R. J. Pankhurst & J. M. Mullin, *Flora of the Outer Hebrides*, pp. 129–133. London: Natural History Museum Publications.

PRESTON, C.D. 1993. Irish Pondweeds IV. *Potamogeton* × *lanceolatus* Smith. *Irish Naturalists' Journal*, **24**: 213–218.

PRESTON, C.D. 1995a. *Potamogeton* × *schreberi* G. Fisch. (*P. natans* L. × *P. nodosus* Poir.) in Dorset, new to the British Isles. *Watsonia*, **20**: 255–262.

PRESTON, C.D. 1995b. Sir George Taylor's studies of the genus *Potamogeton*. *Watsonia*, **20**: 325–326.

PRESTON, C.D. in press. *Potamogeton* × *cognatus* Asch. & Graebn. at Loch Borralie, West Sutherland (v.c. 108), Scotland. *Watsonia*, **20**.

PRESTON, C.D. & STEWART, N.F. 1990. *Potamogeton trichoides* Cham. & Schlecht. in the Bude Canal. *Botanical Cornwall Newsletter*, **4**: 16–18.

PRESTON, C.D. & STEWART, N.F. 1992. Irish Pondweeds III. *Potamogeton* × *griffithii* A. Benn. in Co Donegal, new to Ireland. *Irish Naturalists' Journal*, **24**: 143–147.

PRESTON, C.D. & STEWART, N.F. 1994. Irish Pondweeds V. *Potamogeton* × *suecicus* K. Richter in Co Donegal, new to Ireland. *Irish Naturalists' Journal*, **24**, 485–489.

PRESTON, C.D., STEWART, N.F. & WEBSTER, S.D. 1991. Records of aquatic plants from Connemara and the Burren. *Irish Naturalists' Journal*, **23**: 464–467.

PRESTON, C.D. & WOLFE-MURPHY, S. 1992. Irish Pondweeds II. *Potamogeton* × *lintonii* Fryer. *Irish Naturalists' Journal*, **24**: 117–121.

PROBATOVA, N.S. & SOKOLOVSKAYA, A.P. 1984. Chromosome numbers in the representatives of the families Alismataceae, Hydrocharitaceae, Hypericaceae, Juncaginaceae, Poaceae, Potamogetonaceae, Ruppiaceae, Sparganiaceae, Zannichelliaceae, Zosteraceae from the Soviet Far East. *Botanicheski Zhurnal*, **69**: 1700–1702.

PROBATOVA, N.S. & SOKOLOVSKAYA, A.P. 1986. Chromosome numbers of the vascular plants from the Far East of the USSR. *Botaniceskij Zurnal*, **71**: 1572–1575.

RAUNKIAER, C. 1895–99. *De Danske Blomsterplanters Naturhistorie*, **1**. *Enkimbladede*. Copenhagen: Gyldendalske Bodhandels Forlag.

RAVEN, C.E. 1942. *John Ray Naturalist. His Life and Works*. Cambridge: Cambridge University Press.

RAVEN, J.A. 1984. *Energetics and Transport in aquatic Plants*. New York: Alan R. Liss.

RAY, J. 1660. *Catalogus Plantarum circa Cantabrigiam nascentium*. Cambridge.

RAY, J. 1670. *Catalogus Plantarum Angliae et Insularum adjacentium*. London.

RAY, J. 1686. *Historia Plantarum*, **1**. London.

RAY, J. 1690. *Synopsis methodica Stirpium britannicarum*. London.

RAY, J. 1696. *Synopsis methodica Stirpium britannicarum*. Ed. 2. London.

RAY, J. 1724. *Synopsis methodica Stirpium britannicarum*. Ed. 3. London.

RAYMOND, C.J. & SILVERSIDE, A.J. 1978. Pondweeds in the Forth and Clyde Canal. *Glasgow Naturalist*, **19**: 428–429.

REESE, G. 1962. Zur intragenerischen Taxonomie der Gattung *Ruppia* L. *Zeitschrift für Botanik*, **50**: 237–264.

REESE, G. 1963. Über die deutschen *Ruppia*- und *Zannichellia*-Kategorien und ihre Verbreitung in Schleswig-Holstein. *Schriften des Naturwissenschaftlichen Vereins für Schleswig-Holstein*, **34**: 44–70.

RIDLEY, H.N. 1930. *The Dispersal of Plants throughout the World*. Ashford: L. Reeve & Co.

ROBERTS, M.L. & HAYNES, R.R. 1986. Flavonoid systematics of *Potamogeton* Subsections *Perfoliati* and *Praelongi* (Potamogetonaceae). *Nordic Journal of Botany*, **6**: 291–294.

RODWELL, J.S. (ed.) 1991. *British Plant Communities*, **2**. *Mires and Heaths*. Cambridge: Cambridge University Press.

RODWELL, J.S. (ed.) 1995. *British Plant Communities*, **4**. *Aquatic Communities, Swamps and tall-herb Fens*. Cambridge: Cambridge University Press.

ROGERS, K.H. & BREEN, C.M. 1980. Growth and reproduction of *Potamogeton crispus* in a South African lake. *Journal of Ecology*, **68**: 561–571.

ROSS-CRAIG, S. 1973. *Drawings of British Plants*, **31**. *Lemnaceae–Eriocaulaceae*. London: G. Bell & Sons.

ROWECK, H., WEISS, K. & KOHLER, A. 1986. Zur Verbreitung und Biologie von *Potamogeton coloratus* und *P. polygonifolius* in Bayern und Baden-Württemberg. *Bericht der Bayerischen botanischen Gesellschaft zur Erforschung der heimischen Flora*, **57**: 17–52.

SASTROUTOMO, S.S. 1980. Environmental control of turion formation in curly pondweed (*Potamogeton crispus*). *Physiologia Plantarum*, **49**: 261–264.

SASTROUTOMO, S.S. 1981. Turion formation, dormancy and germination of curly pondweed, *Potamogeton crispus* L. *Aquatic Botany*, **10**: 161–173.

SASTROUTOMO, S.S., IKUSIMA, I., NUMATA, M. & IIZUMI, S. 1979. The importance of turions in the propagation of pondweed (*Potamogeton crispus* L.). *Ecological Review*, **19**: 75–88.

SAUVAGEAU, C. 1893–94. Notes biologiques sur les *Potamogeton*. *Journal de Botanique*, **8**: 1–9, 21–43, 45–58, 98–106, 112–123, 140–148, 165–172.

SCANNELL, M.J.P. 1975. *Ruppia cirrhosa* (Petagne) Grande, an addition to the flora of West Galway. *Irish Naturalists' Journal*, **18**: 220–221.

SCOTT, W. & PALMER, R.C. 1987. *The flowering Plants and Ferns of the Shetland Islands*. Lerwick: Shetland Times.

SCULTHORPE, C.D. 1967. *The Biology of aquatic vascular Plants*. London: Edward Arnold.

SEDDON, B. 1972. Aquatic macrophytes as limnological indicators. *Freshwater Biology*, **2**: 107–130.

SELL, P.D. (ed.) 1967. Taxonomic and nomenclatural notes on the British Flora. *Watsonia*, **6**: 292–318.

SETCHELL, W.A. 1924. *Ruppia* and its environmental factors. *Proceedings of the National Academy of Sciences*, **10**: 286–288.

SETCHELL, W.A. 1946. The genus *Ruppia* L. *Proceedings of the California Academy of Sciences*, **25**: 469–478.

SHARMA, A.K. & CHATTERJEE, T. 1967. Cytotaxonomy of Helobiae with special reference to the mode of evolution. *Cytologia*, **32**: 286–307.

SMITH, B.D., MAITLAND, P.S. & PENNOCK, S.M. 1987. A comparative study of water level regimes and littoral benthic communities in Scottish lochs. *Biological Conservation*, **39**: 291–316.

SMITH, J.E. 1800. *Flora britannica*, **1**. London.

SMITH, J.E. 1804. *English Botany*, **18**. London.

SMITH, J.E. 1809. *English Botany*, **28**. London.

SMITH, S.J., WOLFE-MURPHY, S.A., ENLANDER, I. & GIBSON, C.E. 1991. *The Lakes of Northern Ireland: an annotated Inventory*. Countryside and Wildlife Research Series, no. 3. Belfast: HMSO.

SMITS, A.J.M., VAN RUREMONDE, R. & VAN DER VELDE, G. 1989. Seed dispersal of three nymphaeid macrophytes. *Aquatic Botany*, **35**: 167–180.

SORSA, P. 1988. Pollen morphology of *Potamogeton* and *Groenlandia* (Potamogetonaceae) and its taxonomic significance. *Annales botanici fennici*, **25**: 179–199.

SPENCE, D.H.N. 1964. The macrophytic vegetation of freshwater lochs, swamps and associated fens, in J. H. Burnett (ed.), *The Vegetation of Scotland*, pp. 306–425. Edinburgh & London: Oliver & Boyd.

SPENCE, D.H.N. 1967. Factors controlling the distribution of freshwater macrophytes with particular reference to the lochs of Scotland. *Journal of Ecology*, **55**: 147–170.

SPENCE, D.H.N. 1975. Light and plant response in fresh water, in G. C. Evans, R. Bainbridge & O. Rackham (eds), *Light as an ecological factor:II*, pp. 93–133. Oxford: Blackwell Scientific Publications.

SPENCE, D.H.N. 1981. Light quality and plant responses underwater, in H. Smith (ed.), *Plants and the Daylight Spectrum*, pp. 245–275. London: Academic Press.

SPENCE, D.H.N. 1982. The zonation of plants in freshwater lakes. *Advances in ecological Research*, **12**: 37–125.

SPENCE, D.H.N. & ALLEN, E.D. 1979. The macrophytic vegetation of Loch Urigill and other lochs of the Ullapool area. *Transactions of the botanical Society of Edinburgh*, **43**: 131–144.

SPENCE, D.H.N., ALLEN, E.D. & FRASER, J. 1979. Macrophytic vegetation of fresh and brackish waters in and near the Loch Druidibeg National Nature Reserve, South Uist. *Proceedings of the Royal Society of Edinburgh*, **77B**: 307–328.

SPENCE, D.H.N., BARCLAY, A.M. & ALLEN, E.D. 1984. Limnology and macrophyte vegetation of a deep, clear limestone lake, Loch Borralie. *Transactions of the botanical Society of Edinburgh*, **44**: 187–204.

SPENCE, D.H.N., CAMPBELL, R.M. & CHRYSTAL, J. 1973. Specific leaf areas and zonation of freshwater macrophytes. *Journal of Ecology*, **61**: 317–328.

SPENCE, D.H.N. & CHRYSTAL, J. 1970a. Photosynthesis and zonation of freshwater macrophytes I. Depth distribution and shade tolerance. *New Phytologist*, **69**: 205–215.

SPENCE, D.H.N. & CHRYSTAL, J. 1970b. Photosynthesis and zonation of freshwater macrophytes II. Adaptability of species of deep and shallow water. *New Phytologist*, **69**: 217–227.

SPENCE, D.H.N. & DALE, H.M. 1978. Variations in the shallow water form of *Potamogeton richardsonii* induced by some environmental factors. *Freshwater Biology*, **8**: 251–268.

SPENCE, D.H.N., MILBURN, T.R., NDAWULA-SENYIMBA, M. & ROBERTS, E. 1971. Fruit biology and germination of two tropical *Potamogeton* species. *New Phytologist*, **70**: 197–212.

SPENCER, D.F. 1986. Early growth of *Potamogeton pectinatus* L. in response to temperature and irradiance: morphology and pigment composition. *Aquatic Botany*, **26**: 1–8.

SPENCER, D.F. 1987. Tuber size and planting depth influence growth of *Potamogeton pectinatus* L. *American Midland Naturalist*, **118**: 77–84.

338

SPENCER, D.F. & ANDERSON, L.W.J. 1987. Influence of photoperiod on growth, pigment composition and vegetative propagule formation for *Potamogeton nodosus* Poir. and *Potamogeton pectinatus* L. *Aquatic Botany*, **28**: 103–112.

SPENCER, D.F. & KSANDER, G.G. 1990a. Influence of planting depth on *Potamogeton gramineus* L. *Aquatic Botany*, **36**: 343–350.

SPENCER, D.F. & KSANDER, G.G. 1990b. Influence of temperature, light and nutrient limitation on anthocyanin content of *Potamogeton gramineus* L. *Aquatic Botany*, **38**: 357–367.

SPENCER, D.F. & KSANDER, G.G. 1991. Influence of temperature and light on early growth of *Potamogeton gramineus* L. *Journal of freshwater Ecology*, **6**: 227–235.

SPENCER, D.F. & KSANDER, G.G. 1992. Influence of temperature and moisture on vegetative propagule germination of *Potamogeton* species: implications for aquatic plant management. *Aquatic Botany*, **43**: 351–364.

SPINK, A.J., MURPHY, K.J., SMITH, S.M. & WESTLAKE, D.F. 1993. Effects of eutrophication on *Ranunculus* and *Potamogeton*. *Journal of aquatic Plant Management*, **31**: 113–117.

SQUIRES, R.W. 1983. *The new Navvies. A History of the modern Waterways Restoration Movement*. Chichester: Phillimore & Co.

ST JOHN, H. 1925. A critical consideration of Hagström's work on *Potamogeton*. *Bulletin of the Torrey Botanical Club*, **52**: 461–471.

STACE, C.A. 1991. *New Flora of the British Isles*. Cambridge: Cambridge University Press.

STEARN, W.T. 1973. *Botanical Latin*. Ed. 2. Newton Abbot: David & Charles.

STERN, K.R. 1961. Chromosome numbers in nine taxa of *Potamogeton*. *Bulletin of the Torrey botanical Club*, **88**: 411–414.

STEWART, A., PEARMAN, D.A. & PRESTON, C.D. (comps & eds) 1994. *Scarce Plants in Britain*. Peterborough: Joint Nature Conservation Committee.

STEWART, O.M. & PRESTON, C.D. 1990. *Potamogeton* × *lintonii* – new to Scotland. *B.S.B.I. News*, **54**: 20–21.

STEWART, W.D.P., TUCKWELL, S.B. & MAY, E. 1975. Eutrophication and algal growths in Scottish fresh water lochs, in M. J. Chadwick & G. T. Goodman (eds), *The Ecology of Resource Degradation and Renewal*, pp. 57–80. Oxford: Blackwell Scientific Publications.

STUCKEY, R.L. 1979. Distributional history of *Potamogeton crispus* (Curly Pondweed) in North America. *Bartonia*, **46**: 22–42.

SYME, J.T.B. (ed.) 1869. *English Botany*, **9**. Ed. 3. London: Robert Hardwicke.

SYMOENS, J.J. (ed.) 1988. *Handbook of Vegetation Science*, **15 (1)**. *Vegetation of inland Waters*. Dordrecht: Kluwer Academic Publishers.

SYMOENS, J.J., VAN DE VELDEN, J. & BÜSCHER, P. 1979. Contribution à l'étude de la taxonomie et de la distribution de *Potamogeton nodosus* Poir. et *P. thunbergii* Cham. & Schlechtend. en Afrique. *Bulletin de la Société royale de Botanique de Belgique*, **112**: 79–95.

TAKUSAGAWA, H. 1939. Chromosome numbers in *Potamogeton*, in *Volumen jubilare pro Professore Sadao Yoshida*, **1**, pp. 1066–1067. Osaka: Osaka Natural History Society.

TALAVERA, S., GARCÍA-MURILLO, P. & HERRERA, J. 1993. Chromosome numbers and a new model for karyotype evolution in *Ruppia* L. (Ruppiaceae). *Aquatic Botany*, **45**: 1–13.

TAYLOR, G. 1949. Some observations on British Potamogetons. *South-eastern Naturalist and Antiquary*, **54**: 22–38.

TAYLOR, G. 1977. James Edgar Dandy. *Nature*, **265**: 572.

TAYLOR, J.M. & SLEDGE, W.A. 1944. × *Potamogeton cognatus* Asch. and Graeb. in Britain. *Naturalist*, **1944**: 121–123.

TEESDALE, R. 1800. A supplement to the Plantae Eboracenses printed in the second volume of these transactions. *Transactions of the Linnean Society*, **5**: 36–95.

TELTSCHEROVÁ L. & HEJNY, S. 1973. The germination of some *Potamogeton* species from South-Bohemian fishponds. *Folia geobotanica & phytotaxonomica*, **8**: 231–239.

THOMAS, G.J. 1982. Autumn and winter feeding ecology of waterfowl at the Ouse Washes, England. *Journal of Zoology*, **197**: 131–172.

TOMLINSON, P.B. 1982. *Anatomy of the Monocotyledons, 7. Helobiae (Alismataceae) (including the Seagrasses)*. Oxford: Clarendon Press.

TRIMEN, H. 1879. *Potamogeton Zizii*, M. & K., as a British plant. *Journal of Botany*, **17**: 289–292.

TUR, N.M. 1982. Revisión del género *Potamogeton* L. en la Argentina. *Darwinia*, **24**: 217–265.

TURNER, W. 1548. *The Names of Herbes*. London.

TURNER, W. 1965. *Libellus de Re Herbaria 1538. The Names of Herbes 1548. Facsimiles with introductory matter by James Britten, B. Daydon Jackson & W. T. Stearn*. London: Ray Society.

VAN DIJK, G.M., BREUKELAAR, A.W. & GIJLSTRA, R. 1992. Impact of light climate history on seasonal dynamics of a field population of *Potamogeton pectinatus* L. during a three year period (1986–1988). *Aquatic Botany*, **43**: 17–41.

VAN VIERSSEN, W., VAN KESSEL, C.M. & VAN DER ZEE, J.R. 1984. On the germination of *Ruppia* taxa in western Europe. *Aquatic Botany*, **19**: 381–393.

VAN VIERSSEN, W., VAN WIJK, R.J. & VAN DER ZEE, J.R. 1981. Some additional Notes on the cytotaxonomy of *Ruppia* taxa in western Europe. *Aquatic Botany*, **11**: 297–301.

VAN WIJK, R.J. 1983. Life-cycles and reproductive strategies of *Potamogeton pectinatus* L. in the Netherlands and the Camargue (France). *Proceedings of the international Symposium on aquatic Macrophytes, Nijmegen, 18–23 September, 1983*, pp. 317–321.

VAN WIJK, R.J. 1988. Ecological studies on *Potamogeton pectinatus* L. I. General characteristics, biomass production and life cycles under field conditions. *Aquatic Botany*, **31**: 211–258.

VAN WIJK, R.J. 1989a. Ecological studies on *Potamogeton pectinatus* L. III. Reproductive strategies and germination ecology. *Aquatic Botany*, **33**: 271–299.

VAN WIJK, R.J. 1989b. Ecological studies on *Potamogeton pectinatus* L. IV. Nutritional ecology, field observations. *Aquatic Botany*, **35**: 301–318.

VAN WIJK, R.J. 1989c. Ecological studies on *Potamogeton pectinatus* L. V. Nutritional ecology, in vitro uptake of nutrients and growth limitation. *Aquatic Botany*, **35**: 319–335.

VAN WIJK, R.J. & TROMPENAARS, H.J.A.J. 1985. On the germination of turions and the life cycle of *Potamogeton trichoides* Cham. et Schld. *Aquatic Botany*, **22**: 165–172.

VAN WIJK, R.J. & VERBEEK, P.J.M. 1986. De smalbladige fonteinkruidsoorten in Nederland, herkenning en oecologie. *Wetenschappelijke Mededelingen van der Koninklijke nederlandse natuurhistorische Vereniging*, **177**: 1–37.

VAN WIJK, R.J., VAN GOOR, E.M.J. & VERKLEY, J.A.C. 1988. Ecological studies on *Potamogeton pectinatus* L. II. Autecological characteristics, with emphasis on salt tolerance, intraspecific variation and isoenzyme patterns. *Aquatic Botany*, **32**: 239–260.

VANNEROM, H. & ANDRIESSEN, L. 1987. *Potamogeton × lintonii* Fryer te Zelk (Limburg, Belgie). *Dumortiera*, **37**: 28.

VERHOEVEN, J.T.A. 1975. *Ruppia*-communities in the Camargue, France. Distribution and structure in relation to salinity and salinity fluctuations. *Aquatic Botany*, **1**: 217–241.

VERHOEVEN, J.T.A. 1979. The ecology of *Ruppia*-dominated communities in western Europe. I. Distribution of *Ruppia* representatives in relation to their autecology. *Aquatic Botany*, **6**: 197–268.

VERHOEVEN, J.T.A. 1980a. The ecology of *Ruppia*-dominated communities in western Europe. II. Synecological classification. Structure and dynamics of the macroflora and macrofauna communities. *Aquatic Botany*, **8**: 1–85.

VERHOEVEN, J.T.A. 1980b. The ecology of *Ruppia*-dominated communities in western Europe. III. Aspects of production, consumption and decomposition. *Aquatic Botany*, **8**: 209–253.

VERHOEVEN, J.T.A. & VAN VIERSSEN, W. 1978. Distribution and structure of communities dominated by *Ruppia, Zostera* and *Potamogeton* species in the inland waters of 'De Bol', Texel, The Netherlands. *Estuarine and coastal marine Science*, **6**: 417–428.

VLAMING, V. DE & PROCTOR, V.W. 1968. Dispersal of aquatic organisms: viability of seeds recovered from the droppings of captive killdeer and mallard ducks. *American Journal of Botany*, **55**: 20–26.

VÖGE, M. 1991. Zur Reproduktion von *Potamogeton pectinatus* L. *Floristische Rundbriefe*, **25**: 120–125.

VÖGE, M. 1992. Die Entwicklung von *Potamogeton praelongus* im Grossensee bei Hamburg. *Tuexenia*, **12**: 275–284.

WADE, P.M. & EDWARDS, R.W. 1980. The effect of channel maintenance on the aquatic macrophytes of the drainage channels of the Monmouthshire Levels, South Wales, 1840–1976. *Aquatic Botany*, **8**: 307–322.

WALTERS, S.M., BRADY, A., BRICKELL, C.D., CULLEN, J., GREEN, P.S., LEWIS, J., MATTHEWS, V.A., WEBB, D.A., YEO, P.F. & ALEXANDER, J.C.M. (eds) 1986. *The European Garden Flora*, **1**. *Pteridophyta, Gymnospermae, Angiospermae – Monocotyledons (Part 1)*. Cambridge: Cambridge University Press.

WATERSTON, A.R. & LYSTER, I.H.J. 1979. The macrofauna of brackish and fresh waters of the Loch Druidibeg National Nature Reserve and its neighbourhood, South Uist. *Proceedings of the Royal Society of Edinburgh*, **77B**: 353–376.

WAY, J.M., NEWMAN, J.F., MOORE, N.W. & KNAGGS, F.W. 1971. Some ecological effects of the use of paraquat for the control of weeds in small lakes. *Journal of applied Ecology*, **8**: 509–532.

WEEDA, E.J. 1976. Over het optreden van *Potamogeton praelongus* Wulf., o.a. bij Buinen (Dr.). *Gorteria*, **8**: 89–98.

WEST, G. 1905. A comparative study of the dominant phanerogamic and higher cryptogamic flora of aquatic habit, in three lake areas of Scotland. *Proceedings of the Royal Society of Edinburgh*, **25**: 967–1024.

WEST, G. 1910. A further contribution to a comparative study of the dominant phanerogamic and higher cryptogamic flora of aquatic habit in Scottish lakes. *Proceedings of the Royal Society of Edinburgh*, **30**: 65–182.

WETZEL, R.G. 1988. Water as an environment for plant life, in J.J. Symoens (ed.), *Vegetation of inland waters*, pp. 1–30. Dordrecht: Kluwer Academic Publishers.

WIEGLEB, G. 1983. Bibliography on *Potamogeton alpinus*, part I. *Excerpta botanica*, **23B**: 7–37.

WIEGLEB, G. 1984. Bibliography on *Potamogeton alpinus*, part II. *Excerpta botanica*, **23B**: 145–153.

WIEGLEB, G. 1988a. Analysis of flora and vegetation in rivers: concepts and applications, in J. J. Symoens (ed.), *Vegetation of inland Waters*, pp. 311–340. Dordrecht: Kluwer Academic Publishers.

WIEGLEB, G. 1988b. Notes on pondweeds – outlines for a monographical treatment of the genus *Potamogeton* L. *Repertorium novarum Specierum Regni vegetabilis*, **99**: 249–266.

WIEGLEB, G. 1989. On *Potamogeton coloratus* (Potamogetonaceae) in Turkey. *Willdenowia*, **19**: 121–125.

WIEGLEB, G. 1990a. The importance of stem anatomical characters for the systematics of the genus *Potamogeton* L. *Flora*, **184**: 197–208.

WIEGLEB, G. 1990b. A redescription of *Potamogeton distinctus* including remarks on the taxonomy of the *Potamogeton nodosus* group. *Plant Systematics and Evolution*, **169**: 245–259.

WIEGLEB, G. & BRUX, H. 1991. Comparison of life history characters of broad-leaved species of the genus *Potamogeton* L. I. General characterization of morphology and reproductive strategies. *Aquatic Botany*, **39**: 131–146.

WIEGLEB, G. & HERR, W. 1984. Die Potamogetonaceae Niedersächsischer Fliessgewässer, Teil 1. *Göttinger floristische Rundbriefe*, **18**: 65–86.

WIEGLEB, G. & TODESKINO, D. 1983a. Der biologische Lebenszyklus von *Potamogeton alpinus* und dessen Bedeutung für das Vorkommen der Art. *Verhandlungen der Gesellschaft für Ökologie (Bremen 1983)*, **13**: 191–198.

WIEGLEB, G. & TODESKINO, D. 1983b. Habitat conditions of *Potamogeton alpinus* Balbis stands and relations to the plants biological characters. *Proceedings of the international Symposium on aquatic Macrophytes, Nijmegen, 18–23 September, 1983*, pp. 311–316.

WILLIAMS, G. & HALL, M. 1987. The loss of coastal grazing marshes in south and east England, with special reference to east Essex, England. *Biological Conservation*, **39**: 243–253.

WINGFIELD, M. & WADE, P.M. 1988. Hatfield Chase: the loss of drainage channel habitat. *Naturalist*, **113**: 21–24.

WISNIEWSKA, E. 1931. Rozwój ziarn pylku u *Potamogeton perfoliatus* L. *Acta Societatis Botanicorum Poloniae*, **8**: 157–174.

WITHERING, W. 1787. *A botanical Arrangement of British Plants*. Ed. 2. Birmingham.

WOLFE-MURPHY, S.A., SMITH, S.J. & PRESTON, C.D. 1991. Irish Pondweeds I. A recent record of *Potamogeton* × *cooperi* (Fryer) Fryer from Co Antrim. *Irish Naturalists' Journal*, **23**: 457–458.

WOLFF, P. 1989. *Potamogeton* × *variifolius* Thore dans les Vosges septentrionales – plante nouvelle en Europe centrale. *Bulletin Association philomathique d' Alsace et de Lorraine*, **25**: 5–20.

WOLFF, P. 1992. Das Laichkraut *Potamogeton* × *variifolius* Thore früher in der Pfalz: Erstnachweis für Deutschland. *Pollichia*, **79**: 235–241.

WOODRUFFE-PEACOCK, E.A. 1917. The means of plant dispersal. Wild duck carriage. *Selborne Magazine and Nature Notes*, **28**: 80–83, 97–101, 114–116.

WYSE JACKSON, P.S. 1988. *Groenlandia densa* (L.) Fourr. in Dublin. *Irish Naturalists' Journal*, **22**: 457.

YEO, R.R. 1965. Life history of Sago Pondweed. *Weeds*, **13**: 314–321.

YEO, R.R. 1966. Yields of propagules of certain aquatic plants I. *Weeds*, **14**: 110–113.

YURTSEV, B.A., ZHUKOVA, P.G., PLIEVA, T.V., RASZHIVIN, V.Y. & SEKRETAREVA, N.A. 1975. Interesting floristic finds in the easternmost Chukotka peninsula. III. *Botanicheski Zhurnal*, **60**: 233–247.

GLOSSARY

The more specialised terms used in the Handbook are explained below. Most of the morphological terms are defined and many illustrated in Stearn's *Botanical Latin* (1973), which I have used as the standard reference work when preparing the descriptions. A few terms have, however, been defined more narrowly than usual for the purposes of this Handbook.

Abaxial: the side of an organ facing away from the axis of a stem (cf *adaxial*).

A-chromosome: the normal chromosome, composed of euchromatin and heterochromatin (cf *B-chromosome*).

Acuminate: tapering to a long, fine point.

Acute: narrowed to a point.

Adaxial: the side of an organ facing the axis of the stem (cf *abaxial*).

Adnate: applied to two organs which are attached along their lengths, as if fused together.

Air channel: a tubular channel running along the length of the leaf. Air channels are found on each side of the midrib in *Potamogeton* Subgenus *Coleogeton* and *Ruppia*.

Alternate: arising at different levels on an axis, first on one side and then on another.

Amplexicaul: clasping the stem for at least half its diameter; **semi-amplexicaul**: clasping the stem for less than half its diameter.

Anthesis: the period of flowering.

Apical: situated at the apex.

Apiculate: rounded to obtuse, but terminating in a short point composed partly or entirely of the lamina (cf *mucronate*).

Appressed: pressed against the surface.

Auricle: an ear-like lobe or appendage, usually at the base of a leaf (adjective, **auriculate**).

B-chromosome: a supplementary chromosome, usually composed wholly of heterochromatin (cf *A-chromosome*).

Beak: a point, formed by the persistent style, which projects from the apex of the fruit.

Calcicole: growing in habitats characterised by high concentrations of calcium.

Calcifuge: avoiding habitats characterised by high concentrations of calcium, i.e. found in acidic habitats.

Canaliculate: with a groove along the length of the organ.

Capitate: knob-shaped, borne on a narrower axis (literally, with a head).

Carpel: one of the basic units of the gynoecium, found at the centre of the flower and containing (in the Potamogetonaceae and Ruppiaceae) a single ovule.

Casual: only persisting for a short period, usually a single generation.

Clone: a single genetic individual, spreading vegetatively or propagated asexually (adjective, **clonal**).

Compressed: (of a stem or peduncle) with the longest axis of the cross-section 1.5–2.5 times as long as the shortest; **slightly compressed**: with the longest axis 1.1–1.5 times as long as the shortest; **strongly compressed**: with the longest axis 2.5–3.5 times as long as the shortest (cf *flattened, terete*).

Conductivity: the ability of water to conduct electricity. Conductivity provides an estimate of the total content of dissolved salts; waters with high conductivity are usually eutrophic or brackish.

Contiguous: touching or overlapping.

Cordate: with two rounded lobes at the base separated by a deep sinus.

Coriaceous: with a toughness resembling that of leather. Many leaves so described, including those of *Potamogeton*, are not literally as tough as leather but are relatively tough compared to leaves borne elsewhere on the plant or on related species.

Cuneate: with a V-shaped base.

Denticulate: with small teeth pointing outwards.

Distal: away from the point of attachment (cf *proximal*).

Distant: separated, not touching or overlapping.

Distichous: arranged in two opposite ranks, e.g. alternate leaves in which the first leaf lies directly below the third, the second below the fourth, etc.

Dorsal: the side of the carpel or fruit facing away from the central axis of the flower (cf *ventral*).

Dystrophic: peat-stained. In Britain and Ireland dystrophic waters have very low concentrations of dissolved nutrients and can therefore be included within the more general term *oligotrophic*.

Elliptical: broadest at the middle, narrowing towards each end, with the margins curved.

Emarginate: with a shallowly concave outline at the apex. This is not the normal meaning of emarginate, which means notched at the apex, but I have used it in the apparent absence of a more appropriate word to describe the stipule apex of, for example, *P. crispus*.

Endocarp: the layer of cells below the two thin outer layers of the fruit, the exocarp and the mesocarp. In *Potamogeton* it is composed of sclerified cells and forms the hard 'stone' of the fruit.

Entire: (of an edge) without teeth or lobes.

Erect: standing upright.

Eutrophic: with high concentrations of the nutrients required for plant growth. Eutrophic waters normally support high algal or macrophyte growth in favourable seasons and therefore become depleted of oxygen (cf *meso-trophic*, *oligotrophic*).

Eutrophication: an increase in the concentration of nutrients required for plant growth. Although eutrophication can be a natural phenomenon, the word is usually applied to artificial increases, e.g. those occurring when run-off from fertilised fields enters a water body.

Excurrent: projecting beyond the margin.

Falcate: curved like the blade of a sickle.

Filiform: very narrowly cylindrical (literally, thread-like).

Flattened: (of a stem or peduncle) with the longest axis of the cross-section at least 3.5 times as long as the shortest (cf *terete*, *compressed*).

Flexuous: gently bending alternately inwards and outwards.

Flimsy: a folded piece of thin paper used to contain a plant specimen in the press or before it is mounted on a herbarium sheet.

Fugacious: falling off very rapidly.

Fusiform: (of a solid body) broad in the middle, tapering at both ends (literally, spindle-shaped).

Glabrous: without hairs.

Grazing marsh: low-lying pasture, the fields often separated by ditches (which are sometimes called dykes, reens or rhines).

Heterophyllous: with submerged and floating leaves which differ in morphology (cf *homophyllous*).

Homophyllous: with submerged but no floating leaves (cf *heterophyllous*).

Hyaline: colourless and transparent.

Hypogynous: with the tepals attached beneath the base of the ovary.

Imbricate: closely appressed and overlapping.

Intercostal veins: the veins between the two strong veins or ribs of a stipule. The intercostal veins of open stipules are counted along the closed side.

Keeled: with a ridge running along the longitudinal axis, like the keel of a boat.

Lacunae: pale bands of tissue alongside the midrib or the veins of a leaf.

Lamina: the leaf-blade.

Lanceolate: broadest below the middle and about three times as long as wide.

Lateral veins: the veins running from base to apex of the leaf on either side of the midrib.

Ligule: a hyaline appendage at the apex of the sheath in *Potamogeton* Subgenus *Coleogeton*.

Linear: narrow, with parallel sides.

Loch: Scottish word for lake (diminutive: **lochan**).

Lustrous: shining with reflected light.

Machair lake/loch: a lake influenced by stabilised sand ('machair') on the west coasts of Ireland and Scotland. Machair lakes usually lie at the junction of machair and rocky ground, and therefore demonstrate an interesting range of environmental conditions.

Macrophyte: a macroscopic, submerged or floating water plant.

Marl lake: a lake containing water with a high concentration of dissolved calcium carbonate, which often becomes deposited on plant stems and inorganic objects in the water. Marl lakes usually contain low concentrations of other nutrients (e.g. nitrogen, potassium) and are therefore calcareous but oligotrophic.

Mesotrophic: with moderate concentrations of the nutrients required for plant growth (cf *eutrophic*, *oligotrophic*).

Midrib: the vein which runs along the central line of the leaf from base to apex.

Monopodial: (of a rhizome) a pattern of growth in which the apical bud grows horizontally, the upright shoots developing from lateral buds (cf *sympodial*).

Monotypic: (of a genus or family) containing only one species.

Mucronate: rounded to obtuse, but with a short point composed of the excurrent midrib (cf *apiculate*).

Muricate: rough, with short, hard projections (diminutive: **muriculate**).

Nodal gland: a swelling at the node of the stem. Nodal glands are found in opposite pairs.

Numerous: (of flowers in an inflorescence) more than 20.

Oblanceolate: broadest above the middle and about three times as long as wide (i.e. inverted lanceolate).

Oblong: approximately rectangular, broadest at the middle and with more or less parallel sides.

Obovate: with the outline of a hen's egg, broadest near the apex (i.e. inverted ovate).

Obtuse: blunt (cf *acute*, *rounded*).

Oligotrophic: with low concentrations of the nutrients required for plant growth. Oligotrophic waters normally support low algal or macrophyte growth and therefore retain high concentrations of oxygen (cf *eutrophic*, *mesotrophic*).

Ontogenetic: (of change) occurring during the development of the individual.

Opaque: not transmitting light, i.e. neither transparent nor translucent.

Opposite: arising at the same level on different sides of an axis. Structures so arranged are therefore grouped in pairs.

Orbicular: circular.

Ovate: with the outline of a hen's egg, broadest near the base.

Peduncle: the stalk of an inflorescence.

Persistent: remaining attached.

Petiole: the stalk of a leaf.

Phyllode: a leaf formed from a petiole.

Proximal: towards the point of attachment (cf *distal*).

Recurved: curved back towards the base of an organ.

Reticulate: forming a network.

Rhizome: a modified stem, usually growing within the substrate and bearing roots at the nodes and stems at some nodes (adjective, **rhizomatous**).

Robust: (of a rhizome, stem or peduncle) 2.0–4.0 mm in diameter; **very robust:** over 4.0 mm in diameter (cf *slender*).

Rounded: with an apex which approximates in shape to an arc of a circle (broader than *obtuse*).

Rugose: wrinkled, like the surface of a prune.

Sclerenchymatous strand: a length of strengthening tissue in the lamina of a leaf.

Secondary vein: a vein running from the midrib to one of the inner lateral veins or from one lateral vein to another.

Semi-amplexicaul: see *amplexicaul*.

Serrate: with forwardly-pointing teeth (diminutive: **serrulate**).

Sessile: without a stalk.

Sheath: a structure at the base of a leaf, which enfolds the stem.

Sinuous: with an outline like that of a series of waves.

Slender: (of a rhizome, stem or peduncle) 1.0–2.0 mm in diameter; **very slender:** less than 1.0 mm in diameter (cf *robust*).

Slightly compressed: see *compressed*.

Spike: a cylindrical inflorescence.

Stipule: an appendage at the base of a leaf.

Stylar neck: a narrow connection between the ovary and the stigma.

Sub: a prefix to an adjective indicating that the object approaches the condition described but does not attain it completely.

Submerged: growing entirely under water.

Sympodial: (of a rhizome) a pattern of growth in which the apical bud grows into an aerial stem, the rhizome being continued by a lateral bud from its base (cf *monopodial*).

Tepal: a perianth segment.

Terete: circular and smooth in cross-section, not compressed, flattened, ridged, angled or grooved.

Translucent: allowing light to pass through partially or diffusely (cf *opaque*).

Truncate: ending abruptly, as if cut straight across.

Tuber: a small propagule of non-photosynthetic tissue which develops on the rhizome.

Turion: a reduced branch, with highly modified photosynthetic leaves and stipules, which is borne in a leaf axil or at the apex of a stem.

Undulate: with wave-like folds.

Vein: a strand of conducting tissue running through a leaf or stipule.

Venation: the system of veins in a leaf.

Ventral: the side of the carpel or fruit facing the central axis of the flower (cf *dorsal*).

INDEX

Species are indexed under the accepted scientific and English names and under synonyms which have been widely used in the British and Irish literature. Hybrids are indexed under the parental combination (in alphabetical order), the accepted binomial and widely used synonyms. The **bold figures** refer to the taxon number, not the page number. Synonyms are printed *in italics*; they are equated to a taxon number in this index but are not usually mentioned in the text. The use of some names has changed over the years, and notes on some names which are particularly likely to cause confusion are given in the nomenclature chapter. Infraspecific taxa are only indexed if mentioned in the text.

× cooperi (Fryer) Fryer **41**
coriaceus (Mert. & W. D. J.
  Koch) A. Benn. = **26**
crassifolius Fryer = **23**
crispus L. **19**
crispus × friesii **42**
crispus × lucens **38**
crispus × perfoliatus **41**
crispus × praelongus **40**
crispus × trichoides **43**
decipiens Nolte ex W. D. J. Koch
  = **34**
densus L. = **48**
drucei Fryer = **2**
epihydrus Raf. **10**
epihydrus var. epihydrus see **10**
epihydrus var. ramosus (Peck)
  House see **10**
falcatus Fryer = **4**
filiformis Pers. **20**
filiformis × pectinatus **47**
flabellatus Bab. = **21**
× fluitans Roth **23**
friesii Rupr. **11**
  × gessnacensis G. Fisch. **25**
gramineus L. **4**
gramineus × lucens **26**
gramineus × natans **24**
gramineus × perfoliatus **30**
gramineus × polygonifolius **27**
graminifolius H. & J. Groves = **4**
× griffithii A. Benn. **35**
× grovesii Dandy & G. Taylor **44**
heterophyllus Schreb. = **4**
hibernicus (Hagstr.) Druce = **1**
interruptus Kit. = **21**
involutus (Fryer) H. & J. Groves
  = **30**
johannis Hesl.-Harr. = **36**
kirkii (Hook. f.) Syme ex Hook. f.
  = **24**

lacustris (Pearsall & Pearsall f.)
  Druce = **15**
× lanceolatifolius (Tiselius)
  C. D. Preston **27**
× lanceolatus Sm. **32**
× lintonii Fryer **42**
longifolius auct. = **26**
lucens L. **3**
lucens × natans **23**
lucens × perfoliatus **34**
lundii K. Richt. = **30**
macvicarii A. Benn. = **35**
marinus auct. = **20**
millardii Hesl.-Harr. = **15**
mucronatus Schrad. ex Sond.
  = **11**
natans L. **1**
natans × nodosus **22**
natans × polygonifolius **25**
× nericius Hagstr. **29**
× nerviger Wolfg. **33**
× nitens Weber **30**
nodosus Poir. **2**
oblongus Viv. = **5**
obtusifolius Mert. & W. D. J.
  Koch **14**
× olivaceus Baagöe ex G. Fisch.
  39
panormitanus Biv. = **13**
pectinatus L. **21**
pensylvanicus Willd. ex Cham. &
  Schltdl. = **10**
perfoliatus L. **9**
perfoliatus × praelongus **37**
perpygmaeus Hagstr. ex Druce
  = **32**
plantagineus Ducros ex Roem. &
  Schult. = **6**
polygonifolius Pourr. **5**
polygonifolius forma cancellatus
  Fryer see **5**

BOTANICAL SOCIETY OF THE BRITISH ISLES

The BSBI was founded in 1836 and has a membership of 2,700. It is the major source of information on the status and distribution of British and Irish flowering plants and ferns. This information, which is gathered through a network of county recorders, is vital to their conservation and is the basis of the Red Data Books for vascular plants in Great Britain and Ireland. The Society arranges conferences and field meetings throughout the British Isles and, occasionally, abroad. It organises plant distribution surveys and publishes plant atlases and handbooks on difficult groups of plants. It has a panel of referees available to members to name problematic specimens. Through its Conservation Committee it plays an active part in the protection of our threatened plants. It welcomes as members all botanists, professional and amateur alike.

Details of membership and any other information about the Society may be obtained from:
The Hon. General Secretary,
Botanical Society of the British Isles,
c/o Department of Botany,
The Natural History Museum,
Cromwell Road,
London SW7 5BD.

BSBI Publications

Handbooks

Each Handbook deals in depth with one or more difficult groups of British and Irish plants.

No. 1   *Sedges of the British Isles*
A.C. Jermy, A.O. Chater & R.W. David. Revised edition, 1982. 272 pp., with descriptions, line drawings and distribution maps for all 73 species. Paperback.

No. 2   *Umbellifers of the British Isles*
T.G. Tutin. 1980. 200 pp., with descriptions and line drawings of 73 species. Paperback. Out of print. New edition with distribution maps in preparation; orders being recorded.

No. 3   *Docks and knotweeds of the British Isles*
J.E. Lousley & D.H. Kent. 1981. 208 pp., with descriptions and line drawings of about 80 native and alien taxa. Paperback. Out of print. New edition with distribution maps in preparation; orders being recorded.

No. 4   *Willows and poplars of Great Britain and Ireland*
R.D. Meikle. 1984. 200 pp., with descriptions and line drawings of 65 species, subspecies, varieties and hybrids. Paperback.

No. 5   *Charophytes of Great Britain and Ireland*
J.A. Moore. 1986. 142 pp., with descriptions and line drawings of 39 species and varieties and 17 distribution maps. Paperback.

No. 6   *Crucifers of Great Britain and Ireland*
T.C.G. Rich. 1991. 342 pp., with descriptions of 148 taxa (129 with line drawings) and 60 distribution maps. Paperback.

No. 7   *Roses of Great Britain and Ireland*
G.G. Graham & A.L. Primavesi. 1993. 208 pp., with descriptions and line drawings of 13 native and nine introduced taxa, descriptions of 76 hybrids, and 33 maps. Paperback.

No. 8   *Pondweeds of Great Britain and Ireland*
C.D. Preston. 1995. 352 pp., with descriptions and line drawings of all 50 species and hybrids, most with distribution maps; detailed introductory material and bibliography. Paperback.

Other publications

British and Irish herbaria
D.H. Kent & D.E. Allen, comp. Second edition, 1984. 338 pp. An index to the location of herbaria of British and Irish vascular plants. Paperback.

Atlas of the British flora
F.H. Perring & S.M. Walters, ed. 1990 (smaller reprint of 3rd edition, 1982). 470 pp. Distribution maps for over 1,700 species, including updated maps for 321 Red Data Book species. New index and bibliography to distribution maps published between 1962 and 1989, compiled by C.D. Preston. Paperback.

List of vascular plants of the British Isles
D.H. Kent. 1992. 400 pp. Nomenclature and sequence followed by Clive Stace in *New flora of the British Isles*, with selected synonyms. Paperback.

Alien plants of the British Isles
E.J. Clement & M.C. Foster. 1994. 616 pp. Lists 3,586 recorded alien species, of which 885 are established, with English names, frequency of occurrence, status, areas of origin, location of voucher specimens, references to published descriptions and illustrations, and selected synonyms. Excludes grasses, to be published separately. Paperback.

Scarce plants in Britain
A. Stewart, D.A. Pearman & C.D. Preston, comp. & ed. 1994. 518 pp. Up-to-date accounts of 325 species believed to be nationally scarce (occurring in 16–100 10-km squares in Great Britain) at the start of an NCC / ITE (BRC) / BSBI co-operative venture in 1990, with maps showing records before and since 1970. Accounts of habitats of scarce species, with maps showing numbers of relevant species recorded in each 10-km square. Hardback, published by JNCC, Peterborough.

Available from the official agents for BSBI publications, F. & M. Perring, Green Acre, Wood Lane, Oundle, Peterborough PE8 4JQ (Tel. 01832 273388. Fax 01832 274568).